ULTRASONIC TECHNIQUES
IN BIOLOGY AND MEDICINE

ULTRASONIC TECHNIQUES IN BIOLOGY AND MEDICINE

Editors
B. BROWN, B.Sc., Ph.D. A.Inst.P.
D. GORDON, M.B., D.M.R., D.M.R.D., Sen.M.I.E.E.E.

CHARLES C THOMAS · PUBLISHER
Springfield · Illinois · U.S.A.

© Iliffe Books Ltd., 1967

First Published in Great Britain
in 1967 by Iliffe Books Ltd.,
Dorset House, Stamford Street, London, S.E.1.

Printed in England at the Pitman Press, Bath.

Published and Distributed by
CHARLES C THOMAS · PUBLISHER
Bannerstone House
301–327 East Lawrence Avenue, Springfield, Illinois, U.S.A.

Natchez Plantation House
735 North Atlantic Boulevard, Fort Lauderdale, Florida, U.S.A.

CONTENTS

PREFACE

The applications of ultrasound in biology and medicine are extremely diverse ranging from subjects such as diagnosis and surgery to those of surgical instrument cleaning and the liberation of cell constituents. While some of these applications are well established others are still in an early stage of development.

The development of ultrasonic equipment for a particular application requires close co-operation between medical and scientific staff. At the present time an increased interest in ultrasonics is being shown by the medical profession with the result that more and more hospital physics departments are finding it necessary to have an understanding of ultrasonic waves. This book has been compiled with the prime aim of making clear to hospital physicists and similar workers the basic properties of ultrasound and of introducing them to the various applications of ultrasound in the biological and medical field. It is not intended to be a clinical handbook and clinicians seeking information are adequately catered for in other books and original papers.

The authors are all specialists in their own fields and the editors would like to take this opportunity of thanking them for their respective contributions. Their full co-operation in the production of this book has helped to make the task of the editors less difficult than is usually the case in this type of work.

B. Brown
D. Gordon

1
THE PROPERTIES OF ULTRASONIC WAVES

J. Blitz, M.Sc., F.Inst.P.

1.1 GENERAL CONSIDERATIONS

Ultrasonic waves are sound waves having frequencies which are too high to be detected by the human ear. The highest audible frequency for adults is of the order of 16,000 c/s although, for young children, this upper limit can be as high as 18,000 c/s and, for some animals, even higher.

The physical properties of ultrasonic waves are the same as those of audible sound (or acoustic) waves. However, ultrasonics may be used in preference to audible sound for one or more of the following reasons:

(*a*) they are inaudible,
(*b*) they are directional and can be more easily focussed,
(*c*) because of their shorter wavelengths, they can be used for examining the properties of small quantities of material and for investigating small scale variations in structure,
(*d*) because of their high frequencies, they can be used to investigate certain physical phenomena associated with very short time periods, e.g. viscous relaxation.

The various applications of ultrasonics may be classified under two headings, namely (*a*) low intensity ultrasonics, and (*b*) high intensity ultrasonics. With low intensity applications, the waves are used to investigate the physical properties of the material through which they pass and the material does not suffer any permanent changes. With high intensity applications, actual work is done by the waves on the material, e.g. the production of cavitation, heating, drilling, etc., and irreversible changes in the properties of the material can often take place. In this book both types of applications are described.

1

1.2 VIBRATIONS

1.2.1 GENERAL

Sound waves are produced as a result of some disturbance taking place in a material medium; this disturbance causes the particles from which the medium is formed (e.g. its molecules) to be set into vibration. The vibration of particles in a material is an essential characteristic of acoustic propagation and, for this reason, it is not possible for sound to pass through a vacuum. A disturbance can be either discontinuous, as in the case of an explosion, or regular as in the production of a musical note. We are concerned here only with the applications of regular vibrations at ultrasonic frequencies.

Regular vibrations can be used to produce either a pure or a complex note. A source producing a pure tone, e.g. a tuning fork, vibrates with what is known as *simple harmonic motion*. A complex tone, such as one produced by most musical instruments is made up of a number of pure tones resulting from simple harmonic motions having different frequencies.

1.2.2 SIMPLE HARMONIC MOTION (OR SIMPLE PERIODIC MOTION)

Simple harmonic motion is that motion along a line for which the acceleration of a body *towards* some fixed point on that line varies in proportion to the displacement of the body *away* from that point. If one can imagine the motion of a particle with uniform speed around the circumference of a circle, the projection of the particle on the diameter (i.e. the point where the perpendicular line from the particle to the diameter crosses the latter) can be shown to perform simple harmonic motion. Familiar examples include the motions of the bob of a clock pendulum and of a child on a swing. If a graph is plotted of the displacement

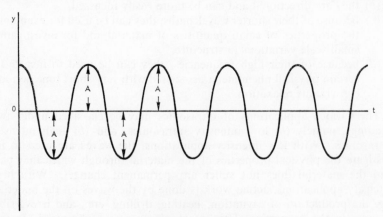

Fig. 1.1. Variation of displacement y with time t for a body executing simple harmonic motion

y of a body from the position the body will occupy when at rest against the time t, the curve shown in Fig. 1.1 will be obtained. This is called a sine curve, for reasons which will presently become apparent, and consists of peaks and troughs located at regular intervals. The peaks indicate the maximum displacement of the body to one side (say the right) of the normal position of rest and the troughs indicate the maximum displacement to the other side (i.e. the minimum displacement, if motion to the right is regarded as being positive). The curve repeats its form for the time of duration of the vibrations and sections of equal length, each representing equal times, can be superimposed on one another. These equal times are each known as the *time period*, which is the time taken for the body to complete a single vibration (or oscillation). Thus, for the pendulum, it is the time taken to complete a swing from its normal position of rest to the extreme right, then back through the position of rest to the extreme left, and finally to its original position.

The number of complete vibrations executed in one second is known as the *frequency f*, which is equal to the reciprocal of the time period T, i.e.

$$f = 1/T \qquad (1.1)$$

If T is measured in seconds, f is expressed in cycles per second (c/s). A frequency of one thousand cycles per second is called the *kilocycle* per second (kc/s) and the corresponding time period (i.e. one thousandth of a second) is called the *milli-second* (msec). A frequency of one million cycles per second is called the *megacycle* per second (Mc/s) and the corresponding time period (i.e. one millionth of a second) is called the *micro-second* (μsec).

Recently by international agreement the term Hertz has been adopted as the unit of frequency. One Hertz is a frequency of one cycle per second, a Kilohertz is a frequency of one thousand cycles per second and a Megahertz is a frequency of one million cycles per second.

The pitch of a note is related to the frequency of the vibrations producing it. The pitch is raised by one octave when the frequency is doubled, by two octaves when the frequency is quadrupled, and so on. If a source of sound is vibrating in a complex but periodic manner, it can be shown to be describing a number of simple harmonic motions of different frequencies simultaneously (see Fig. 1.2). In general, the frequencies are related to one another in a simple manner. The higher frequencies, i.e. the *overtones*, which may be described as *harmonics*, are multiples of the *fundamental* frequency, i.e. the frequency of the note having the lowest pitch. Thus the second harmonic has a frequency which is twice that of the fundamental, the third harmonic a frequency which is three times that of the fundamental, and so on. In most cases the intensity of a harmonic decreases as its order increases. Normal practice, where possible, is to excite a source at its fundamental frequency.

The maximum displacement of a vibrating particle from its normal position of rest is called the *displacement amplitude* (marked A in Fig. 1.1) and the maximum velocity of the particle, which will be observed as it passes through its normal position of rest (i.e. zero displacement), is

3

called the *velocity amplitude*. The form of the curve shown in Fig. 1.1, can be expressed mathematically by either of the following equations:

$$y = A \sin 2\pi ft \tag{1.2a}$$

$$y = A \sin \omega t \tag{1.2b}$$

where y is the particle displacement at any time t and $\omega = 2\pi f$ is the *angular frequency* or *pulsatance*. The alternative expressions $2\pi ft$ and ωt are each called the *phase angle*, which indicates the progress of the oscillations at a given time t. During one complete vibration there is a change in phase angle of 2π or 360 degrees.

1.2.3 DAMPED FREE VIBRATIONS

Let us now consider the vibrations of a pendulum which is initially displaced and then released so as to swing freely. Because of friction at the support and the viscosity of the air, the pendulum undergoes free damped vibrations, for which the amplitude decreases progressively in an exponential manner, as shown in Fig. 1.3. Other well-known examples of free damped vibrations include the effect of striking a bell, sounding a note on a piano, and plucking a guitar string. At ultrasonic frequencies an important example is that of the vibrations of a piezoelectric crystal when it is excited by a momentary d.c. voltage applied across its electrodes.

Where the damping is very high, oscillations will not take place and the motion of the body is called *anharmonic* or *aperiodic*. After its initial

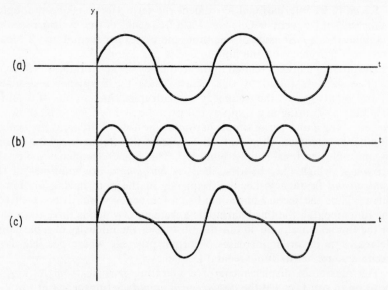

Fig. 1.2. Complex periodic motion: (a) simple harmonic motion at the fundamental frequency, (b) simple harmonic motion at the second harmonic, (c) resultant of (a) and (b)

4

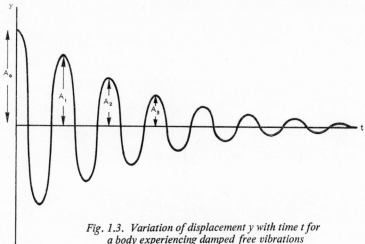

Fig. 1.3. Variation of displacement y with time t for
a body experiencing damped free vibrations

displacement the system returns slowly to its normal position of rest, the
time taken depending on the degree of damping. A well-known example
of this type of motion is that of a door fitted with a damper to prevent
it from slamming.

The frequency of the free vibrations of a body, i.e. its *natural frequency*,
depends on the size and also on the physical properties of the body (see
Sect. 1.8). At this stage it can be said that, for a given material, the
smaller the dimensions the higher the natural frequency. For example,
the time period of a vibrating pendulum is expressed by the formula:

$$T = 2\pi\sqrt{[l/\mathbf{g}]}$$

where l represents the length of the pendulum and $\mathbf{g}$ the acceleration due
to gravity. The degree of damping is expressed by the *logarithmic decre-*
ment, or *damping coefficient* δ as follows:

$$\delta = 2\cdot303 \log_{10}(A_2/A_1) \tag{1.3}$$

where A_1 and A_2 are the amplitudes of two successive vibrations (see
Fig. 1.3). This can also be expressed in terms of the *Q factor*, for which:

$$Q = \pi/\delta = \pi/2\cdot303 \log_{10}(A_2/A_1) \tag{1.4}$$

In practice, because δ has a finite value, the oscillations take place not
at a single frequency but at frequencies extending over a continuous range,
known as the *frequency bandwidth*, on both sides of a frequency f_0 at
which the amplitude is a maximum. The variation of amplitude with
frequency is illustrated in Fig. 1.4. If A_0 is the value of the amplitude at
the frequency f_0, it is usual to define the frequency bandwidth as the difference $f_2 - f_1$, where f_1 and f_2 are the frequencies on either side of f_0 at
which the amplitude is reduced to the value $A_0/\sqrt{2}$ (i.e. by about 3 dB).
The bandwidth $f_2 - f_1$ increases with the value of δ and thus decreases

5

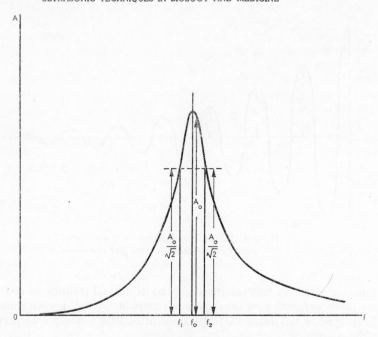

Fig. 1.4. Variation of amplitude A with frequency f for a body subjected to forced harmonic oscillations

with the value of Q, i.e. the heavier the damping the wider the frequency band. It can be shown that the value of Q is approximately equal to the ratio $f_0/(f_2 - f_1)$. In the ideal case where there is no damping, the oscillations take place only at the single frequency f_0.

1.2.4 FORCED VIBRATIONS AND RESONANCE

The vibrations of a system can be sustained for any desired length of time by the application of an external periodic force, varying in the same way as the displacement of a particle undergoing simple harmonic motion, as described by the Eqns. 1.2a and 1.2b. These vibrations will then depend partly on the characteristics of the applied force and partly on the properties of the vibrating system, although the system will oscillate at the frequency of the applied force. This force is exerted by a *transducer*, a device which converts energy of one kind to that of another, in this case to energy of mechanical vibrations. The transducers most commonly used for generating ultrasonics are piezoelectric and magnetostrictive oscillators, which convert electrical energy supplied by a high frequency a.c. generator to mechanical vibrational energy. An everyday example of forced vibrations is the sustaining of the motion of a child's swing by pushing it at regular intervals.

The amplitude of forced vibrations will be a maximum when the vibrating system is excited externally at one of its natural frequencies, either at the fundamental or at a harmonic (see Sect. 1.2.1). In this case we have a state of *resonance* and, once the vibrations have settled down to a steady state, the energy supplied externally is used up only in overcoming those losses which would give rise to damping if the system were oscillating freely. The degree of resonance, i.e. the magnitude of the amplitude at the resonance frequency, intensifies with the Q factor of the system and thus diminishes as the damping coefficient δ is increased. If it were possible to have a completely undamped system, the value of the Q factor would be equal to infinity and the oscillations would build up, at resonance, to an infinite amplitude.

1.3 WAVE MOTION

Let our source of sound be a flat plate vibrating uniformly with simple harmonic motion in a direction perpendicular to its radiating surface, the plate being in contact with the medium through which the sound waves are to be propagated. Imagine the medium to be divided up into very thin parallel layers of equal thickness, as indicated by the letters A, B, C, D, etc. in Fig. 1.5, with their surfaces parallel with the surface of the source. Energy from the vibrations of the source is transmitted to the layer A which then oscillates at the same frequency as the source. Because of the finite amount of time taken for the energy to pass from the source to the layer A, the vibrations of A will lag in phase behind the vibrations of the source (see Fig. 1.6). In the same way B is set into oscillations as a result of energy passing to it from A and, because of the additional time taken, the vibrations of B will lag in phase behind those of the source by a greater amount than those of A. Acoustical energy thus passes

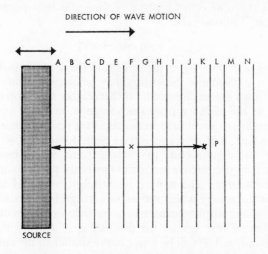

Fig. 1.5. Division of medium, in which plane waves are propagated, into parallel layers

7

progressively through the medium and arrives eventually at some receiver, such as a microphone or the diaphragm of a human ear, which will be set into vibration at the same frequency as the source but lagging behind it in phase. This phase lag will depend on the time taken for the waves to travel from the source to the receiver which, in turn, depends on the distance travelled by the waves and the speed of sound in the medium.

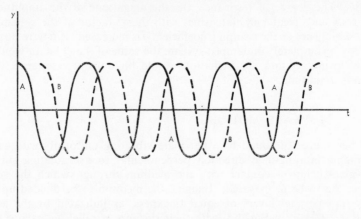

Fig. 1.6. Variation of displacement y with time t for layers A and B (Fig. 1.5.), showing the phase lag of B with respect to A

The speed of sound is a constant quantity for a medium in a given state and depends only on its physical properties, as shown by Eqns. 1.8 to 1.13.

Consider some point P at a distance x from the source (see Fig. 1.5). The time taken for the sound to arrive at P from the source is equal to an amount x/c, where c is the speed of sound in the medium. Thus if we apply Eqn. 1.2 to describe the vibrations of a particle of the medium at P, provided that the source has a plane surface and thus propagates plane waves (see Sect. 1.6), we have:

$$y = A \sin \omega(t - x/c) \tag{1.5}$$

The vibrations of P thus lag in phase behind the vibrations of the source by an angle $\omega x/c$. Some of the energy may be converted into heat during its passage through the medium and, for this reason, there will be a decrease in amplitude as the distance from the source is increased (see Sect. 1.6). A further decrease in amplitude may arise as a result of the beam being diffracted (see Sect. 1.9) or scattered (see Sect. 1.10).

It must be made quite clear that when sound waves pass through a material there is no progressive motion of any of the particles of the medium away from the source. The motion is entirely vibrational about a fixed position; it is the *energy* which moves in a progressive manner.

The graph of the displacement y of a particle in the medium from its normal position of rest against the distance x of P from the source, at some time t, (see Fig. 1.7) will be a sine curve similar to the curve shown in Fig. 1.1. Because t is constant, the only variables in Eqn. 1.5 are y and x.

8

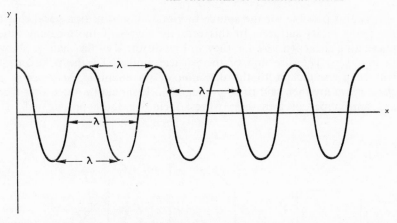

Fig. 1.7. Variation of particle displacement y with distance x from a source of plane waves

An important property of wave-motion is the *wavelength*. This is defined as the distance travelled by the sound waves in a single time period T and is, by convention, identified by the symbol λ. Thus:

$$\lambda = cT = c/f \qquad (1.6)$$

The wavelength can be seen to be equal to the distance between two successive peaks or two successive troughs of the curve shown in Fig. 1.7, which is sometimes called the *wave-form*. In general, the wavelength is given by the distance between two positions in the waves for which the phase difference is 360 degrees. Eqn. 1.5 can be re-written in either of the following forms:

$$y = A \sin (\omega t - 2\pi x/\lambda) \qquad (1.7a)$$

$$y = A \sin (\omega t - kx) \qquad (1.7b)$$

where $k = 2\pi/\lambda$ is called the *wave-number*. Eqns. 1.5a, 1.5b, 1.7a, and 1.7b show clearly that the particle displacement y in a medium depends both on the distance x from the source of the mean position P of the particle and the time t under consideration.

1.4 LONGITUDINAL AND TRANSVERSE WAVES

In the example illustrated in Fig. 1.3, the vibrations of the source take place in the direction of propagation of the waves, i.e. perpendicular to the plane of the vibrating surface. The layers of the medium then suffer alternating compressions and expansions, and the vibrations of the particles will thus be in the direction of the wave-motion. We then say that *longitudinal* or *compressional waves* are propagated. Because the vibrations of the particles all lie in a given direction, i.e. in the direction of propagation of the vibrations, they are said to be *polarized*.

9

2

It is also possible for the source to vibrate in a direction parallel with the plane of its surface. In this case the layers of the medium suffer alternating shear stresses, i.e. they will be distorted in the manner shown in Fig. 1.8. The direction of the particle motion, i.e. the polarization, will be perpendicular to the direction of wave-motion. *Transverse* or *shear waves* are then said to be propagated. It should be noted that there are some types of transverse waves, including those propagated in a

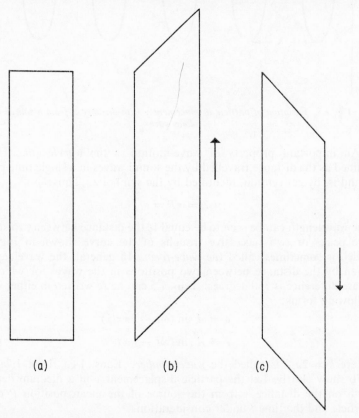

(a)   (b)   (c)

Fig. 1.8. Distortion of a body acted upon by a shear stress: (a) unstressed body, (b) shear stress in positive direction, (c) shear stress in negative direction

stretched string and in a vibrating rod, which are not shear waves. These, however, will rarely concern the student of ultrasonics.

Longitudinal waves can be passed through all types of media, whereas transverse waves, in general, can travel only through solids. This is because liquids and gases cannot, under normal circumstances, support shear stresses. Exceptions arise for certain types of liquids, called visco-elastic fluids, through which it is possible, under certain conditions, to pass shear waves for very short distances of the order of a fraction of a millimetre.

10

1.5 THE SPEED OF SOUND

It was mentioned earlier that the speed of sound in a given medium is a quantity which depends on the physical properties of that medium. The mathematical relationships for different types of material are as follows:

For a solid rod for which the wavelength is considerably greater than the cross-sectional dimensions:

$$c = \sqrt{(Y/\rho)} \text{ for longitudinal waves} \qquad (1.8)$$

where Y is the Young's modulus for the material and ρ the density,

$$c = \sqrt{(G/\rho)} \text{ for torsional waves} \qquad (1.9)$$

i.e. for shear waves polarized along arcs of circles concentric with the curved surface of the rod, where G is the shear modulus or the rigidity of the material.

For solids in bulk, for which the wavelength is small compared with any of the cross-sectional dimensions:

$$c = \sqrt{[(K + 4G/3)/\rho]} \text{ for longitudinal waves} \qquad (1.10)$$

where K is the bulk or volume modulus, and

$$c = \sqrt{[G/\rho]} \text{ for transverse waves} \qquad (1.11)$$

For a liquid or gas (logitudinal waves only):

$$c = \sqrt{[K/\rho]} \qquad (1.12)$$

In the case of an ideal (or perfect gas), Eqn. 1.12 reduces to:

$$c = \sqrt{[\gamma P/\rho]} \qquad (1.13)$$

where P is the static pressure of the gas and γ the ratio of its specific heat at constant pressure to its specific heat at constant volume. The quantities represented by the symbols Y, K, and G are known generally as elastic moduli and further information about them can be found in any standard college text-book of General Physics[1]. Because the elastic moduli and density for a given material varies with the temperature, the speed of sound will also vary with the temperature, generally increasing with rise in temperature.

Table 1.1 gives values of acoustic speeds for a number of commonly used materials, at room temperature and standard pressure. The table shows that the values of the speeds in solids are the highest, those in liquids are somewhat lower, and those in gases very much lower. It is seen that transverse waves travel at roughly half the speed of longitudinal waves in a given solid.

1.6 THE CHARACTERISTICS OF SOUND WAVES

Up to now it has been assumed that the source has been a plane surface from which *plane waves* are generated and that the *wavefront* (i.e. the leading surface of the advancing waves) is plane. Where the source

11

Table 1.1 ACOUSTIC SPEEDS AND CHARACTERISTIC IMPEDANCES FOR SOME COMMON MATERIALS AT ROOM TEMPERATURE AND STANDARD PRESSURE

Material	Longitudinal Waves		Transverse Waves
	Speed m/sec	Characteristic Impedance c.g.s. units	Speed m/sec
Aluminium	6400	$1 \cdot 7 \times 10^6$	3100
Copper	4700	$4 \cdot 2 \times 10^6$	2300
Nickel	5600	$5 \cdot 0 \times 10^6$	2900
Steel	6000	$4 \cdot 7 \times 10^6$	2900
Barium titanate	5000	$2 \cdot 7 \times 10^6$	
Perspex	2700	$3 \cdot 2 \times 10^5$	
Quartz (X-cut)	5700	$1 \cdot 5 \times 10^6$	
Lubricating oil	1400	$1 \cdot 1 \times 10^5$	
Water	1400	$1 \cdot 4 \times 10^5$	
Air	330	43	
Hydrogen	1300	11	

is very small in size compared with the wavelength, it can be regarded as being virtually a point, with the result that the wavefront is spherical in shape, i.e. *spherical waves* are propagated (see Fig. 1.9). However, at a sufficiently large distance from the source, where the curvature of the wavefront is small, spherical waves approximate very closely to plane waves.

Sound waves are characterized by the quantities *acoustic pressure p*, *particle velocity u*, and *intensity I*, as well as the particle displacement *y*. The acoustic pressure is the excess pressure, at a given point in the medium at a given time, which gives rise to a compression (or expansion where *p* is negative) as a result of the action of the sound waves. The particle velocity is the velocity of a vibrating particle at a given point in the medium at a given time; this should not be confused with the speed of sound. Both *p* and *u* vary in the same way as the particle displacement as shown by Eqn. 1.7. The maximum values of these quantities are called, respectively, the acoustic pressure amplitude p_0 and the particle velocity amplitude u_0. The ratio p/u is called the *specific acoustic impedance* and, for plane waves, it can be shown that this quantity is equal to the product ρc, which is known as the *characteristic impedance* of the medium. The importance of this quantity in the study of acoustics becomes evident in Sect. 1.7.

The intensity at any point in a wave is defined as the rate of flow of energy through a unit area, at right-angles to the direction of wave-motion, about that point. It is related to the quantities p_0, u_0, ρc, and the particle displacement amplitude A as follows:

$$I = \tfrac{1}{2}p_0 u_0 = \tfrac{1}{2}p_0^2/\rho c = \tfrac{1}{2}u_0^2 \rho c = \tfrac{1}{2}\omega^2 A^2 \rho c \qquad (1.14)$$

Thus the value of intensity can be obtained from any one of these alternative expressions. The usual method of determining the intensity is to couple an acoustic receiver, placed in the required position, to an a.c. voltmeter, the reading of which is directly proportional to the pressure

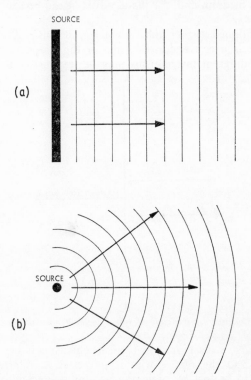

Fig. 1.9. Wavefront positions for (a) plane waves and (b) spherical waves

amplitude p_0 and, hence, the displacement amplitude A. It is common practice to relate the intensity to some reference value using the decibel scale, as follows:

Number of decibels (dB) $= 10 \log_{10}(I/I_0) = 20 \log_{10}(A/A_0)$

$$= 20 \log_{10}(V/V_0) \qquad (1.15)$$

where the suffix 0 corresponds to some arbitrary reference value and V represents the reading of the voltmeter. Eqn. 1.15 is also used to denote a change of intensity from a value I_0 to another value I as, for example, when considering a decrease in intensity with distance from the source due to the spreading of the beam or to attenuation.

13

For plane waves, the intensity I is constant for all positions in the beam of sound, if we ignore attenuation, but for spherical waves there is a decrease in intensity in accordance with the inverse square law, as follows:

$$I_2/I_1 = d_1{}^2/d_2{}^2 \tag{1.16}$$

where I_1 and I_2 are the intensities at distances d_1 and d_2, respectively, from the centre of the source, again ignoring attenuation.

The *energy density* is defined as the amount of energy contained in unit volume of the medium and, for plane waves, it can be shown to be equal to the product cI.

It was mentioned earlier that when sound waves travel through a material there is a conversion of some of the sound energy into heat. A number of different mechanisms may be responsible for these energy

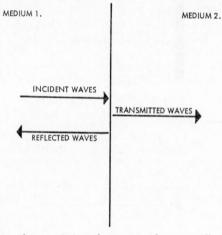

Fig. 1.10. Reflection and transmission of waves incident normally to a plane boundary

losses. However, a discussion of these mechanisms is beyond the scope of this book and the reader who is interested is referred elsewhere.[2] Energy can also be lost by such processes as scattering and diffraction, which are explained later in this chapter. Losses of acoustic energy can be expressed in terms of the *attenuation* or *absorption coefficient* α, having as its unit the neper per cm, and defined, for plane waves, by the following equations:

$$A = A_0 \exp(-\alpha x) \tag{1.17a}$$

or
$$I = I_0 \exp(-2\alpha x) \tag{1.17b}$$

where A_0 and I_0 are the amplitude and intensity, respectively, at some reference position in the sound waves and A and I their values at a further distance x from the source. By taking logarithms to the base 10 these equations can be rewritten as follows:

$$2 \cdot 303 \log_{10}(A/A_0) = -\alpha x \tag{1.17c}$$

or
$$2 \cdot 303 \log_{10}(I/I_0) = -2\alpha x \tag{1.17d}$$

14

A comparison of these equations with Eqn. 1.15 shows that attenuation can also be expressed in decibels per cm. It can easily be seen that 1 neper is equivalent to about 8·7 dB.

1.7 THE REFLECTION AND TRANSMISSION OF PLANE WAVES

1.7.1 REFLECTION AND TRANSMISSION AT NORMAL INCIDENCE

Let us consider a beam of plane waves incident at right-angles to a plane boundary separating two media (1) and (2) in Fig. 1.10. At the boundary, some of the energy of the incident waves is reflected and the remainder transmitted into the second medium. The relative intensities of the transmitted and reflected waves with respect to the incident waves are expressed by the transmission and reflection coefficients, which depend on the characteristic impedances $\rho_1 c_1$ and $\rho_2 c_2$, respectively, of the two media.

The *transmission coefficient* α_t is defined as the ratio of the intensity of the transmitted waves at the boundary to that of the incident waves and can be shown, for normal incidence, to be given by the expression:

$$\alpha_t = \frac{4\rho_1 c_1 \rho_2 c_2}{(\rho_1 c_1 + \rho_2 c_2)^2} \tag{1.18}$$

The *reflection coefficient* α_r is defined as the ratio of the intensity of the reflected waves at the boundary to that of the incident waves and, for normal incidence, is given by the expression:

$$\alpha_r = \left(\frac{\rho_2 c_2 - \rho_1 c_1}{\rho_2 c_2 + \rho_1 c_1}\right)^2 \tag{1.19}$$

α_t and α_r may be expressed as either fractions or percentages. If for a given boundary, they are added together, the result is equal to unity, i.e. 100 per cent.

Table 1.1 gives values of characteristic impedances for a number of different materials. As a useful exercise the reader can calculate values of α_t and α_r for a number of pairs of materials. For example, it will be found that, because gases have very low characteristic impedances, almost 100 per cent reflection and practically no transmission will take place at a boundary between a gas and a solid or liquid. At a boundary between a solid and a liquid the value of the transmission coefficient may be of the order of 10 per cent. This may appear to be low but, in practice, it represents a drop in intensity of only a few decibels, which would still leave plenty of acoustic energy available for use.

The efficiency of the transfer of sound energy from one material to another, as expressed by the transmission coefficient, is known as the degree of acoustic *matching* or *coupling*. Where α_t is very low, the two media are said to be poorly matched or coupled but where the value of α_t is sufficiently high for a loss of only a few decibels (say a value of about

15

10 per cent) the media are said to be well matched. Ultrasonic waves are often propagated in a solid material by a crystal or a magnetostrictive transducer. If the surfaces of the transducer and the solid are placed together, unless they are both flat to a very high degree of precision (i.e. optically flat), they will be in contact in only a few places and, in practice, a layer of air will separate them. This results in very little sound energy being transmitted. However, if a liquid fills the air gap between the surfaces (a film of oil would do), the degree of coupling is greatly improved because of the very large increase in the characteristic impedance of the intervening layer. Alternatively, both the transducer and the solid medium can be immersed in a liquid in such a way that their surfaces are kept at some fixed distance apart.

The introduction of a third medium, however, does give rise to certain complications and the resultant value of the transmission coefficient may not necessarily be obtained by multiplying together the coefficients for each of the two boundaries. Much will depend on the thickness and the characteristic impedance of the material of the intervening layer and also on the wavelength.

Thus, if the thickness of the layer is equal to a whole number of half-wavelengths, sound will be transmitted as though the intervening medium were non-existent. This is, however, an ideal situation which is difficult to apply in practice to ultrasonic waves for two reasons. The first is that, because the wavelengths used are short, a high degree of precision is required for the determination of the thickness of the layer. The second is that transmission does not take place at a single frequency but over a band of frequencies extending to both sides of the centre frequency (see Sect. 1.2.3). For pulsed waves this band may be very wide (see Sect. 1.13) and a given thickness will be equal to an exact number of half-wavelengths for only one of the frequencies in the band. However, where the frequency band is reasonably narrow and the characteristic impedance of the intervening layer is not too far removed in value from the characteristic impedances of the outer media (e.g. where a liquid lies between two solids), a departure of not more than a decibel or two from the ideal case might be expected.

Where the intervening medium is thin compared with any of the wavelengths of the propagated sound and the characteristic impedance of this medium does not differ too much from that of the other two media, we have another example of transmission taking place as though the intervening medium were absent. This would, of course, not apply to a thin air gap between two solids where the frequency is high, because (a) the characteristic impedances differ greatly and (b) the wavelength in air is short and may not be large compared with the thickness of the gap, e.g. at a frequency of 1 Mc/s the wavelength in air is about 0·3 mm as compared with about 5 mm is metals.

A special case arises where the thickness of the intervening medium is equal to a quarter-wavelength or an odd number of quarter-wavelengths. Where the characteristic impedance has a value which is the mean of that of the characteristic impedances for the two outer media, the resultant transmission coefficient will amount to almost 100 per cent. A well-known example of this occurs in optics where the technique of 'blooming' is applied to the design of lenses.

1.7.2 REFLECTION AND TRANSMISSION AT OBLIQUE INCIDENCE

An interesting phenomenon is observed when a beam of longitudinal waves in a liquid strikes a plane solid surface at some oblique angle i to the normal (see Fig. 1.11). There will be, as one might expect, a beam of

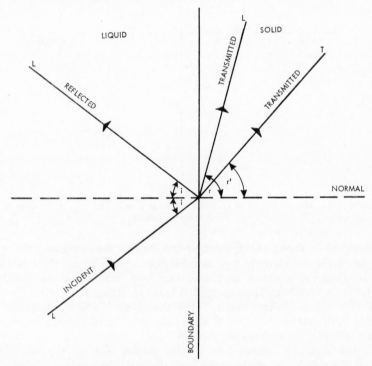

Fig. 1.11. *Double refraction of sound waves in a solid (L—longitudinal waves, T—transverse waves)*

longitudinal waves reflected back into the liquid on the other side of the normal at the same angle i. However, in general, two beams will be transmitted into the solid, refracted at different angles r and r', respectively, to the normal. The first of these consists of longitudinal waves and the second of transverse waves polarized in planes perpendicular to the surface. The speeds c_1 of the longitudinal waves in the liquid, c_2 of the longitudinal waves in the solid, and c_2' of the transverse waves in the solid are related as follows:

$$c_1/\sin i = c_2/\sin r = c_2'/\sin r' \qquad (1.20)$$

17

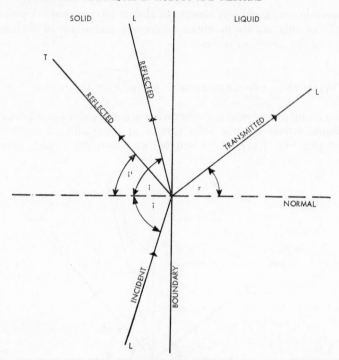

Fig. 1.12. Double reflection of sound waves in a solid (L—longitudinal waves, T—transverse waves)

The equation shows that r' must always be less than r because the speed of the transverse waves in a given solid must always be less than the speed of longitudinal waves in that solid (see Sect. 1.5). Now the speeds of longitudinal waves in liquids are nearly always less than those of longitudinal waves in solids. In this case c_1 is less than both c_2 and c_2', so that r and r' are both greater than i, with the result that the transmitted beams are both refracted away from the normal.

If the angle i is increased to a value greater than i_{c1}, the first critical angle, for which r would be equal to 90 degrees, only transverse waves can pass through the solid. On increasing the angle i still further, a second critical angle i_{c2} is reached, for which the transverse waves would be refracted at an angle of 90 degrees, i.e. they are propagated along the surface of the solid. These are called *surface waves* and have properties which differ from those of transverse waves in materials in bulk. For values of i greater than i_{c2}, propagation in the solid is no longer possible.

On the other hand, when a beam of longitudinal waves in a solid strikes a boundary with a liquid at an angle i to the normal as in Fig. 1.12, a beam of longitudinal waves passes into the liquid at some angle r to the normal, as expected, and two beams are reflected back into the solid. The first contains longitudinal waves reflected at the angle i and the second contains transverse waves polarized, as before in planes perpen-

18

dicular to the boundary. In the latter case the angle of reflection is i', which is related to the other angles as follows:

$$c_1/\sin i = c_1'/\sin i' = c_2/\sin r \qquad (1.21)$$

where, this time, c_1 represents the speed of longitudinal waves and c_1' the speed of transverse waves in the solid, c_1 being greater than c_1'. c_2 is the speed of longitudinal waves in the liquid. It is seen that because c_1' must be less than c_1, i' will always be less than i.

The phenomenon, just described, where transverse waves are produced as a result of the reflection or refraction of longitudinal waves is usually called *mode conversion*.

1.8 STATIONARY OR STANDING WAVES

We have already seen that when a beam of sound waves strikes, at right-angles, a boundary between two media, some of the waves are reflected backwards. Where the reflected waves form a continuous beam, they will interfere with the incident waves and give rise to *stationary* or *standing waves*. Stationary waves are characterized by the appearance of fixed and equally spaced positions of maximum and minimum amplitude, called

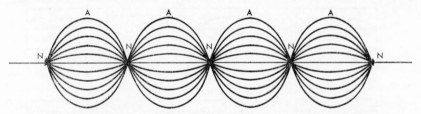

Fig. 1.13. Envelope of stationary waves, showing nodes N and antinodes A

antinodes and *nodes*, respectively (see Fig. 1.13). The wave-form resulting from the superimposed waves will vary in position with time but will always lie within the envelope shown in the diagram.

Perfect nodes will appear only when the amplitude minima are equal to zero, as would be the case when the reflection coefficient at the boundary is 100 per cent and when there is no absorption. In practice there will always be some small finite value of amplitude at a nodal position, depending on what is known as the *standing-wave ratio* (SWR), as given by the following relationship:

$$\text{SWR} = (A_i + A_r)/(A_i - A_r) \qquad (1.22)$$

where A_i is the amplitude of the incident waves and A_r the amplitude of the reflected waves at the boundary. The appearance of perfect nodes would, if this were possible, be indicated by a value of infinity for the standing-wave ratio.

In practice a stationary wave system will be found in any finite sized medium. The sound travels backwards and forwards due to reflection at

19

the end boundaries and, because of losses of energy on reflection and absorption, the intensity of the travelling waves eventually diminishes to zero. For certain values of the length of the medium, the phenomenon of resonance will occur. One can have either *half-wavelength resonance* or *quarter-wavelength resonance*, depending on the nature of the system.

1.8.1 HALF-WAVELENGTH RESONANCE

Half-wavelength resonance is observed in a body which has its end surfaces perpendicular to the direction of propogation of the waves, when its length is equal to a whole number of half-wavelengths. There will be, at each end, either particle displacement antinodes (for a solid immersed in a liquid or gas) or particle displacement nodes (for a fluid bounded at each end by solid surfaces or for a gas having a liquid at one boundary and a solid at the other). The amplitude to which the waves build up at the antinodes determines the Q factor for the system (see Sects. 1.2.3 and 1.2.4), high values of Q being obtained for high reflection coefficients and low absorption, i.e. for high values of the standing-wave ratio.

A body resonates at its fundamental frequency when its length is exactly one half-wavelength and at its second harmonic when it is two

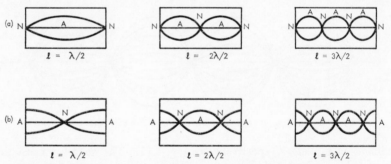

Fig. 1.14. Half-wave length resonances for: (a) displacement nodes at both ends of the medium, (b) displacement antinodes at both ends of the medium

half-wavelengths (i.e. one wavelength) long. The order of the harmonic is equal to the number of half-wavelengths contained by the body (see Fig. 1.14). Resonances can be improved in quality by clamping the body at the nodes and can be suppressed by clamping it at the antinodes.

1.8.2 QUARTER-WAVELENGTH RESONANCE

Quarter-wavelength resonance occurs in a body when it has an antinode at one end and a node at the other, thus containing an odd number of quarter-wavelengths. This can be observed in a liquid, having a solid at one boundary and a gas at the opposite boundary, and also in a solid clamped at one end and left free at its other. The order of the harmonic is determined by the number of quarter-wavelengths contained by the body. However only the fundamental frequency and the *odd* harmonics (i.e. 3rd, 5th . . .) can be excited (see Fig. 1.15).

Let us suppose that a rod is clamped at its centre so that its ends are left free. The fundamental frequency will correspond to the rod being one half-wavelength long. If the clamp is moved to one of the ends of

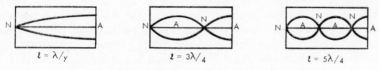

$$l = \lambda/y \qquad l = 3\lambda/4 \qquad l = 5\lambda/4$$

Fig. 1.15. Quarter-wavelength resonances

the rod, to provide a node in that position, the fundamental frequency will be halved because the rod is now a quarter wavelength resonator corresponding to a wavelength twice that as before.

1.9 DIFFRACTION

It has been assumed up to now that a parallel beam of sound waves will emerge from a source having a plane surface and vibrating with simple harmonic motion. This would be true only if the area of the surface were infinite in extent. In practice, because of the finite size of the source, the emergent beam will spread out. This phenomenon is called *diffraction* which is well-known in the study of optics.

Let us consider a source in the form of a plane circular disc vibrating in a piston-like manner in the direction perpendicular to its flat surfaces.

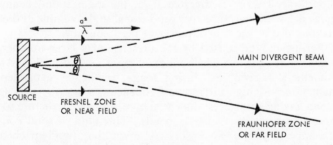

Fig. 1.16. Diffraction of waves from a circular source vibrating in a piston-like manner

It can be shown that within an approximate distance of $D^2/4\lambda$ from the radiating surface, D being the diameter of the disc and λ the wavelength, the beam will be approximately parallel. For distances greater than this the beam is divergent. The divergent beam consists of a main part having a semi-angle of divergence equal to θ and a number of side lobes

21

of very much reduced intensity, all of which appear to originate from near the centre of the radiating surface of the source (see Fig. 1.16). The value of the angle θ is given by the following expression:

$$\sin \theta = 1 \cdot 22 \lambda / D \qquad (1.23)$$

The region where the beam is parallel is called the *Fresnel zone* or the *near field* and the region where the beam is divergent is called the *Fraunhofer zone* or the *far field*.

Thus if D is small compared with λ, the waves diverge at a very short distance in front of the source, i.e. we have, in effect, spherical waves. Consider, for example, the propagation of ultrasonic waves in water, in which the speed of sound is 1,500 m/sec, by a source 2·5 cm (say 1 in) in diameter. At a frequency of 100 kc/s the wavelength is 1·5 cm and the Fresnel zone is about 1 cm in length. On the other hand, at a frequency of 10 Mc/s, the wavelength is only 0·015 cm and the Fresnel zone is over a metre long. In the latter case, where the diameter of the source contains a large number of wavelengths, the beam is said to be highly directional.

1.10 THE SCATTERING OF ULTRASONIC WAVES

Reflection of sound waves will always take place where there is a discontinuity in characteristic impedance. At a plane boundary having dimensions large compared with the wavelength, regular reflection take place in the same way as light is reflected from a mirror. Where, however, the boundary has dimensions which are comparable with or less than one wavelength, scattering takes place, i.e. the beam is reflected in all directions. In the study of ultrasonics the Rayleigh type of scattering, which occurs at boundaries having dimensions small compared with the wavelength, is important. Energy is diverted from the main sound beam and the observed attenuation is directly proportional to the volume of the scattered object and also to the fourth power of the frequency.

Scattering may be caused by the presence of a large number of small particles evenly distributed in liquids and gases (i.e. hydrosols and aerosols); the quietness experienced during foggy weather is explained by this phenomenon. At high ultrasonic frequencies, scattering may take place in a solid having a polycrystalline structure, a type of structure to be found in most commercially available metals. This kind of solid consists of a large number of tiny single crystals, i.e. crystallites, tightly packed together and orientated at random. Now most single crystals are anisotropic, i.e. some of the physical properties, including the speed of sound, vary with direction. Consequently, a beam of sound waves entering a polycrystalline body in a given direction changes its speed in a discontinuous manner on crossing the boundary between adjacent crystallites. Reflection takes place at each boundary and, when the dimensions of the crystallites are small compared with the acoustic wavelength, Rayleigh type scattering occurs.

1.11 THE FOCUSING OF ULTRASONIC WAVES

One method of increasing the acoustic intensity, for example to produce cavitation, without increasing the power of the source, is to focus the beam, i.e. to cause the sound waves to converge to a point. This can be done by using either a concave transducer or an ultrasonic lens (see Fig. 1.17). Because of diffraction, the beam does not actually come to a focus at a point and a high intensity is observed over a small finite region.

Where a concave transducer is used, the focal region will be around the centre of curvature of the surface of the transducer.

Where an ultrasonic lens is used, the focal length F is related to the radii of curvature R_1 and R_2 of its surfaces by the following formula:

$$1/F = [(c_2 - c_1)/c_1](1/R_1 + 1/R_2) \qquad (1.24)$$

where c_1 is the speed of sound in the lens and c_2 the speed in the surrounding medium. For the system to be convergent, R_1 and R_2 must both be positive when c_2 is greater than c_1 or both be negative when c_2 is less than c_1. By the 'real is positive' convention used in optics, R is positive when

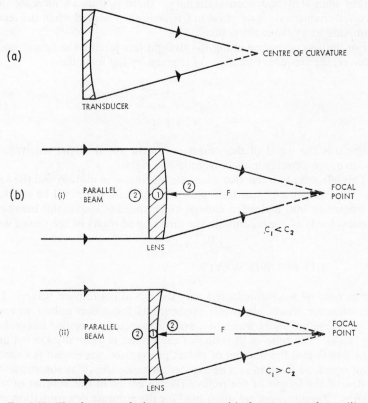

Fig. 1.17. The focusing of ultrasonic waves: (a) focusing transducer, (b) focusing lens, (i) plano-convex lens, (ii) plano-concave lens

23

the convex side of the surface faces the medium having the higher value of c. Thus a converging system is produced by a convex lens when c_2 is greater than c_1 and by a concave lens when c_2 is less than c_1. In practice it is usual to use a plano-convex or plano-concave lens for which R_1 is infinite, i.e. $1/R_1$ is equal to zero.

1.12 THE DOPPLER EFFECT

Where the source or receiver of sound waves is in motion, a change in frequency may be observed. This is called the *Doppler effect*. For example, if one stands by the side of the road and listens to the note emitted by the engine of a passing car travelling at a constant speed, there is a sudden drop in pitch as the car passes. Where the source is travelling towards a stationary receiver, the latter registers an increase in frequency caused by a decrease in wavelength due to the compression of the wavefronts. Where the source is moving away from the receiver, a decrease in frequency of the source is observed. On the other hand, where the receiver is moving towards a stationary source, it receives the wavefronts earlier than if it had been stationary; there is thus an increase in the received frequency. A decrease in frequency is observed when the receiver is moving away from the source.

For motion occurring along the straight line joining the source and the receiver, the frequency change Δf is given by the formula:

$$\Delta f = f \, \frac{1 \pm \dfrac{v}{c}}{1 \pm \dfrac{u}{c}} \tag{1.25}$$

where u is the speed of the source and v the speed of the receiver. The positive sign denotes motion from left to right.

This effect is observed also when the medium is in motion and the source and the receiver are both stationary. In this case there will be no change in frequency but, instead, a change in the speed of sound, this being equal to the velocity of the medium in the direction of travel of the sound waves.

1.13 PULSED WAVES

Up to now we have considered only the use of continuous waves. There are, however, many ultrasonic applications for which pulsed waves are used. These are short trains of waves propagated at regular intervals (see Fig. 1.18). The time of duration of each pulse is generally known as the *pulse length* and the number of pulses propagated per second is called the *pulse repetition frequency*. The expression 'pulse length' is sometimes used to denote the length of the pulse either in cm or in the number of wavelengths. Pulsed waves are often used for the accurate determination of the speed of sound and for the location of defects in materials, because of the

24

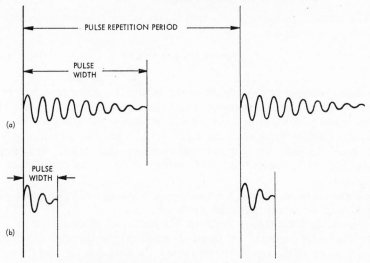

Fig. 1.18. Pulsed waves: (a) light damping, (b) heavy damping

ease of measurement of the time of travel of a short pulse compared with that of a long train of waves. Pulsed waves are also used where the employment of continuous waves would give rise to overheating of either the transducer or the medium.

To obtain pulses of finite length, the transducer should be sufficiently damped for the oscillations to disappear immediately after the required number of waves has been propagated. This operation is usually carried out by mechanical means; for a piezoelectric transducer it is usual for some highly absorbent material to be placed in contact with the rear surface of the crystal, so that the latter executes heavily damped free vibrations when the exciting current has been switched off. In Sect. 1.2.3 it was shown that an increase in the damping of an oscillator results in an increase in the frequency bandwidth. Thus a short pulse may carry a very wide band of frequencies. This must be taken into account for those applications which are frequency dependent.

1.14 HIGH INTENSITY ULTRASONICS

It was mentioned at the beginning of this chapter that high intensity ultrasonic waves are used for doing work on the material being studied and, for this purpose, one or more of the effects of these waves are employed. Some of these effects, such as heating, can take place directly as a result of agitation but others may occur because of the phenomenon of *cavitation*.

Cavitation appears in a liquid as a result of the application of high alternating pressures. It will be observed in boiling water and also in water in the vicinity of a rotating ship's propeller. At sufficiently high intensities. cavitation can be produced by ultrasound.

25

3

The acoustic pressure p in sound waves varies in accordance with the following relationship:

$$p = p_0 \sin(\omega t - kx) \tag{1.26}$$

and has a maximum value of $+p_0$ and a minimum value of $-p_0$. The resultant pressure in any region of the liquid at a given time will be the sum of the hydrostatic pressure P and the acoustic pressure p, the latter being either positive or negative, depending on the phase of the vibrations. Any air bubbles present in the liquid will be subjected to this variable pressure and will thus expand and contract alternately. Where p_0 is sufficiently high, the bubbles will collapse suddenly on contraction and release large amounts of energy almost instantaneously; this is the phenomenon of cavitation. Cavitation can be recognized by an accompanying hissing sound called 'cavitation noise.'

The minimum intensity required for the onset of cavitation is called the *threshold of cavitation* (or *threshold intensity*) and this quantity depends on the nature of the liquid, the frequency, the temperature, and the hydrostatic pressure. An increase in the threshold intensity will occur with increase in frequency and in pressure. Its variation with temperature is governed by the temperature variation of the surface tension and the saturation vapour pressure for the bubble. For water at room temperature, the cavitation threshold remains fairly constant with frequency in the audible range and then increases slowly, at first, and then rapidly at frequencies above about 40 kc/s. Thus cavitation is more easily produced at audible frequencies but this would involve the production of intense highly pitched audible notes which could be extremely unpleasant to anyone in the vicinity. Hence the frequency range 20 to 40 kc/s is normally used for the production of cavitation.

When a coupling fluid is used to pass acoustic energy from the transducer to the working area, unwanted cavitation in this liquid is suppressed by raising its pressure in order to increase the threshold of cavitation by the required amount. Another method is to focus the waves to the region where cavitation is required (see Sect. 1.11).

As one might expect, the onset of cavitation will depend on whether or not bubbles are present in the liquid. Cavitation can be produced in a liquid entirely free from gas bubbles when the acoustic pressure amplitude is greater than the static pressure P. During part of the negative half of each cycle of vibration in a given region of the liquid, the quantity $P - p_0$ becomes negative and the fluid will be under tension. This results in the neighbouring molecules being 'torn apart' and the consequent formation of what are known as 'cavitation voids,' i.e. bubbles containing only the vapour of the liquid. The threshold intensity is very much higher for a liquid entirely free from gas bubbles.

REFERENCES

1. NEWMAN, F. H. and SEARLE, V. H. L., *The General Properties of Matter*, 5th Ed., Arnold, London (1957).
2. BLITZ, J., *Fundamentals of Ultrasonics*, 2nd Ed., Butterworths, London (1967).

2

PRODUCTION OF ULTRASONIC WAVES

B. Brown, B.Sc., Ph.D., A.Inst.P.

2.1 INTRODUCTION

The production of ultrasonic waves can be accomplished in various ways which can be conveniently grouped under three headings; mechanical, piezoelectric and magnetostrictive generators. Ultrasonic energy is produced by the conversion of another form of energy and hence the means for carrying out this conversion is generally referred to by the term 'transducer.' Thus, one refers to a piezoelectric transducer or a magnetostrictive transducer, etc. The type of transducer used in a particular application depends on a number of factors. These include the intensity and frequency required, and the conditions under which the ultrasonic wave is to be propagated, i.e. whether in a gas, liquid, or solid.

Originally all ultrasonic waves were produced by mechanical means, i.e. tuning forks and whistles. Today tuning forks have no practical use although certain types of whistle are useful for processes such as homogenization. In the field of medical ultrasonics, however, mechanical generators play no part in the production of ultrasonic waves and we are only concerned with magnetostrictive and piezoelectric transducers. With these types of transducer electrical oscillations at ultrasonic frequencies and at powers ranging from a fraction of a watt up to several kilowatts are supplied to the transducer. These oscillations are then converted by the transducer into mechanical vibrations in order to produce the ultrasonic waves. As mentioned earlier, the particular application usually determines the type of transducer to be used although in some applications there is a choice, e.g. in the field of hospital cleaning either piezoelectric or magnetostrictive transducers may be used.

In this chapter basic facts concerning the operation of the various types

27

of ultrasonic generator are provided and it is hoped that these will assist the reader to understand how particular ultrasonic generators work and why a certain type of transducer is necessary in a particular application. In addition the importance of correct application of transducers in order to obtain the best results is discussed.

2.2 MAGNETOSTRICTIVE TRANSDUCERS

Magnetostrictive transducers can be used to transform electrical energy to mechanical energy or vice versa. For the production of ultrasonic waves the first effect is utilized and an electrical energy input is converted into mechanical vibrations. The ability of the transducer to convert energy from one form to another is due to its magnetostrictive properties. The magnetostrictive effect was discovered by Joule and refers to the

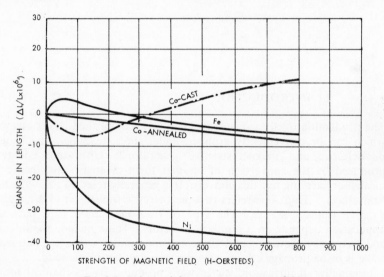

Fig. 2.1. *Relative deformation in magnetic field*

ability of a magnetic material to change its dimensions when it is subjected to a magnetic field. This phenomenon is due to the existence of small regions of magnetic moments in magnetic materials referred to as domains. When a ferromagnetic material is unmagnetized the domains are randomly aligned in one of several directions of so-called easy magnetization. When an external magnetic field is applied to the material the domains begin to move towards the direction of the applied field and during this process the material expands or contracts externally.

The actual changes in dimensions produced by this effect are very small, the relative deformation dl/l being of the order of 10^{-4} to 10^{-6} where dl is the change in length experienced by a rod of length l. If conditions are such that the ferromagnetic rod is subjected to a varying magnetic field

28

so that it is at mechanical resonance, then the relative deformation can be greater, up to 10^{-3}, but limitations are normally imposed by the stresses the material can stand. The actual deformation can be positive or negative and depends on the material. Fig. 2.1 shows the relative deformation of various materials at varying field strengths.

The magnetostrictive effect is also temperature dependent and as the temperature is increased the materials experience a reduction in their magnetic and magnetostrictive properties. Ultimately when the temperature reaches the so-called Curie Point of a particular material then the material loses its magnetic properties completely. Table 2.1 shows the Curie

Table 2.1 CURIE POINTS OF TRANSDUCER MATERIALS

Material	Curie Point °C
Nickel (annealed)	365
Cobalt-Nickel (4% Co-Ni)	410
Cobalt-Nickel (18% Co-Ni)	570
Permalloy (45% Ni-Fe)	440
Alfenol (13% Al-Fe)	500
7 A 2 Ferrite (Ni, Cu, Co ferrite)	530

temperature for several materials used in the construction of magneto-strictive transducers and it is seen that these are fairly high. In the medical and biological applications of ultrasound the temperature is always well below the Curie Points quoted.

Magnetostrictive transducers generally consist of laminated metal stacks upon which a coil is wound. Electrical oscillations from a suitable generator are applied to the coil thereby producing an oscillating magnetic field and hence periodic changes in the length of the metal stack.

For a varying external magnetic field there are two directions of easy magnetization within the magnetic material and thus the average movement would cancel out under ordinary conditions. However an initial magnetization is given to the magnetic material by passing a d.c. polarizing current through the coil and under these conditions when the varying magnetic field is imposed one domain movement is considerably greater than the other thus providing a correspondingly greater change in length.

If the frequency of the oscillatory current and hence of the magnetic field variation is adjusted to be the same as the natural frequency of the rod of magnetic material being used so that it is at mechanical resonance, then the amplitude of vibration becomes quite large. For this reason magnetostrictive transducers are always operated at resonance. In the case of a transducer oscillating freely at its fundamental frequency then its length is equal to a half wavelength of the sound radiated by it and hence its resonant frequency can be calculated by using the formula:

$$f = \frac{V}{2l} \tag{2.1}$$

where V is the velocity of sound in the magnetic material and l is the length of the rod. For a magnetostrictive transducer therefore its operating frequency is determined by the material of which it is made and its length. It will be realized that in order to wind a coil on it a magnetostrictive transducer must have a certain minimum length below which its use becomes impracticable. If it is borne in mind that the velocity of sound in nickel and similar ferromagnetic materials is of the order of 5×10^5 cm/sec then assuming a minimum transducer length of a few cm it is easily seen that the maximum frequency at which a magnetostrictive transducer can operate is about 40 kc/s. As the transducer length is increased so the resonant frequency is decreased. Ultimately a stage is reached where the physical size of the transducers becomes unwieldy and though some Russian workers have used transducers operating at 8 kc/s most commercial transducers are designed to be resonant in the range 13–25 kc/s. Thus magnetostrictive transducers are limited to use at low frequency only. It must also be realized that a particular transducer is only resonant at one particular frequency determined by its length. If an experiment is designed in which frequency variation is necessary then a different transducer must be used for each frequency. Although magnetostrictive transducers are limited to use at low frequencies they can be operated at high power levels and they are particularly useful for the production of intense cavitation since the intensity of cavitation increases with decrease in frequency and increase in power level.

The efficiency of a magnetostrictive transducer, i.e. its ability to convert electrical energy into mechanical vibration, depends on its construction but generally most magnetostrictive transducers operate at efficiencies

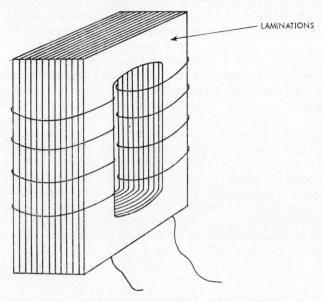

LAMINATIONS

Fig. 2.2. Window type magnetostrictive transducer

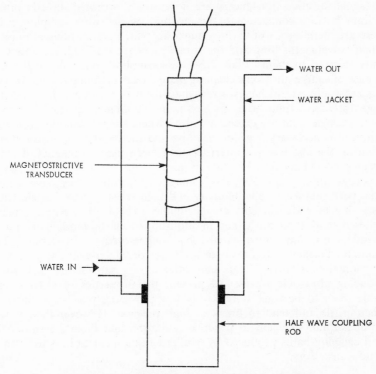

WATER OUT

WATER JACKET

MAGNETOSTRICTIVE
TRANSDUCER

WATER IN

HALF WAVE COUPLING
ROD

Fig. 2.3. Nodally mounted magnetostrictive transducer

of between 30 and 65 per cent. These values can be exceeded by well designed transducers and some commercially available transducers claim to have an efficiency of well over 65 per cent but published figures are not available.

The shape of a magnetostrictive transducer is often determined by the use for which it is intended. The simplest form of transducer is a rod of suitable ferromagnetic material around which the exciting coil is wound. To reduce the effect of eddy currents the rod is usually built up of thin laminations electrically insulated from each other. Plate 2.1 shows a laminated bar transducer designed to operate at 13 kc/s. With such a simple construction, transducers are fairly cheap to produce and easy to replace when necessary. As the operating frequency is increased the transducer length must be decreased and hence its length to diameter ratio decreases. Under these conditions there is a considerable loss of magnetic flux at the end faces and to overcome this loss, window type transducers are used which provide a closed path for the flux. This type of transducer is shown in Fig. 2.2.

Cooling of the transducer is necessary at a high power level and this is accomplished either by immersing the transducer in a water jacket, nodally mounted on a half-wave coupling rod as in Fig. 2.3, or by incorporating a fan to blow air onto the transducer.

31

Magnetostrictive transducers are not usually operated directly into a medium but are connected to the medium by half-wave coupling rods. These are merely rods of various materials which are an integral number of half wavelengths long and the transducers are soldered, cemented, or firmly screwed to them. Plate 2.2 shows coupling rods passing through the base of a large ultrasonic cleaning plant. Each coupling rod has several magnetostrictive transducers screwed to its base as shown in Plate 2.1. Magnetostrictive transducers possess many suitable properties for use at low frequencies and are extensively used where the production of intense cavitation is necessary, e.g. for cleaning and the breakdown of cell walls.

During the last few years ferrites have been used as magnetostrictive transducers. Many ferrites, such as nickel-zinc ferrite possess magnetic properties similar to those of ferromagnetic metals. They have a high initial permeability, small coercivity and high resistivity so that electrical losses due to eddy currents are negligible. The Curie Point for many ferrites is more than 500°C and in addition the elastic modulus is not so dependent on temperature as in other magnetostrictive materials. The potential efficiency of ferrites is of the order of 90 per cent and their cost of production is small. Thus they offer a very satisfactory method of producing ultrasonic waves. At present the properties of ferrites only enable them to be used at relatively low power outputs since they are rather brittle and tend to break at high powers. However their power output is quite sufficient to produce cavitation and Plate 2.3 shows the small cleaning baths produced by Mullard Equipment Ltd., which utilize ferrite transducers.

2.3 POWER SUPPLIES FOR MAGNETOSTRICTIVE TRANSDUCERS

The source of power for magnetostrictive transducers has the task of converting the frequency of the supply network of the locality where the equipment is to operate into electrical oscillations of high frequency. The size and power output of the generator depends entirely on the radiating area of the transducer or transducers to be driven by it and on the level of power required. Valve generators are used and for high output powers, generators with a number of stages are used. The functional diagram of a typical circuit is shown in Fig. 2.4. The frequency is determined by the self-excited oscillator, which can be a variable frequency Wien bridge oscillator. This oscillator is stable only when working at low power and hence for increased power output, voltage and power amplification is necessary. Thus the oscillator feeds an amplifier stage which in turn feeds a push-pull driver stage and a push-pull power amplifier. The output is then taken through the output transformer to the transducers. The generator must also supply the d.c. polarizing current necessary with magnetostrictive transducers and this varies up to 10 A. The d.c. supply is separated from the oscillatory circuit by choke-capacitance coupling. The power output of the generator is usually governed by a

32

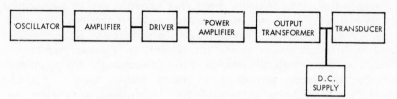

Fig. 2.4. Block diagram of valve generator for driving a magnetostrictive
transducer

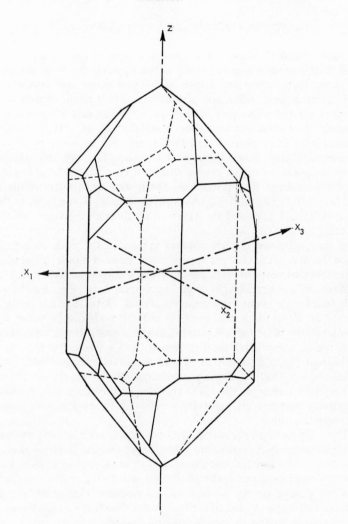

Fig. 2.5. A quartz crystal

control in the amplifier stage. Frequency variation can be accomplished by manual control although in some cases an electro-mechanical feedback system controls the frequency of oscillation so that one generator can be used to drive any one of several transducers, the optimum working frequency being automatically selected. Most generators for driving magnetostrictive transducers provide a continuous output whereas generators for driving piezoelectric transducers may be required to provide a continuous output or a pulsed output depending on the application.

2.4 PIEZOELECTRIC TRANSDUCERS

In 1880 J. and P. Curie found that if a slice of quartz was cut from a crystal in a certain manner, then if the opposite faces of the slice were subjected to pressure, these faces developed equal and opposite charges with a consequent difference of potential. This phenomenon was called the piezoelectric effect and besides quartz it was also observed in several other crystals such as tourmaline, Rochelle salt, etc. It is found that all crystals exhibiting piezoelectricity possess one or more polar axes, i.e. an axis such that, when the crystal is turned through 180° about it, the new configuration of the crystal does not coincide with its configuration prior to turning. The polar axes for quartz are illustrated in Fig. 2.5 and labelled X_1, X_2, and X_3. Axes perpendicular to the faces of the prism are called the Y axes and the axis passing through the vertex of the prism is called the Z axis. When the crystal is subjected to pressure or tension then the maximum electric charges appear at the ends of a polar axis. Since the maximum charges appear at the ends of a polar axis, plates used in piezoelectric experiments are cut from a crystal in such a way that one pair of surfaces are at right angles to a polar axis. Fig. 2.6 shows how a cylindrical plate is cut from a quartz crystal. A plate cut in this manner is termed an X-cut plate, and similarly a Y-cut plate can be cut in which the normal to the plate faces is parallel to the Y-axis. In the case of an X-cut plate pressure applied in the direction of the X-axis charges the two surfaces normal to the X-axis positively and negatively respectively, and this is called the longitudinal direct piezoelectric effect. Tension in the direction of the Y-axis charges the same surfaces in the same way positively and negatively respectively, and it is referred to as the transverse direct piezoelectric effect.

The reciprocal piezoelectric effect was discovered in 1881 by the Curies. If a piezoelectric crystal is brought into an electric field, so that the field direction is the same as the direction of the piezoelectric axis, the crystal changes its dimensions in certain directions. In the case of an X-cut plate, positive charge on the surface bl and negative charge on the opposite surface cause the crystal to expand in the direction of the X-axis and this is referred to as the reciprocal longitudinal piezoelectric effect. Similarly positive charge on the surface bl and negative charge on the opposite surface causes the crystal to be compressed in the direction of the Y-axis and this is known as the reciprocal transverse piezoelectric effect. If the

34

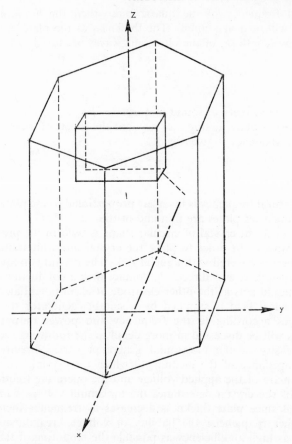

Fig. 2.6. How an X-cut plate is obtained from Fig. 2.5

sign of the charges is reversed then the expansion becomes a contraction and vice versa. The crystal deformation along the X-axis is determined only by the imposed potential difference across the opposite surfaces and it is independent of the crystal dimensions. Deformation along the y-axis is greater as the ratio l/b increases. The actual deformation produced is very small being of the order of $10^{-6} - 10^{-7}$ cm for a potential difference of thousands of volts across a quartz crystal.

The analogy between the inverse piezoelectric effect and the magneto-striction effect is thus obvious and in fact in the case of the piezoelectric effect the relationship between the field acting and the mechanical deformation produced is much simpler than in the case of the magneto-strictive effect. If a piezoelectric quartz crystal is placed in an alternating electric field so that a polar axis is in the direction of the field then the quartz will be alternately expanded and compressed, producing longitudinal ultrasonic oscillations in the surrounding medium. If the electrical frequency is adjusted to be at resonance with the fundamental

35

mechanical frequency of the quartz plate then the amplitude of the oscillation will be a maximum. The thickness of the plate, l, is equal to half the wavelength, λ, of the ultrasonic waves produced so that

$$l = \frac{\lambda}{2} = \frac{V}{2\nu} \qquad (2.2)$$

where V is the velocity of sound in quartz.

For an X-cut plate, taking into account the effects of transverse waves, the natural frequency is given by,

$$f = \frac{2 \cdot 87 \times 10^5}{l} \text{ c/s}$$

Since the natural frequency is inversely proportional to the plate thickness, at high frequencies plates are thin and brittle.

Usually an X-cut crystal of circular shape is used in the production of ultrasonic waves. In order to place the crystal in an alternating electric field, one face is covered with a metal foil. The crystal is frequently used so that the active face is directly in contact with a conducting liquid and hence the liquid acts as the other electrode at earth potential. The alternating electrical field is supplied by a suitable generator the design of which varies according to the frequency and power output required. Generators will be discussed in more detail in the following sections.

The intensity of the ultrasound generated varies directly with the acoustic impedance of the medium to which the crystal is coupled and with the square of the applied voltage and the operating frequency. The thickness of the crystal determines the maximum voltage which can be applied and since plate thickness decreases as frequency increases then at the higher frequencies the liability of voltage breakdown increases. To obtain as high an efficiency as possible the mounting of the crystal is important in order to avoid damping. The method of mounting depend on the application and a number of different types of crystal holders have been designed. These are described in the various chapters dealing with applications.

Provided the ratio of the crystal diameter to the wavelength of the ultrasound produced is large then the ultrasonic beam is propagated in an almost parallel beam perpendicular to the crystal face. However, due to the finite dimensions of the crystal surface and to inhomogeneity in the plate it is found that there is a slight divergence of the beam as it leaves the crystal surface. This divergence must be taken into account when it is required to irradiate only a limited area of human tissue.

The power output obtainable from a quartz transducer represents quite a high acoustic intensity per unit area of transducer radiating face. For instance in the treatment of Ménière's disease the Federici equipment uses a quartz crystal 4·1 cm in diameter. The applied voltage across the crystal which operates at 1 Mc/s is 3500 V and this enables an output of up to 6 W/cm^2 to be obtained. Occasionally it may be necessary to achieve even higher intensities at a particular point and this may be done by the use

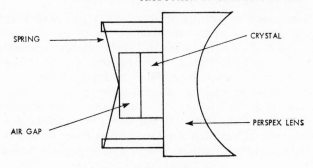

SPRING

CRYSTAL

AIR GAP

PERSPEX LENS

Fig. 2.7. Plano-concave lens

of acoustic lenses and reflectors. Synthetic resin lenses have been used to focus ultrasonic waves and the general arrangement is shown in Fig. 2.7. The material of which the lenses are made is important since in many materials acoustic losses are high and considerable internal temperature rises take place. Reflectors normally consist of concave metal mirrors and these are useful for focusing ultrasound in liquids. To a large extent however the use of reflectors has been superseded by the development of synthetic piezoelectric materials which can be moulded into any desired shape and hence, which may be constructed in such a way as to produce a focussed ultrasound beam at a particular point.

These materials include barium titanate ($BaTiO_3$) and lead zirconate-titanate and in the last few years they have largely replaced quartz as a piezoelectric material for ultrasonic transducers. The ability of barium titanate to act as a piezoelectric material is due to its ferro-electric properties, i.e. its ability to change its electrical polar structure under the influence of a strong electric field and then to retain the new orientation after removal of the field. Thus whereas the originally prepared ceramic is not piezoelectric, after a polarizing process, it possesses an overall polarity and piezoelectric properties. If a small alternating electric field is subsequently applied to the crystal then the crystal will alternately become thicker and thinner respectively according to whether the a.c. field is in the same direction as the resonant polarization in the crystal or in opposition to it. Provided the material is constructed in a suitable shape it may thus be conveniently used as an ultrasonic transducer.

Barium titanate offers several advantages over quartz as a transducer material. From a commercial viewpoint it is far cheaper to produce and it is also much easier to construct transducers of complex shape and large area. Since the polar axis is determined completely by the direction of the initial external applied electric field, transducers can be made in a concave shape which, by their focusing action can produce high intensity ultrasonic radiation at a point as shown in Fig. 2.8. For instance Gordon has used a barium titanate bowl transducer with focal length 10 cm in his work. Barium titanate has a relatively low electrical impedance and quite low voltages are used to excite the crystal into vibration. In a typical case to obtain the same ultrasonic output from a barium titanate or a quartz

37

crystal would require voltages of about 100 V and 1000 V respectively. The disadvantages of barium titanate are mainly its comparatively low efficiency and fairly low Curie point. The efficiency is probably greater than 50 per cent but it is certainly inferior to that of quartz. The low Curie point of barium titanate, about 100°C to 120°C, limits its use at high intensities since at high powers internal energy losses give rise to heat in the crystal and sufficient heating can result in the crystal being depolarized.

Recently a new and improved polycrystalline ceramic for use as a transducer material has been developed. It is based on a solid solution of lead zirconate-titanate and has several advantages over barium titanate,

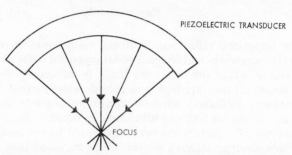

Fig. 2.8. Ceramic bowl transducer to produce a focused beam

an important one being its high Curie point of about 250°C to 320°C. This enables the transducers to be used under temperatures well above those possible with barium titanate. In addition, it enables coupling stubs (to be discussed later) or protecting plates to be soft soldered to the crystal without causing depolarization. The dielectric loss of the material is low and this reduces the production of internal heat. The actual tensile strength of the material is about the same as that of barium titanate but the increased dielectric strength enables the limit to be more nearly approached. Lead zirconate-titanate can be driven at much larger strain amplitudes than most ceramics and hence for the same power handling capacity smaller volume crystals can be used. The many advantages of lead zirconate-titanate are resulting in a widespread use of the material in ultrasonic equipment and most new equipment being manufactured which is based on piezoelectric transducers utilizes lead zirconate-titanate crystals. Like barium titanate, the material can be manufactured in a variety of shapes and at present various sizes of discs, tubes, and blocks are available. Crystals can be obtained to produce vibrations over a wide frequency range, from 25 kc/s, in sandwich form, for applications such as cleaning, to 3 Mc/s as in surgical therapy equipment.

Compound oscillators, i.e. a combination of a piezoelectric material and a metal plate or plates, are also used to obtain ultrasonic oscillations. The first use of this type of transducer was described by Langevin in 1921 who used a quartz plate sandwiched between two steel plates. The sandwich transducer oscillates as a whole and has an advantage over a quartz plate with the same resonant frequency in that its impedance is

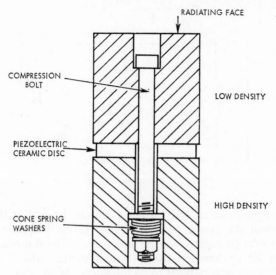

Fig. 2.9. Modern sandwich transducer

considerably reduced and it provides a higher power output. In the original sandwich transducers the components were firmly cemented together but in modern sandwich transducers, no cement is used, the transducer elements being merely pressed together by bolts. Fig. 2.9 shows the general form of a modern sandwich type transducer. These transducers provide a higher efficiency than barium titanate transducers and they are also much more robust. They have a low mechanical Q value which is an advantage in so far as it overcomes the necessity for exact tuning to resonance required with other types of transducer. Currently lead zirconate-titanate sandwich transducers are extensively used in low frequency high power applications.

2.5 POWER SUPPLIES FOR PIEZOELECTRIC TRANSDUCERS

The design of the oscillatory circuit used to supply electrical oscillations to the piezoelectric transducer depends on the type of material used as a transducer. Whereas one circuit may be quite useful for driving a quartz crystal, a different circuit design is necessary for lead zirconate-titanate. In addition the circuit design is also governed by the frequency output required and the power output necessary.

A circuit useful for driving quartz transducers in air or gases is due to Pierce and is illustrated in Fig. 2.10. The quartz crystal is connected between the grid and anode of the valve. A milli-ammeter is incorporated into the circuit to indicate changes in the intensity of vibrations of the crystal. If the quartz is set into its natural vibration by a disturbance the mechanical deformation produces alternating voltages at its electrodes

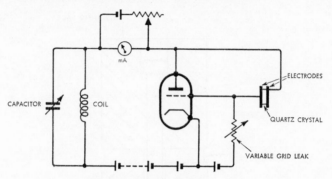

Fig. 2.10. Pierce oscillatory circuit

by the direct piezoelectric effect. These act on the grid at the valve and thereby control the anode current at the correct frequency. Thus the quartz is set into stronger vibration and so on. The stationary condition of vibration set up has a frequency equal to the natural frequency of vibration of the crystal parallel to its thickness. While this circuit is quite suitable for the production of ultrasonic waves in gases, it is quite unsuitable for the generation of waves in liquids and solids as the damping of the crystal stops the reaction.

To overcome damping of the crystal it is more usual to employ a Hartley oscillator, the circuit diagram of which is shown in Fig. 2.11. In this circuit the quartz crystal is placed in parallel with the capacitance of the oscillatory circuit, the oscillatory circuit being made up of an inductance and a variable capacitance. The oscillations produced are imposed on the quartz crystal and adjusted to the natural frequency of the crystal by variation of the capacitance. It has previously been mentioned that the amplitude of vibration of the quartz crystal is proportional to the applied voltage. Hence when a high power output is required it is usual to transform up the alternating voltage produced by the oscillator.

Power supplies for barium titanate and lead zirconate-titanate transducers are somewhat different from those used for driving quartz crystals. A lower voltage output is required and thus fewer insulation problems arise. The impedances of ceramic transducers vary according to the frequency of operation and size of the crystal and there is relatively little variation between one ceramic material and another. As the frequency of operation increases problems arise since as the crystal becomes thinner its capacitance rises and its impedance falls. This necessitates a step-down transformer of larger ratio being used in the generator circuit which results in a lower efficiency. This disadvantage can be overcome to some extent by using a thicker crystal and operating it at an odd harmonic. Thus the capacitance which has to be tuned is reduced and the load impedance which has to be matched is increased.

In the use of quartz it can normally be assumed that the correct operating frequency is a fixed quantity and this can be ensured by a technique such as the crystal controlled oscillator. This assumption cannot be made in

Plate 2.1.   Laminated 13 kc/s magneto-strictive transducers (Courtesy Ultrasonics Ltd.)

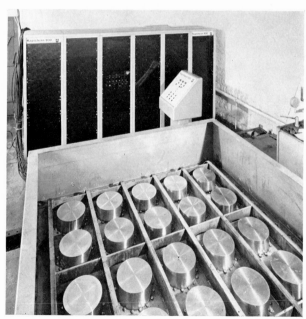

Plate 2.2.   Half-wave coupling rods (Courtesy Ultrasonics Ltd.)

Plate 2.3. *Cleaning ferrite components with ultrasonic equipment.* (Left) *the 100-watt amplifier and* (right) *the 4-litre cleansing bath.* (*Courtesy M.E.L. Equipment Co. Ltd.*)

Plate 2.4. *Step transformer being used to emulsify oil and water.* (*Courtesy Dawe Inst. Ltd.*)

the case of ceramic crystals however. The large temperature coefficient of the material may cause a variation in frequency of more than 1 per cent and hence variable frequency tuning is necessary. If the generator is to be used to drive different transducers the variable frequency tuning is even more necessary.

In one ultrasonic generator for use in the medical field, the Friston Mark 5 generator, a tetrode oscillator valve is provided with a plug-in coil which is tuned by two variable capacitors, a small one controlled from the panel and also a larger pre-set which can only be reached when the chassis is removed from its case. The driving voltage can be controlled by varying the screen volts and this permits automatic control of the power level.

Practically, variations in the power level cause changes in the valve capacitances and supply voltages which prevent the frequency from remaining stable. Thus it is essential to have some form of tuning indicator and in early generator design a rough indication was provided by incorporating a meter in the anode circuit of the power stage. Another method adopted was the use of a diode voltmeter connected to a separate silvered area on the crystal, i.e. a monitoring electrode. While this indicates the approximate optimum frequency it is unsatisfactory since it is possible to show large voltages when there is little acoustic output at frequencies slightly off optimum.

More exact tuning is accomplished by utilizing the Lissajous figures produced on a cathode ray oscilloscope. Basically these figures are produced by connecting the active drive electrode of the transducer to an X-plate and the monitoring electrode to a Y-plate of the oscilloscope. In practice a phase-shift network is placed between the end of the transducer cable and the deflection plates. It consists of an inductance and variable capacitor in parallel with one end earthed and the other connected to the deflection plate and through a resistance to the transducer cable. When the capacitor and inductance are in resonance the system becomes a voltage divider and the resistance can be varied to change the sensitivity of the tuning indicator. With similar phase-shift arrangements in both leads it is possible to find capacitor settings such that when the tuning is

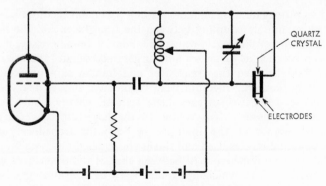

Fig. 2.11. Hartley oscillatory circuit

41

4

correct, as measured by the acoustic power, the Lissajous figure is a straight line. At all other frequencies it is an oval. With the tuning indicator correctly adjusted the relationship between the acoustic power and the square of the monitor voltage is approximately linear. Thus the voltmeter may be calibrated in watts on a square law.

For ultrasonic generators supplying high power at low frequencies, such as in cleaning applications, it is quite a simple matter to make the system self oscillating and thus the frequency varies as required. This is usually accomplished by providing the transducer with a large silvered area connected to the power stage of the oscillator and a small silvered area provided with an amplifier which feeds the power stage. At the higher frequencies used in medical applications this method of self oscillation is not suitable as it is found that the circuit tends to tune itself to a point just off resonance. Also at low power levels the system will not operate at all. This disadvantage has been overcome to some extent by the introduction of various modifications in the circuit and a self oscillatory system is particularly useful in applications where a long period of ultrasonic irradiation is required, such as the treatment of Ménière's disease.

Thus it is clear that the design of an ultrasonic generator for a particular application obviously depends on the requirements of the particular application. Factors which affect the circuit design are choice of frequency, intensity output required, pulsed or continuous output, degree of tuning necessary and so on. Several circuits have been designed for specific applications and the interested reader can refer to the references provided.

Transistorized power supplies are available but only when a small power output is required, i.e. in the treatment of Ménière's disease. Small cleaning units also incorporate transistors. However for higher power outputs at the present time it is more reliable and economical to utilize valve generators. It is possible however that in the near future transistorized supplies may also be available over the whole range of power output.

2.6 TRANSDUCER COUPLING AND VELOCITY TRANSFORMERS

In order to propagate ultrasonic waves in a particular medium it is necessary to have suitable coupling between the transducer and the medium. The propagation of ultrasonic waves in solids, i.e. human tissue, necessary in applications such as diagnosis and surgery necessitates the use of some coupling fluid between the transducer and human skin on which it is placed. If no coupling medium were used, then, due to the very poor contact between the two surfaces, little acoustic energy would be transmitted into the tissue. This is due to the large difference in specific acoustic impedance at the interface between the transducer and air. Hence a coupling fluid is used and this is chosen as far as possible to have a specific acoustic impedance in between that of the transducer material and the medium into which the sound is to be transmitted. Coupling fluids used in medical applications depend on the part of the body being treated. For ophthalmic examination and diagnosis water coupling between the transducer and eye has been found excellent. For abdominal examination and diagnosis the transducer can be pressed fairly close to the skin and a suitable cream can be used as a coupling medium. Olive oil has also been used. For diagnosis or ultrasonic surgical treatment of the head, coupling between the transducer and skull is not as easy due to the hard bony nature of the skull. Some workers have reported the use of a mixture of polyethylene glycol 1500 and polyethylene glycol 400 as a coupling medium. Another technique is to place the head in a tank filled with water, the water acting as the coupling medium. This technique of water immersion has been used for examination of various parts of the body, the advantage being that the transducer probe can be moved round in the water to scan the part in every direction. By this technique most of the soft tissue structures in the neck and limbs can be seen. The method does have the disadvantage, however, that it subjects the patient to some inconvenience and from this aspect the other coupling methods described are better.

For high intensity applications where the transducer is required to propagate the ultrasonic waves in liquids, e.g. cleaning, disruption of cell walls, etc., other methods are used to couple the transducer to the liquid. Theoretically of course, the simplest method of coupling is to place the transducer directly in the liquid concerned. However, with crystal transducers the damping effect of the liquid on the crystal surface may be appreciable. In addition, many liquids are not sufficiently good insulators, particularly in the case of quartz which requires a high operating voltage. Liquids may also be corrosive and attack the transducer material. Generally, therefore, transducers are not placed directly in liquids but are coupled, the exact mechanism of the coupling depending on the type of transducer.

Quartz crystals are normally used in holders which expose only one side of the crystal to the liquid. Barium titanate and lead zirconate-titanate transducers can be bonded with an epoxy resin to the outside wall of a chamber in which the liquid is placed.

For applications which require local application of high intensity vibration at a particular point both barium titanate and lead zirconate-titanate transducers can be coupled to the medium by half-wavelength rods. Velocity transformers to provide larger amplitudes of vibration are also used and several different applications have been reported.

As mentioned earlier, magnetostrictive transducers are normally coupled to liquid media by the use of half-wave rods, this enabling cooling of the transducer to be conveniently carried out. In small scale work, usually only one transducer is used, but in large scale applications as shown earlier, several transducers can be attached to a coupling stub. The length of a half wave rod of a particular material can readily be calculated knowing the velocity of sound in the material and the desired frequency of vibration.

It is often desirable to obtain high ultrasonic intensities at a particular point and in order to accomplish this velocity transformers can be used. These consist of metal half-wave rods but of tapering rather than uniform

43

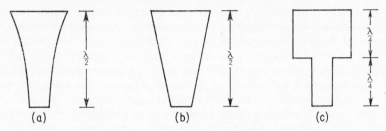

Fig. 2.12. Velocity transformers: (a) Exponential, (b) Conical, (c) Quarter wave cylindrical step transformer

diameter. Such transformers are analogous to the acoustic horns used with loudspeakers. Any type of tapering will give an increase in the amplitude of motion and three types of tapers are in common use, the exponential, the conical, and the cylindrical quarter wave step taper. These are illustrated in Fig. 2.12.

In the case of a resonant exponential taper, the particle velocity is increased at the small end in the ratio of the square root of the inverse area ratio or more simply in the inverse diameter ratio, i.e. the velocity transformation ratio is

$$R = \frac{d_1}{d_2}$$

where d_1 and d_2 are the large input and small output diameters respectively.

In the case of a resonant conical taper the particle velocity is increased at the small end in a rather more complicated manner than in the exponential taper. The transformation ratio is given by

$$R = \frac{d_1}{d_2}\left[\cos\left(\frac{2\pi l}{\lambda}\right) - \frac{(d_1/d_2 - 1)}{\frac{d_1 2\pi l}{\lambda d_2}} \cdot \sin\left(\frac{2\pi l}{\lambda}\right)\right]$$

where l is the length of the taper and λ is the wavelength of shear waves in the material.

A velocity transformer frequently used is the double quarter wave cylindrical step transformer. This can be conveniently produced and consists of two cylinders each a quarter of a wavelength long joined together to form a transformer half a wavelength long. Normally this type of transformer is produced by the machining of a single block of metal. For an input diameter d_1 and output diameter d_2 the velocity transformation ratio is given by

$$R = \left(\frac{d_1}{d_2}\right)^2$$

Thus this type of transformer provides a large transformation but it also gives rise to a large stress at the centre and if the ratio of the end diameters is too great it is common for the transformer to fracture.

44

Velocity transformers are used over a wide range of frequencies and for various applications. Plate 2.4 illustrates a step transformer being used to demonstrate ultrasonic emulsification. The transformer is attached to a lead zirconate-titanate transducer operating at a frequency of 20 kc/s. This particular apparatus is very useful in the breakdown of cell walls in order to extract the contents. Fig. 9.6 shows a section through a transducer assembly developed for the treatment of Ménière's disease. The operational frequency is 3 Mc/s and it may be seen that the conical applicator results in an increase in ultrasonic intensity at the point of application. Further details of various velocity transformers are provided in the appropriate chapters.

BIBLIOGRAPHY

CRAWFORD, A. E., *Ultrasonic Engineering*, Butterworth (1955).
HUETER, T. F. and BOLT, R. H., *Sonics*, Wiley (1955).
BROWN, B. and GOODMAN, J. E., *High Intensity Ultrasonics*, Iliffe Books Ltd. (1965).
BERGMANN, L., *Der Ultraschall*, Hirzel (1954).

3

ENERGY MEASUREMENT

E. A. Lloyd, B.Sc., Grad. Inst. P., Grad. I.E.R.E.

3.1 INTRODUCTION

When ultrasonic equipment is used in physical experiments, the parameters which must be known to allow for the interpretation and reproducibility of results are:

1. The frequency, duration and mode of the transducer's operation (i.e. pulsed, A.M., F.M., C.W. etc.).
2. Its total effective radiating area.
3. The total power delivered by the transducer to the medium to which it is coupled. (Gross Acoustic Power Transfer, G.A.P.T.).
4. The Intensity distribution within the field of the transducer.

Power is defined in Physics generally as work done or transferred per unit time and is measured in Watts or ergs/sec (1 W = 10⁷ ergs/sec). In this context G.A.P.T. is the power delivered by the transducer to the medium of interest and does not include the power losses in the transducer mount, electrical power losses etc. Sound intensity, ultrasonic or otherwise, is the amount of energy passing through unit area normal to the direction of propagation and is measured either in W/m² or ergs/cm². The sound intensity (I) of a plane progressive wave in the direction of propagation is defined by the following equations:

$$I = \rho c(\omega A)^2 = \rho c u^2 = p^2/\rho c = pu \qquad (3.1)$$

A represents the r.m.s. amplitude of the mechanical waves in a medium of density ρ in which the waves of angular frequency ω propagate at a velocity c. The r.m.s. amplitude of the particle pressure is denoted by p and u is the r.m.s. value of the particle velocity. Evidently, measurement

46

of the sound intensity at any point within the field of an ultrasonic transducer involves the measurement of one or more of the following quantities:

(a) The particle velocity amplitude (u).
(b) The particle pressure amplitude (p); or
(c) The amplitude (A) of the waves in the medium.

To specify completely the characteristics at a point within the field, the direction of the particle velocity and the phase relationship between the pressure and the particle velocity ought also to be measured. In order to respond to any of these parameters, the dimensions of the detecting device must be small compared with the wavelength of the ultrasound in the medium. Few devices are so dimensioned and those that are, usually respond to only a single field characteristic.

The piezoelectric probe which can be made very small, responds to the particle pressure and can usefully be used in liquids up to a frequency of 20 Mc/s. The thermoelectric probe can yield directly a measure of both the particle velocity and pressure amplitudes in acoustic fields of all types including plane progressive and standing-wave. For a plane progressive field the probe yields directly a measure of the acoustic intensity, since energy is transported in fields of this type, whereas in a standing-wave field the probe measures the energy density.

When used at ultrasonic frequencies, particularly in liquids, Rayleigh discs, pressure membranes and other forms of mechanical receiver generally fail to measure, directly, any of these quantities. This is principally because their dimensions are in practice considerably greater than those of the sound waves they are intended to measure. Mechanical receivers have nevertheless long been applied, with success, to the measurement of ultrasonic powers and intensity, but rely for their operation on the force exerted on an object placed in a beam of ultrasound. When an ultrasonic beam traverses a medium, energy is transported and is accompanied by a flow of momentum. At an interface between acoustically dissimilar materials there is a change of momentum per unit area of interface. It is the rate at which this change of momentum occurs which constitutes a radiation pressure at the interface and it is to this quantity that most mechanical receivers respond. For a plane progressive wave of infinite extent in a loss-less medium, there is no rate of change of momentum and no radiation pressure effects are observed. In a lossy medium however, there is a continuous change in the rate of change of momentum due to absorption, and the radiation force on the medium gives rise to a mass flow in the direction of ultrasonic propagation. This streaming effect, acoustic or quartz wind, as it is often described, is in fact a very sensitive indication that absorption is taking place.

Apart from these direct methods optical and calorimetric methods have been widely used. So too has the effect of ultrasonic radiation on photographic and other organic films. Recently ultrasonic waves traversing electrolytes and other solutions have been observed to develop vibration potentials within the medium. Developments of this sort should in the future add to the means available for ultrasonic power and intensity measurements.

47

3.2 ULTRASONIC POWER MEASUREMENT

Before examining the means now available for power measurement in greater detail it is advisable to examine the effects of the environment in which measurements are made on the accuracies attainable. The simplest model for this examination is that of a power meter terminating, for example, water-borne ultrasound at normal incidence. There can be no interaction between transmitter and power meter due to reflected energy in this case because the source is assumed at infinity. For power meters of the absorbing calorimeter type, the power available at the meter and the power actually indicated by the meter will vary with the specific acoustic impedance presented by the meter to the water column. If the impedances of the water and meter are equal the Impedance Ratio of the meter is unity and the power indicated by the meter (P_1) is a maximum. If P_0 is the power available at a meter with an Impedance Ratio (I.R.) which differs from unity, the power delivered to and capable of being indicated by the meter is

$$P_1 = P_0(1 - \alpha_m) \tag{3.2}$$

where α_m is defined as the reflection factor of the meter and is equal to

$$\alpha_m = (r - 1)^2/(r + 1)^2 \tag{3.2}$$

and $\qquad r = \text{Impedance Ratio of the meter} = Z_m/Z_0$

Z_m and Z_0 are the characteristic impedances of the meter and water column respectively and are numerically equal to the moduli of the complex specific acoustic impedances $\hat{Z}_m$ and $\hat{Z}_0$.

In practice therefore

$$r = Z_m/Z_0 = \rho_m c_m/\rho_0 c_0$$

To illustrate this point, consider the case of a water borne column of ultrasound terminated at normal incidence by absorption meters of in one case castor oil and in the other polystyrene. The characteristic impedances of these materials are:

$$\text{Water } (Z_0) = (\rho_0 c_0) = 0 \cdot 143 \times 10^6$$
$$\text{Castor oil } (Z_m)_2 = (\rho_m c_m)_1 = 0 \cdot 141 \times 10^6$$
$$\text{Polystyrene } (Z_m)_2 = (\rho_m c_m)_2 = 0 \cdot 294 \times 10^6$$

Substituting these quantities into the relevant equations the result is that if the incident power is 1 W, the castor oil meter will indicate 1 W whereas the polystyrene meter would indicate 0·89 W.

A similar treatment applied to meters of the scattering or reflecting type show that the maximum power indicated by the meter $(P_1)^1$ is given by:

$$P_1{}^1 = P_0 \alpha_m \quad \text{where} \quad \alpha_m \text{ is defined as before}$$

Meters of this type approximate to the infinitely rigid reflector ($u = 0$ at the surface) and the air cell type of reflector ($p = 0$ at the surface). In the first case $Z_m = \infty$ whereas in the latter case $Z_m = 0$. Substitution of these values into the expression indicates that for an incident energy of 1 W the rigid reflector will indicate 1 W whereas the air reflector would indicate an incident energy of twice this value.

These simplified examples have been used to illustrate the need for the proper selection of detector material and have shown that an *a priori* knowledge of the materials used, could enable meter indications to be corrected. However, the simplifying assumption that the meter terminates an infinite transmission line does not often occur in practice. The separation between source and meter is finite and interaction is an all too common occurrence. When source and meter are able to interact freely the indicated power is a function of both the amplitude and phase of the meter and source reflection factors. Theoretically it should be possible to terminate the line in a meter whose impedance is the conjugate of that of the source (i.e. resistive components equal, reactive components equal but of opposite sign). In this case the meter would give a true indication of the incident power. In practice, however, the complex impedance ratio at both source and meter cannot be measured and only the modulus of this factor can be determined from known values of the characteristic impedances of the various materials used. On this basis it is only possible to indicate that if a given source, with impedance ratio r_0, is attached through a column of material to a meter, with impedance ratio r_m, the power delivered and indicated by the meter would lie within a range with limits $P_{1\ max}$ and $P_{1\ min}$ where:

$$P_{1\ max} = P_m[1 - (\alpha_m)_1]; \quad (\alpha_m)_1 = (r_m r_0 - 1)^2/(r_m r_0 + 1)^2$$

and

$$P_{1\ min} = P_m[1 - (\alpha_m)_2]; \quad (\alpha_m)_2 = (r_m/r_0 - 1)^2/(r_m/r_0 + 1)^2$$

For matched meters of the castor oil type with $r_m \cong 1$, both these equations reduce to:

$$\alpha_m = (r_0 - 1)^2/(r_0 + 1)^2$$

and
$$P_{1\ max} = P_{1\ min} = P_{in}(1 - \alpha_m)$$

This is identical with the result obtainable if the same transducer is considered to operate into an infinite water column. In this case the power delivered by the transducer P_0 operating at a power level P_{in} is given by:

$$P_0 = P_{in}(1 - \alpha_0); \quad \alpha_0 = (r_0 - 1)^2/(r_0 + 1)^2$$

Evidently for the matched meter case the power indicated by the meter is a true estimate of the power delivered by the transducer.

For mis-matched meters of the polystyrene type (I.R. $\cong$ 2) and transducers of the lead zirconate type (I.R. $\cong$ 8):

$$(\alpha_m)_1 = 0 \cdot 9 \quad \text{and} \quad (\alpha_m)_2 = 0 \cdot 6$$
$$P_{in} = 5 \cdot 2 P_1 \quad \text{or} \quad P_{in} = 1 \cdot 6 P_1$$

If the meter indicates $P_1 = 1$ W, the transducer drive is estimated as lying within the range 5·2 and 1·6 W. The best estimate for the drive power is, therefore, 3·4 ± 1·8 W (±53 per cent). P_1 as a measure of P_0

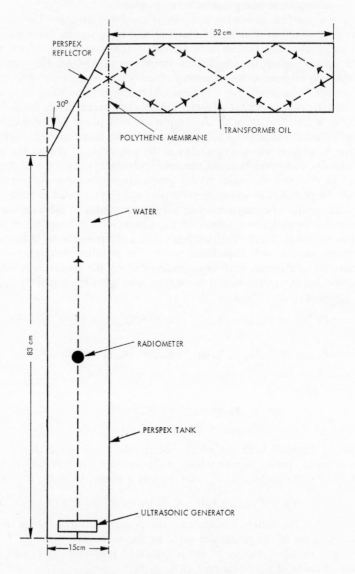

Fig. 3.1. An anechoic tank with main line termination

the power in the ultrasonic field cannot as a result be better than $P_0 = 1 \pm 0\cdot53$ W. Clearly uncertainties of this order could not be tolerated in a practical measurement and it is for this reason that particular care is taken to prevent source and meter interacting in practice. Ideally meters which absorb energy should be properly matched to the line which they terminate and reflect as little as possible of the incident energy. Meters which reflect should be totally reflecting and so shaped that all the incident energy is reflected away from the transducer preferably into some absorbing medium.

When the meter is dimensionally less than the cross section of the incident ultrasound and particularly when the sound field is probed by meters with dimensions comparable with the wavelength of the ultrasound, some form of main line termination is necessary. Various forms of anechoic tank have been developed, but the most successful have been based on the design illustrated in Fig. 3.1. With this particular design the incident ultrasound is deflected into a terminating load by a 30° reflector plate. After successive reflections the beam of ultrasound returns to the reflector plate at normal incidence to be reflected back along its own path. By this means a finite length of absorber can be arranged to provide a very long path for the ultrasound so that finite quantities of highly absorbing material can effectively terminate the transducer in a quasi-infinite section of lossy transmission line. Few anechoic tanks are ideal and some energy is inevitably scattered in the process of power measurement and may ultimately react with the power meter. Meters with highly directional properties are less prone to errors in these circumstances. A directivity coefficient delta δ has been defined by Hueter and Bolt[1] where $\delta = I_0/I_R$. I_0 is the indication on the power meter due to an axial source at some distance x from the meter and I_R is the average indication by the same meter placed at the centre of a uniform spherical source of radius R generating the same total power. Values for δ can range from ± 1 for detectors with spherical symmetry to large numbers for highly directional devices.

The major sources of error in any measurement can be attributed to the meter being neither a perfect reflector or absorber; an error contribution due to lack of proper main line termination and errors due to effects in the region where the meter is mounted. An empirical relationship between the ratio of indicated power (P_1) and power available for measurement (P_0) is given by:

$$P_1/P_0 = A\,(1 + \underset{\substack{\text{(meter} \\ \text{mismatch} \\ \text{error)}}}{\gamma\alpha_t/\delta} + \underset{\substack{\text{(main} \\ \text{line} \\ \text{error)}}}{\beta\alpha_w\alpha_m/\delta}) \tag{3.4}$$

where $A = A_a = (1 - \alpha_m)$ for absorption and $A = A_r = \alpha_m$ for reflection type meters respectively. α_t, α_w and α_m are respectively the reflection factors of the main line termination, the material surrounding the meter and of the meter itself, γ and β are constants.

For the ratio of the power indicated to the power available to approach unity the necessary conditions are:

51

1. The main line should be terminated in a reflectionless load so that α_t approaches zero.
2. The meter should be totally absorbing so that α_m approaches zero.
3. If α_t and α_m cannot be made to approach zero, highly directional meters should be used.
4. Where highly directional properties are not available, the precaution of mounting the meter in a reflectionless enclosure should be taken.

Condition (1) can normally be satisfied by choosing anechoic conditions for the measurement. Condition (2) is usually satisfied by the calorimetric type of meter. Conditions (3) and (4) can only be approximated to by the choice of pulse techniques for power measurement purposes when pulses of ultrasonic power are received by the meter which are time resolved from secondary effects and as such the measurement system has a directivity approaching infinity. The proper choice of absorber with which to surround the meter enclosure further serves to reduce secondary reflection effects.

3.3 DIFFRACTION PHENOMENA

When energy is emitted by a circular piston source many wavelengths in diameter, measurements may be made in either the Fresnel or Fraunhofer regions of that transducer's field. The usual arguments using Fresnel half period zones show that the Fresnel field of a transducer diameter d operating at a frequency with wavelength λ extends as far as points $x_0 = d^2/4\lambda$, distant from the transducer surface. Within this region diffraction effects occur and in a plane normal to the axis of the transducer the field consists of a series of concentric rings, the number of rings increasing with decreasing distance from the transducer surface. Beyond x_0 the beam begins to diverge and the interference pattern begins to disappear until at sufficiently large separations the intensity falls off as x^{-2}. In order that accurate measurements can be made these phenomena have to be taken into consideration.

If power measurement is carried out in the Fresnel region with a meter small compared with the sources dimensions, then a knowledge of the polar distribution is required before it is possible to sum indicated powers in order to arrive at a value for the total power in the field. If on the other hand a perfectly plane detecting system, larger than the source, is set perpendicular to the axis, the measured intensity involves a summation over the whole diffraction pattern. The manner of this summation can be very different for different types of meters. If a meter responds to radiation pressure it is insensitive to phase and the appropriate summation is the arithmetic sum of the intensities at all points. When a piezoelectric material is used as the detector the result is the vector sum of the pressure amplitudes at all points intercepted by the detector. This property makes it very difficult to interpret measurements made in the Fresnel field using large piezoelectric receivers because of their high sensitivity to angular displacement. In particular the output from a square section piezoelectric receiver placed in the Fresnel field of a transducer would drop from a maximum value to zero for an angular displacement from the normal of $\Delta\theta = \lambda/d$, where d is the length of one side of the square section. At frequencies between 5 and 10 Mc/s with wavelengths of approximately 0·2 mm in water, this would require an angular setting accuracy for maximum response from the receiver of better than 24 minutes of arc. Plane piezoelectric detectors as such are not widely used for measurements in the Fresnel field and this is why piezoelectric probes for near field applications are usually spherically symmetric in shape. Otherwise all forms of meters may be used in the Fresnel field for it is most often in this region that measurements are made. Typical laboratory transducers are some 3 cm in diameter, and operate at between 5 and 10 Mc/s into columns of water or dilute salt solutions. As such they have Fresnel fields which extend to a metre or more from their surface and few laboratory enclosures have dimensions very much greater than this.

3.4 PIEZOELECTRIC RECEIVERS

Though piezoelectric crystals are the most widely used form of mechanical receiver of ultrasonic energy they are hardly ever used as absolute standards for ultrasonic power or intensity measurements. Measurement of the total output power from a transducer can be accomplished by using a separate receiver or in the pulse reflection method by using the transducer itself as the receiver. This type of measurement is difficult and can only reasonably be carried out if the separation between source and receiver is beyond the limits of the Fresnel field. The response of the piezoelectric receiver is the vector sum of the pressure distribution over the face of the receiving crystal and as such the output is particularly sensitive to misorientation if mounted in the Fresnel region. If the error involved in treating the crystal and reflector as plane surfaces is less than $\lambda/4$, then in the case of a square crystal of side d the amplitude of the received echo will fall to zero if the reflector is twisted from the setting for maximum received signal by an angle $\Delta\theta = \lambda/2d$. In the new setting the signal received by one half of the crystal exactly cancels that received by the other half. For a circular crystal, the value for $\Delta\theta$ is modified by a numerical factor very near to unity. For accurate measurement therefore a convenient specification is that the signal received by the crystal should not fall by more than a small fraction of it's amplitude when the reflector is plane and parallel with the source. This definition can conveniently be restated as $\Delta\theta \ll \lambda/d$. For water at 20°C, if $\lambda = 0·2$ mm and $d = 30$ mm this means that $\Delta\theta$ must be very much less than 24 minutes of arc. Accurate mechanical design is therefore very necessary for this type of measurement. Even when operating in the Fraunhofer region a plane transducer does not intercept a plane wavefront and indications have to be corrected for the finite size of the receiving crystal[2].

Small circular plate transducers, less than 5 wavelengths in diameter are less sensitive to misorientation problems and are sometimes used to probe a transducer's far Fresnel field. The corrections for transducers of this type, are small and can be neglected for practical purposes. However for reliable operation in both the Fresnel and Fraunhofer regions an ideal probe receiver should be completely non-directional and insensitive to the phase characteristics of the field in which it is placed. Such devices can only be manufactured from piezoelectric materials when the device takes the form of a sphere less than a wavelength in diameter. Few such devices have been manufactured, the majority of probes being made from small cylinders of a ceramic material. Such devices have a cylindrical uniformity of response, which has proved quite adequate for most practical purposes.

In general, piezoelectric receivers are designed for wide-band operation; achieved by operation at frequencies below resonance where the system has a flat response. In this region the frequency dependent terms are neglected and the dynamic sensitivity of an open circuited receiver is given by:

$$V/F = k_c^2(1 + k_c^2)/\alpha \qquad (3.5)$$

where α is the transformation constant used to convert electrical impedances (Z_{el}) into mechanical impedances (Z_{mech}) and k_c is the electromechanical coupling coefficient.

$$k_c^2 = \alpha^2 Z_{el}/Z_{mech} \qquad (3.6)$$

For maximum sensitivity and the highest attainable efficiency, the probe system should be a half wavelength in thickness operated at its self resonant frequency and with its capacitive reactance tuned out using a shunt inductor. In applications where this is possible, particularly in the pulse-reflection method, the pressure sensitivity of the device, ignoring losses, is given by:

$$V/p = 4\alpha(1/R_1 + 4\alpha^2/\rho_0 cS)/\rho_0 c \qquad (3.7)$$

For maximum power transfer, i.e. matched receiver, the load resistance R_1 is made equal to:

$$R_1 = \rho_0 cS/4\alpha^2$$

and
$$V/p = 32\alpha^3/\rho_0^2 c^2 S \qquad (3.8)$$

Under these conditions the voltage generated in the transducer by the received energy leads to the destructive interference of reflected waves by emitting waves of equal amplitude but opposite in phase[3]. Only under these conditions is the receiver perfectly matched, acting as a totally absorbing meter and reflecting no energy from the crystal face.

For small cylindrical transducers there are at least three principal modes in which the device can resonate; the Length, Radial and Thickness modes, and the dimensions which govern these modes must be taken into account when designing a probe for flat frequency response. In general there is considerable coupling between the length and radial modes whereas the thickness mode is relatively independent of these two. Above the critical region ($1/d = 1.5$) where most coupling occurs, the radial resonant frequency is given by:

54

$$\omega_r^2 = 4Y_0 d_m^2/(1 - \sigma^2)\rho \qquad (3.9)$$

in which $\omega_r = 2\pi f_r$, f_r is the radial resonant frequency, d_m is the mean diameter of the tube, Y_0 is the Young's modulus, σ is Poisson's ratio, and ρ is the material density, Since this is the lowest frequency at which the device will resonate, probes for wide-band operation should only be used at frequencies below this value. Langevin[4] has also shown that in designing receivers of this type, the choice of the ratio of wall thickness (t) to outside diameter (d_0) is not unrestricted. Because a uniform pressure gives rise to both radial and tangential stresses, the coupling coefficient k involves both the radial and tangential piezoelectric constants. These constants have opposite signs and the degree of cancellation depends on the thickness to diameter ratio. When t/d_0 has a value between 0·22 and 0·35 the response of cylindrical transducers is poor and it is for this reason that thin walled ceramic cylinders with t/d_0 values less than 0·2 are most commonly used.

Few piezoelectric devices have a performance characteristic which can be accurately predicted. Sensitivity values obtained from the simple theory are very rarely attained in practice, principally due to the uncontrolled losses associated with the method of mounting, the necessary electrical connections to the two surfaces and the uncertainties in the manufacture of the material from which the receiver is manufactured. Few devices exceed 60 per cent of their theoretical efficiency. For these reasons all piezoelectric receivers are standardized, usually against a radiation pressure type of meter. Alternatively the 'self reciprocity' technique of Carstensen[5] can be used. The transducer is excited to emit short pulses which are reflected from a perfect reflecting surface and in turn received by the same element. This system is difficult to apply in practice and calibration using a radiation pressure method is to be preferred.

3.5 THERMOELECTRIC PROBE

For some applications the thermoelectric probe has distinct advantages over the piezoelectric probes in that it yields directly values of the particle velocity and pressure amplitude in both free and standing wave fields. It can be very small, accurate to within ±2 per cent and is often used to study the fine structure of ultrasonic fields, particularly in the higher megacycle range.

A detailed theoretical analysis of the thermoelectric probe has been given by Fry and Fry[6] and thermoelectric probes based on their design have been used by Dunn and Fry[7] in the precision calibration of ultrasonic fields. In these measurements they have used probes of the type illustrated in Fig. 3.2. A thermocouple probe etched down to between 0·0003 and 0·0005 in. in diameter in the neighbourhood of the junction, is embedded in a small quantity of acoustic absorbing material. Where measurements have to be carried out in water or in any of the many salt solutions now used in research, castor oil is a suitable embedding material.

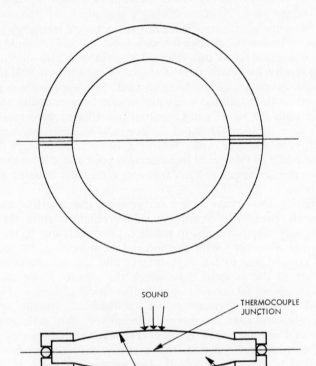

Fig. 3.2. Thermoelectric probe (after Dunn and Fry[7])

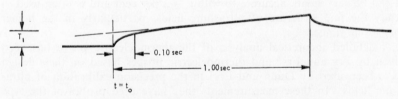

Fig. 3.3. Typical waveform recorded by a thermoelectric probe

In practice the absorber is contained in a cell with polythene membrane end windows through which the ultrasound is transmitted. Polythene can present a mismatch to the incident ultrasound but by the proper choice of membrane thickness it is possible to transmit without significant loss the incident ultrasound. Sproule,[8] Biquard[9] and others have investigated the transparency to the passage of sound of materials varying in thickness and have shown that for maximum transmission the membrane should be either very thin compared with the wavelength of ultrasound in the material itself (λ_m), or that the thickness (d) should be a small number of wavelengths thick, i.e.

$$d \ll \lambda_m \quad \text{or} \quad d = n\lambda_m \quad \text{where} \quad n < 5 \tag{3.10}$$

The probe functions in the following manner. The source is excited to produce acoustic pulses of one second duration in every three or four. Energy is absorbed by the oil and its temperature, measured by the thermocouple, rises. This transient temperature rise is normally observed on an oscilloscope and photographed for measurement or recorded directly on a high speed recorder with response times of tens of milliseconds. With either method additional highly stable d.c. amplification is often necessary because of the very small output from thermocouples fabricated from materials available in wire form. Increased sensitivities have been reported using probes of copper constantan and iron constantan thermocouples with soldered lap junctions.

A typical recorded waveform is illustrated in Fig. 3.3. A relatively rapid rise in temperature is observed soon after the initiation of the pulse followed by an almost linear rise for the remainder of the pulse's duration. On cessation of the pulse there is a rapid fall in temperature followed by a slow return to the unperturbed temperature of the medium. Where repeated measurements are being made it is advisable to allow a two to three second interval for the medium to return to its original temperature. Apart from recording the wave form it is necessary to record the temperature of the absorbing material at the time of measurement, for, like castor oil, the absorption coefficients of most absorbing liquid media are markedly temperature dependent. This is perhaps the most serious limitation of this technique, because such data is not always readily available. Fry and Fry have shown that the initial rise in temperature results from the conversion of acoustic energy into heat by viscous forces acting between the wire and fluid medium. The temperature rise generated by this process approaches an equilibrium value very rapidly and for this reason high speed recording devices are necessary. The second much slower and linear rise in temperature which follows is brought about by the bulk absorption of the ultrasound in the absorbing medium. In this respect the probe functions as a simple constant volume calorimeter. The equation basic to the operation of the device in this phase is:

$$\mu I = \rho_0 c (dT/dt)_0 \tag{3.11}$$

μ is the acoustic absorption coefficient of the absorbing medium and $(dT/dt)_0$ is the time rate of temperature rise near the origin or initiation

57

5

of the pulse. For short pulses ($\leqslant 1$ sec), this is closely approximated to by the slope of the recorded waveform during the second phase. An accurate knowledge of the acoustic intensity absorption coefficient could therefore lead to absolute acoustic intensity measurements.

For thermocouple wire diameters very much less that the acoustic wavelength in the medium, the equilibrium temperature T_1, due to the action of the viscous forces, is given by the relationship:

$$T_1 = \gamma_0 (dT/dt)_0 t \tag{3.12}$$

where γ_0 is defined as the ratio of the equilibrium temperature rise at the thermocouple junction due to the viscous forces acting three and the temperature rise due to absorption in time t. An approximate expression for γ_0 is given by:

$$\gamma_0 = Q_v \rho_0 c (1 + \log r_2/r_0)/2\pi k \mu It \tag{3.13}$$

Q_v is the heat generated per second per unit length of wire by the viscous forces, r_0 is the radius of the wire, r_2 is a quantity dependent on the velocity distribution in the sound beam and k is the thermal conductivity coefficient of the absorbing medium. In order to arrive at values for Q_v, values for r_2 and T_1 have to be determined. Fry and Fry in their original paper have computed values for particular field distributions and T_1 may be obtained by measurement from the recording. From Fig. 3.3 T_1 is the height of the vertical from t_0 to the intercept with the slope (dT/dt) projected to t_0. By this means information related to the velocity and pressure amplitude of the ultrasonic waves may be obtained. From these results the pressure and intensity distribution within a transducer's field can be obtained using the relationships in Eqn. 3.1.

3.6 THE CALORIMETRIC METHOD

Methods of ultrasonic power measurement which rely for their operation on the degradation of ultrasonic energy into thermal energy are both direct and capable of high precision. There are in general three basic systems all of which depend upon a measurable rate of rise in temperature of an absorber of closely controlled mass and specific heat. They are:

1. The steady flow system.
2. The transient system; and
3. The substitution system.

In all three cases a beam of ultrasound is directed into a volume of absorbing media. For water borne ultrasound castor oil is a suitable material because of its high coefficient of absorption and other physical properties which make it an excellent match to water. In this respect it is an admirable material for use as a well matched power meter. The castor oil or other absorbing material is usually separated from the medium in which the ultrasound is being propagated by a membrane capable of transmitting all the incident energy. The conditions which this membrane

must satisfy, are identical with those necessary for the satisfactory operation of the thermoelectric probe and in general it should be very thin.

In category (1) the castor oil or other absorbing medium flows at a
constant rate through the system terminating the beam of ultrasound.
The steady state difference between the inlet and outlet temperature
(T_1 and T_2) is, as the following equation shows, a direct measure of the
incident ultrasound under ideal conditions.

$$P_1 = \text{mass flow} \times \text{specific heat} \times \text{temperature difference}$$
$$= MJS(T_2 - T_1)/t \tag{3.14}$$

M is the mass of absorber contained in the calorimeter, J the mechanical
equivalent of heat, S the specific heat of the absorbing material and t is
the time taken for a mass M of the absorber to flow through the calorimeter. A typical calorimeter of this type is illustrated in Fig. 3.4. The

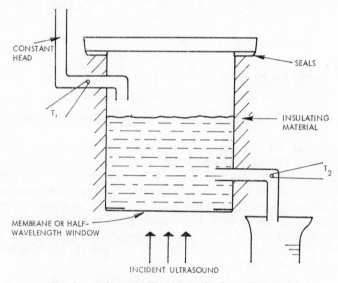

Fig. 3.4. Schematic illustration of a flow calorimeter

conditions necessary for optimum performance are that all the incident
ultrasound should be absorbed and that there should be no heat lost to
the medium in which the ultrasound is normally propagated. These
requirements are often in conflict. For wideband operation and low-loss
transmission the membrane should be thin and as such it cannot prevent
heat losses from the calorimeter. When operating at a particular test
frequency the calorimeter can be acoustically coupled to and thermally
isolated from the medium using half wave plates. Materials like fused
quartz, certain of the ceramics and titanium alloys with their low acoustic
loss and low thermal conductivity can be used in plate form, a specific
number of half wavelengths thick. Half wave plates of this type are very
frequency sensitive and careful adjustment of the system for operation

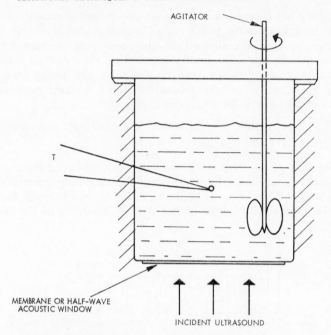

AGITATOR

T

MEMBRANE OR HALF-WAVE
ACOUSTIC WINDOW

INCIDENT ULTRASOUND

Fig. 3.5. Schematic illustration of a constant volume calorimeter

at a particular test frequency must be made. For these reasons the steady-flow system is infrequently used in practice.

In the transient calorimetric method of category (2), Fig. 3.5, a measured quantity of absorber is raised in temperature by the incident ultrasound. The problem of providing a low-loss window to acoustic transmission whilst providing good thermal isolation remains. Steps must also be taken to prevent loss of absorber by evaporation and allowance should be made for convective heat transfer away from the calorimeter. The equation for the system is:

$$P_1 = MJS(\mathrm{d}T/\mathrm{d}t)_0 \tag{3.15}$$

In practice the transducer is switched on and the temperature with time curve for the calorimeter obtained. This curve can be recorded automatically with a thermistor, as the temperature sensing device, connected into a wheatstone bridge circuit. The main advantage in using a thermistor instead of thermometer is that the former is much more sensitive and has a lower heat capacity. Compared with the thermocouple used in the thermo-electric probe, which also acts as a transient calorimeter in the second phase, the thermistor has a more rapid response, greater sensitivity and does not need a reference temperature source. When automatic recording is used, the source can be 100 per cent modulated with square waves and the transient temperature with time curve recorded. Alternatively a temperature with time curve could be obtained by observation and plotting. In practice $(\mathrm{d}T/\mathrm{d}t)_0$ is obtained from the slope of the curve very near the origin. In this region errors due to convection have their least value and little is gained by plotting the whole heating curve when all the necessary information is contained in the transient response to a short term pulse. Transient automatic recording systems which can respond to this initial rise in temperature have much to recommend them.

The substitutional system of category (3) Fig. 3.6 is the method most widely adopted. This method has the advantage that when the incident ultrasound is completely absorbed, the heating of the absorber by the ultrasound can be simulated by dissipating a measured amount of electrical power in a heater element embedded in the calorimeter. By this means thermal losses from the calorimeter are the same in both cases so that by monitoring the amount of electrical power needed to simulate the heating effect of the ultrasound, a direct measure of the absorbed ultrasonic energy can be obtained. Because of this the window through which the ultrasound is coupled need not be too good a thermal isolator and can

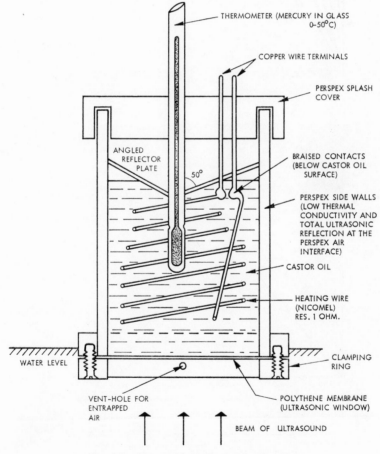

Fig. 3.6. A practical substitutional calorimeter

61

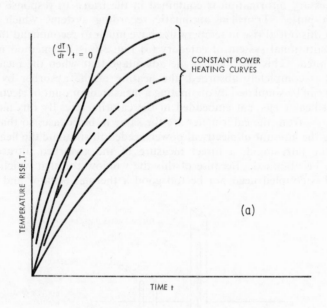

(a)

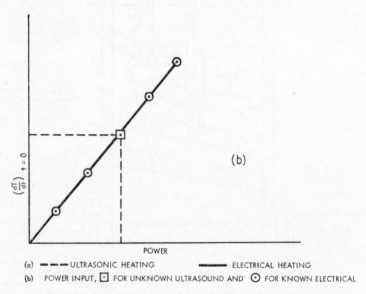

(b)

(a) ━━━ ULTRASONIC HEATING ━━━━ ELECTRICAL HEATING

(b) POWER INPUT, ⊡ FOR UNKNOWN ULTRASOUND AND ⊙ FOR KNOWN ELECTRICAL

Fig. 3.7. Calibration curves for a substitutional calorimeter

be made thin so that wide-band frequency operation is possible. The performance of this type of calorimeter depends in practice on how well the heater coil, as an energy source, can be regarded as a true substitute for the absorbed ultrasound. As heat sources they are very different; the latter a bulk effect, the former essentially a local source. Some equalization of these effects can be obtained by agitating the absorber using air jet or mechanical agitators. Either method increases the uncertainty with which measurements can be made because of the increased heat losses and the need to keep these constant during calibration and subsequent measurements.

To calibrate the instrument, heating curves are obtained for both ultrasonic and electrical inputs, Fig. 3.7. These are compared over their whole range and must be very similar in their characteristics. In fact this method can only usefully be interpreted when the electrical heating curves are identical in shape with those due to ultrasonic heating. In order to achieve this some modification usually has to be made to the internal structure of the calorimeter and some redisposition of the heating element. Once the characteristics of the calorimeter have been optimized, calibration curves of temperature against time are obtained for various values of electrical power input. From these $(dT/dt)_0$ values are plotted against electrical power input. When the electrical power inputs sensibly span the expected values of ultrasonic power to be measured they provide a means for correction against possible errors in calibration. Using the relationships:

$$(\Delta T/\Delta t)_0/P_1 = (MJS)^{-1} \tag{3.16}$$

the slope of the calibration curve $(\Delta T/\Delta t)_0 P_1$ is a straight line with slope $(MJS)^{-1}$ and any minor variations in the calibration can be corrected for by drawing the best straight line through the results. By this means it is possible both to arrive at an accurate calibration curve and also to estimate the interpretive errors involved in the measurement process. With little effort the method can be made accurate to better than ± 10 %.

Calorimeters in general have tended to be bulky and rather slow in their operation. These disadvantages have been overcome in more recent designs particularly those reported by Szilard and Wiederhielm.[10] The latter is interesting because with it the author has been able to probe the field of transducers operating in the frequency range 0·5 to 20 Mc/s. A functional diagram of this meter is illustrated in Fig. 3.8. Points of particular interest include the extensive use of agar both to prevent the formation of standing waves and to act as a matched couplant for the ultrasound into the 10 cc of water forming the calorimeter proper. In order to probe the fine structure of the transducer's field the orifice through which the ultrasound is coupled is restricted to a diameter of 5 wavelengths in agar. Smaller orifices cannot be used because diffraction effects would begin to introduce a variable. The apparatus cannot be regarded as a low level meter. Reliable results have been obtained down to intensities of 2 W/cm², requiring a total power input to the calorimeter of 0·6 W.

Increased sensitivity and the reduction of errors involved in calorimetric measurements can be obtained by using a device in which it is not

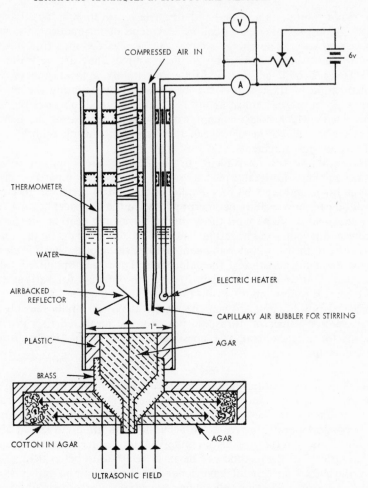

COMPRESSED AIR IN

THERMOMETER

WATER

AIRBACKED REFLECTOR

PLASTIC

BRASS

COTTON IN AGAR

ULTRASONIC FIELD

ELECTRIC HEATER

CAPILLARY AIR BUBBLER FOR STIRRING

AGAR

AGAR

Fig. 3.8. A probe calorimeter (after Szilard and Wiederhielm[10])

the rise in temperature that is measured but the consequent thermal expansion of the liquid in a fixed volume calorimeter. Mikhailov[11] in a recent article reports on the development of such devices. Because the thermal expansion of the calorimetric liquid does not depend on the point at which heating takes place, the calibration of the instrument by electrical means need not involve any of the precautions necessary with the rate of temperature rise with time methods. The calorimeters which he has developed are illustrated in Fig. 3.9. To minimize heat losses the calorimetric liquid is housed in a thin double walled Dewar type of vessel. When the air between the walls is evacuated there is very little thermal loss. End windows of acetate, polystyrene and nylon with thicknesses between 50 and 100 μ have been used and the coefficient of reflection found to be less than 2 per cent. The apparatus is calibrated by measuring

64

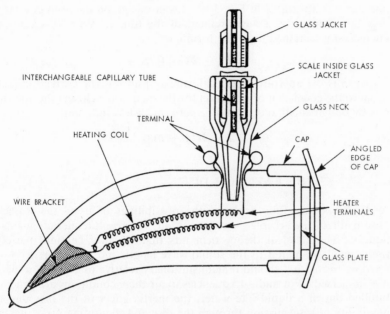

Fig. 3.9. An expansion calorimeter (after Mikhailov[11])

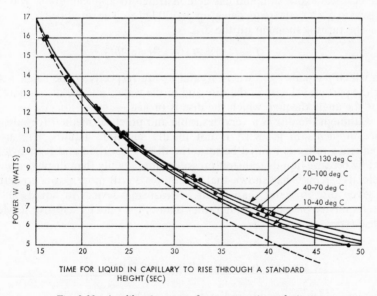

Fig. 3.10. A calibration curve for an expansion calorimeter

the power fed to the heating coil and observing the time (t) taken for the level in the capillary to move between two fixed points. A typical calibration curve is illustrated in Fig. 3.10. From this graph the total power (W) may be obtained by a measurement of the time t. With W known the intensity I is obtained from the formula:

$$I(1 - \delta) = W/S \tag{3.17}$$

Where S is the aperture of the calorimeter and δ is the correction factor equal to the coefficient of reflection for the membrane closing the aperture. δ is by design small and should be very much less than unity so that:

$$I = W(1 + \delta)/S \tag{3.18}$$

3.7 THE RAYLEIGH DISC

A. B. Wood has fully explored the possibilities of using the Rayleigh Disc method, the accepted standard in air, for absolute measurements in liquids. The classical theory demands that the disc be thin, perfectly rigid, small compared to the sound wave length and that apart from the freedom to rotate it should remain stationary relative to the fluid in which it is immersed. For audio-frequencies in air these conditions are generally fulfilled but in a liquid like water, the inertia effect of the medium, the possibility of transmission through the disc and the setting up of flexural vibrations are among the factors which detract from agreement between theory and practice. Wood[12] has however developed a modified form of the classical expression and has demonstrated its applicability to Rayleigh Discs in water at frequencies up to 20 kc/s. The modified expression for the turning moment on the disc is:

$$T = 4\rho a^3 v_w^2 (1 - \beta^2) \sin 2\theta/3 \tag{3.19}$$

In which β equals v_d/v_w where v_d and v_w are respectively the r.m.s. values of the particle velocity in the disc and in the water, a is the disc radius and θ is the angle through which the disc is turned.

Although the disc is a very desirable and practical method for intensity measurements in gases, it is not ideally suited to liquids. It's useful frequency range is limited because the disc is not rigid and it's sensitivity is low because liquids transmit pressure more readily than displacement or velocity. King[13] has shown that it requires 35 dB more power to actuate a given disc in water than in air. Measuring devices in liquids should preferably be pressure sensing rather than of the velocity sensitive Rayleigh Disc type.

3.8 RADIATION PRESSURE METHOD

Devices which respond to radiation pressure have been the most successful and widely used form of mechanical receiver. At a boundary between acoustically dissimilar materials, a radiation pressure is developed and the force exerted on the interface is a direct measure of the ultrasonic intensity in that region. The phenomena of radiation pressure has been widely investigated[14] and it is now understood that there are two forms; the Rayleigh pressure and the Langmuir pressure. The former operates on obstacles whose dimensions are small compared with the wavelength of the incident ultrasound whereas the Langmuir pressure is experienced only by large obstacles. Beyer and Borgnis[15] have developed the relationship between radiation pressure and intensity and have shown that the mean force (F) exerted on an obstacle intercepting the whole of a sound beam is:

$$\bar{F} = Y\int(\rho u^2)_A \, d_a = Y\bar{I}A/C \tag{3.20}$$

where I is the mean acoustic intensity, Y a constant dependent on the acoustic and geometric properties of the obstacle and A is the cross-sectional area of the beam. The particle velocity u has two components, u_a the aperiodic acoustic velocity and u_0 the flow velocity. In a medium under constant hydrostatic pressure p_0 therefore the mean force F has two components:

$$P_0 A + \bar{\pi} = \int(p_0 + \bar{p} + \rho u_a^2) \, da$$

and $\qquad\qquad P \text{ (flow)} = \int(\rho_0 u_0^2) \, da \tag{3.21}$

where $\bar{p}$ is the average excess pressure, $\bar{\pi}$ is the average acoustic radiation pressure and $\bar{P}$ (flow) is the pressure due to hydrodynamic flow. Therefore,

$$\bar{F} = Y(\bar{\pi} + \bar{P} \text{ (flow)}) = Y\bar{I}A/C = Y\bar{E}A \tag{3.22}$$

where E is the mean energy density in the sound beam. The total output from an ultrasonic transducer (W) is therefore:

$$W = \bar{E}A = F/Y = (\bar{\pi} + \bar{P} \text{ (flow)})/Y \tag{3.23}$$

By this means the total output from a transducer may be obtained by interrupting the beam with an obstacle of known acoustic and geometric properties and measuring the force exerted on it.

In many investigations the energy density or intensity distribution within the beam is to be measured. In this case the obstacle used to probe the field must interact with only that portion of the sound field which is local to the obstacle. Radiation pressure is a local effect but hydrodynamic flow is not and without some form of protection the obstacle would experience the contributions to hydrodynamic flow from many other points in the acoustic field. It is for this reason that a membrane, transparent to the transmission of ultrasound but mechanically preventing hydrodynamic flow, is placed between source and as close as is physically possible to the detector in any localized field measurement.

In the practical application of this phenomena to power and intensity measurements there is a wide choice of material which can be used for the obstacle. This range includes total absorbers, near perfect to poor reflectors and non-reflectors which introduce a change of velocity across the interface. Fig. 3.11 illustrates the relationship between the net force exerted on plane specimens of this type and ultrasonic energy density. An air/liquid interface or a metal/liquid interface both approximate to the perfectly reflecting obstacle. They are convenient to manufacture and as Fig. 3.11 shows they have the greatest sensitivity; experiencing a force equal to twice the energy density. For these reasons air-cell and metal reflectors are most commonly used. The geometry of the detection device too plays a major role in the sensitivity with which measurements can be made. Geometrically simple targets are usually adopted and take the form of discs or spheres. Small spherical obstacles with dimensions comparable with the ultrasonic wavelength have been shown by King[13] to have sensitivities nearly twenty times as great in plane-progressive fields and nearly four times greater in a standing wave field as that of a disc of the same radius and manufactured from the same material. When designing probes there is no doubt that totally reflecting spheres provide

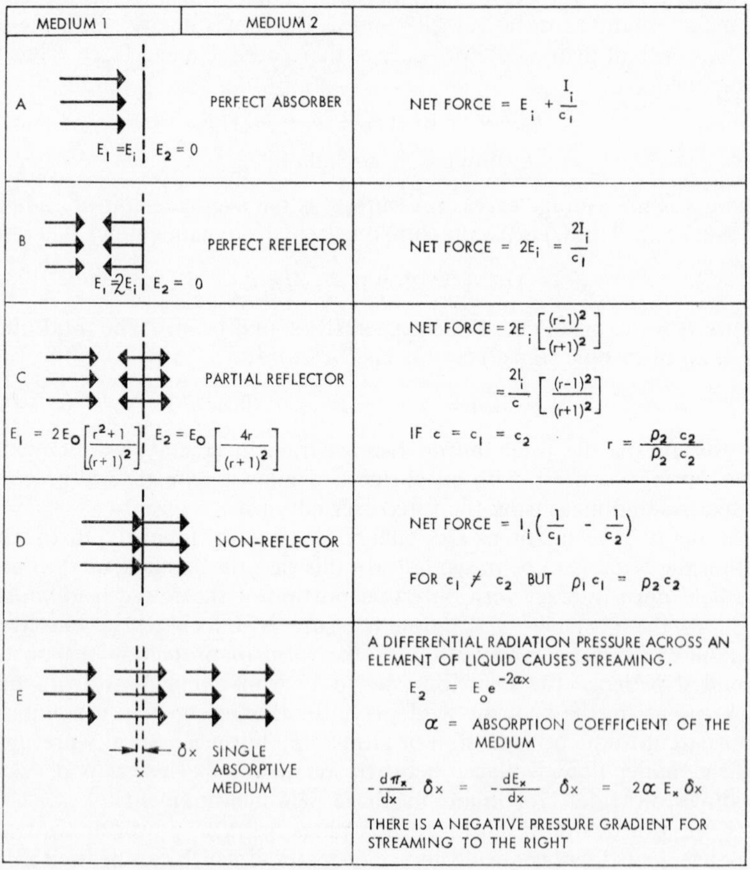

Fig. 3.11. Net acoustic force on unit area of the interface $= \pi_1 - \pi_2 = E_1 - E_2$
i denotes quantities in the incident beam of ultrasound. Suffixes 1 and 2 denote mediums 1 and 2

68

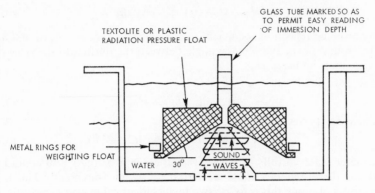

Fig. 3.12. Radiation pressure float (after Henry[17])

the most sensitive means of measuring ultrasonic intensities in liquids now available.

There are several ways in which radiation pressure can be used to measure sound intensity. If the sound beam is directed vertically in a column of liquid, a cone or plate may be suspended in the sound field, and its apparent weight measured both in the presence and absence of the ultrasound. Devices of this type have been widely reported,[16] they intercept the whole of the beam area, and measurement of weight changes are made using precision chemical balances. More recently Henry[17] has developed radiation pressure floats which are independent of any external connections or mountings. This type of intensity meter is buoy shaped (Fig. 3.12) and made from a material with a mean density slightly less than that of the medium in which it is to be used. In use the buoy is sunk using 'sinker' rings until it reaches an equilibrium position below the liquid surface. When the beam is switched on the float rises, and the weight required to restore the float to its equilibrium position is a direct measure of the incident sound power. As an aid to the precision with which measurements can be made, the front surfaces of these totally reflecting meters are coned at an angle of 30° ensuring that all the incident radiation is reflected away from the transducer and can be directed into some suitable absorbing medium. Kossoff[18] uses similar floats but directs the beam of ultrasound downwards onto the float (Fig. 3.13). The weight of this type of float is adjusted so that it just sinks in water and its stem is immersed in carbon tetrachloride to achieve equilibrium. The radiation pressure makes the float stem sink further into the carbon tetrachloride and it is this increased insertion, previously calibrated in grammes weight change which is used as a measure of radiation pressure. The main advantage with this arrangement is that the instrument sensitivity can be altered simply by adjustment of the stem diameter for a fixed diameter of carbon tetrachloride container. For buoys of this type forces within the range of 1 gramme weight can be measured and the range of forces measured extends from zero up to 50 g or more. The general relationship between force exerted and mean intensity is given by:

$$\bar{I} = Mgc/A(1 + r \cos 2\theta) \qquad (3.24)$$

where r is the reflection coefficient of the meter, A the cross-sectional area of the sound beam and θ is the angle between the normal to the reflecting surface and the beam axis.

For perfectly absorbing meters:

$$r = 0 \quad \text{and} \quad \bar{I}a = Mgc/A \qquad (3.25)$$

whereas for perfect reflectors:

$$r = 1 \quad \text{and} \quad \bar{I}r = Mgc/A(2 \cos^2 \theta) \qquad (3.26)$$

No meter material fully satisfies either the $r = 1$ or the $r = 0$ conditions and for these meters r must be obtained by measurement. The most direct way of doing this is to use two meters identical in every way differing only in their angle θ. Results obtained when the two buoys ($\theta_1 = 30°$ and $\theta_2 = 15°$ typically) make the same measurement of $\bar{I}$ can be solved simultaneously to yield a value for r the only unknown.

Both the methods so far described have been free-field measurements in which certain precautions have been taken to ensure that this is so.

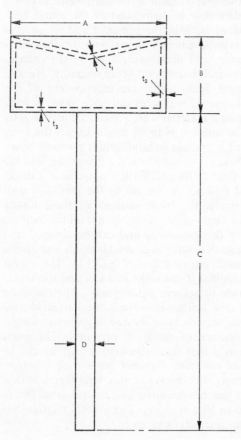

Fig. 3.13. *Radiation pressure float (after Kossoff[18])*

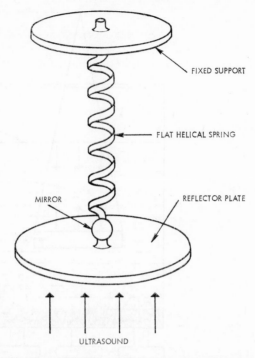

Fig. 3.14. Radiation pressure meter (after Klein[19])

FIXED SUPPORT

FLAT HELICAL SPRING

MIRROR

REFLECTOR PLATE

ULTRASOUND

Methods have however been developed for total output power and mean intensity measurements where source and reflector have been designed to interact. The two most interesting of these are due to Klein[19] and Cady and Gittings.[20] Klein's apparatus, Fig. 3.14 uses a helical spring to support a disc at its free end. The incident beam of ultrasound lifts the disc against gravitational forces reducing the extension of the spring. This spring is so designed that a very small contraction or elongation of its length introduces a large axial rotation. Cady and Gittings' apparatus Fig. 3.15 differs in that the reaction force exerted on a transducer irradiating a water-air interface is measured. Their argument is that if there is a force acting at the interface then by Newtons Third Law there should be an equal and opposite reaction, measurable at the transducer. In both these methods the beam is not disturbed or scattered, but is totally reflected by a surface normal to the direction of wave propagation. Total normal reflection is assumed in both cases so that by adjusting the distance between source and reflecting surface a perfect standing wave system can be set up with a maximum force registered on either the disc in the one case and the transducer in the other. Under these conditions the radiation pressure actuating the measurement device is equal to twice the energy density in the medium, $\pi = 2\bar{E}$.

Where vertically beamed ultrasound measurements are generally concerned with gross power measurements, the horizontally beamed configuration is usually adopted when the intensity distribution within the field of a transducer is to be investigated. For fine structure work discs

71

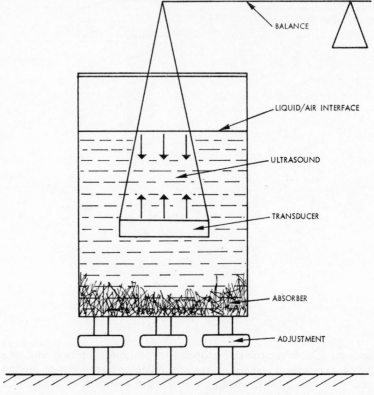

Fig. 3.15. A method of measuring the output from a transducer proposed by Cady and Gittings[12]

or spheres of reflecting material suspended from long wires or mounted as the vane of a torsion balance form the basis for most devices. Small condenser microphones too have been used, the radiation pressure altering the separation between plates, and intensity is measured indirectly as a change in capacitance.

The need for high sensitivity devices is well illustrated by an examination of the equation relating radiation pressure and acoustic intensity:

$$\bar{\pi} \propto \bar{E} = \bar{I}/c$$

The force exerted per square centimetre surface of a detector in a field of water borne ultrasound (c $1\cdot48 \times 10^5$ cm/sec) with intensity I equal to 1 W/cm^2 (10^7 ergs/cm^2) is:

$$\pi = 67\cdot4 \text{ dynes/cm}^2 = 0\cdot069 \text{ g w/cm}^2 \tag{3.27}$$

In practice target areas for typical probes can range between $0\cdot1$ and $0\cdot01$ cm^2. Also when strictly free field measurements of the intensity distribution within the field of a transducer operating into a water load are to be made, cavitation effects must be avoided. Cavitation can be

avoided if the instantaneous particle pressure within the medium is prevented from falling below zero, that is the excess pressure should not
exceed the hydrostatic pressure. Boyle and Taylor[21] have shown that
when a dissolved gas is present, the excess pressure should not exceed
$(p_a - p_v)$, where p_a and p_v are the atmospheric and vapour pressures
respectively. In practice distilled water is used and degassed by high
energy ultrasound prior to measurements being made, so that the maximum
permissible excess pressure is very nearly equal to the atmospheric pressure.
For a plane progressive wave in water at atmospheric pressure, the average
intensity $\bar{I}$ is related to the r.m.s. value of the excess pressure p_e by:

$$\bar{I} = p_e^2/\rho_0 c \qquad (3.28)$$

When p_e is equal to one atmosphere, $\bar{I}$ is limited to values less than
0·3 W/cm² below 100 kc/s but increases rapidly to as high as 100 W/cm²
at 1 Mc/s. Taking both these factors into account, a probe with an area
of approximately 0·05 cm² in the non-cavitating fields of transducers
operating at 100 kc/s into water loads, would experience a weight change of
0·45 × 10⁻³ g.wt or twice this value if it were a total reflector. Furthermore,

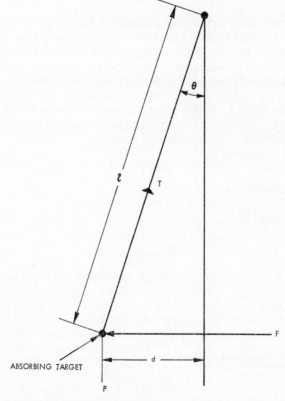

Fig. 3.16. A simple sphere suspension used in radiometric measurements

assuming that the field intensity range, maximum to minimum intensity, of interest is just under ten to one, the instrument should respond to changes in weight of 50×10^{-6} g. To measure this quantity with an accuracy of ± 5 per cent, the weight measuring instrument would need to have an accuracy of better than $\pm 5 \times 10^{-6}$ g. Most high precision chemical and torsion balances have the necessary accuracy but have not been used because surface tension effects interfere with the movement of the coupling wire across the liquid/air interface. The total force (ϕ) involved has been shown by Wells et al.[22] to be equal to:

$$\phi = 2 \, dT \tag{3.29}$$

where d is the diameter of the wire and T the value of surface tension at the liquid/air interface. For a wire of 0·005 cm diameter moving across a water/air interface ($T = 70$ dyne/cm):

$$\phi = 0.7 \times 10^{-3} \text{ g.wt}$$

Theoretically this force need not introduce an error if measurements are made under equilibrium conditions. In practice however the effect is to cause 'stiction' of the detector in the vicinity of the balance point and reduces the accuracy with which apparent weight changes can be measured.

To overcome these difficulties, the probes are more often suspended from very long wires from a fixed point and their weight chosen so that the intercepted ultrasound deflects the probe from its equilibrium position a small distance d. This distance d is purposely kept small so that measurements are made with the region of interest and also to satisfy the necessary condition that d/l, where l is the length of suspension, makes a very small angle with the vertical. Under these conditions, the system can be represented by Fig. 3.16, where F is the total horizontal force and Mg is the weight of the probe acting through its vertical.

Resolving horizontally,
$$F = T \sin \theta$$

Resolving vertically,
$$Mg = T \cos \theta$$

When θ is small
$$\tan \theta = d/l$$

and
$$F_r = Mg \, d/l \tag{3.30}$$

In practice d is usually small enough to require measurement using a travelling microscope. For larger deflections Wells et al. have obtained an exact relationship between F and d by considering the suspension in catenary form. Even with long wire suspensions surface effects are capable of introducing errors due to the change in angle of contact between wire and liquid (Fig. 3.17). The force tending to restore the wire, previously considered, is not likely to exceed:

$$\Delta\phi = \phi \sin \theta \tag{3.31}$$

For a movement of 0·02 cm and a suspension length of 100 cm,

$$\sin \theta = \theta = 2 \times 10^{-4}$$

therefore $$\Delta\phi = 1\cdot4 \times 10^{-7} \text{ g.wt}$$

This value is an order less than the sensitivity required of the instrument and unlikely therefore to introduce significant errors. Long suspensions could however introduce other errors the most significant of which are due to the resilience and change of length of the suspension wire with temperature and stress. Both these factors can be reduced to negligible proportions by the proper choice of suspension material. Phosphor bronze is particularly suitable.

Few investigators have considered the possible effect of convection currents on the accuracies attainable. The greater the suspension length immersed, to overcome surface tension effects, the greater is to be the contribution from convection currents in the liquid. There appears to be no simple means of overcoming this effect but it should receive serious consideration when radiation pressure measurements are to be carried out at very low intensities.

In any investigation which involves the determination of absolute sound intensity the constant Y relating the radiation pressure experienced by a material detector and the sound intensity in the medium must be known. This constant can be obtained for a particular obstacle by setting up a Huyghen Wave pattern which fully reproduces all the field characteristics of the obstacle (reflection, diffraction, and shadow formation) by

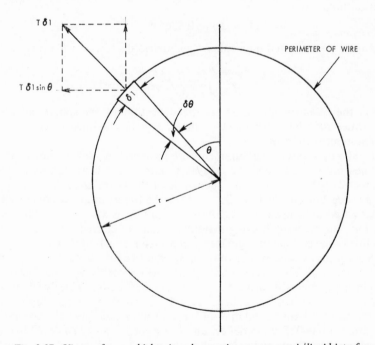

Fig. 3.17. Viscous forces which arise when a wire crosses an air/liquid interface

75

interference with the undisturbed field. Few such calculations have been made with the notable exception of King's work[23] on spheres and discs in plane progressive fields and Embleton's work[24] on the radiation force experienced by a sphere in a cylindrical sound field. King has shown that spheres are more sensitive to radiation pressure than discs of the same dimension and that the greater the density of the sphere material compared with that of the medium, results obtained with spheres greater than 5λ in diameter approximate to the simple radiation theory which is less dependent on the field distribution. With these proviso's Fox's[25] development of King's theory can be applied to near field measurements which are neither plane-progressive nor strictly Fresnel. In Fox's equation relating ultrasonic intensity and the force acting on a sphere two constants are introduced

$$\alpha = 2\pi R/\lambda_m \quad \text{and} \quad \beta = \rho_0/\rho_1 \tag{3.32}$$

where R is the sphere radius, λ_m the ultrasound wavelength in the medium with density ρ_0 and ρ_1 the density of the sphere material. In practice β is chosen to be as large as possible even to the extent of using platinum-iridium alloys with a density of over 21 g/cm³. With these two constants determined, Fox has published graphs from which a value for Y relating mean radiation pressure and mean total energy E may be obtained:

$$Y = \bar{P}/\bar{E} \tag{3.33}$$

For the range of particular interest, α greater than 15, the following approximation holds true:

$$(1 - Y) = 0\cdot7365\,e^{-1.156\alpha} \tag{3.34}$$

The total force exerted on a sphere (geometric shadow $= \pi R^2$) is equal to:

$$F_T = \bar{P}\pi R^2 = Y\bar{I}\pi R^2/C \tag{3.35}$$

or $$\bar{I} = F_T C/(Y\pi R^2) \tag{3.36}$$

F_T is the quantity measured by the deflection of the sphere, all other quantities may be determined so that $\bar{I}$ can be obtained directly as an absolute measurement.

Total output power measurements too have been made with horizontally beamed ultrasound when the measuring interface is large compared with the wavelength and interrupts the whole of the beam area. To overcome the surface tension effects Wells et al.[26] used a totally immersed balance but experienced difficulties at low power measurements due to irregularities in the fulcrum. Kossoff[27] using a similar totally immersed system, suitably modified to overcome fulcrum effects reported a sensitivity $3\cdot3 \times 10^{-6}$ g. wt indicating that a total power of 0·5 mW could be measured with a ±5 per cent accuracy. The disadvantage with their systems was the need for weight adjustments in order to obtain zero deflection. Totally immersed torsion balances too have been used by Newell[28] who has reported a deflection of 0·1 cm for 60 mW of incident ultrasonic power. Accuracies to within $\pm0\cdot00025$ cm in deflection measurement can be achieved using a travelling microscope giving Newell's apparatus a sensitivity of $\pm0\cdot15$ mW.

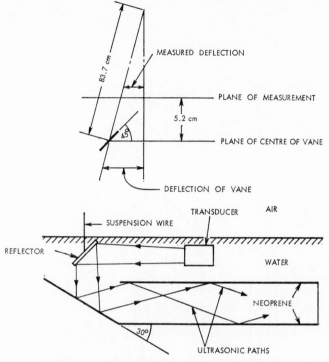

Fig. 3.18. A schematic illustration of Wells' apparatus

Recently Wells *et al.* after careful consideration of the errors involved, have developed a very sensitive system capable of measuring the total power in a 2 mW beam with an accuracy of ±3 per cent. In their system a hollow metal vane, air backed so that there is total reflection, is suspended from two very long phosphor bronze wires. The vane is angled at 45° so that the reflected rays are deflected away from the transducer and absorbed in neoprene. The arrangement is illustrated in Fig. 3.18. The equation relating the force experienced by the totally reflecting vane and the mean energy density in the medium is:

$$F = 2\bar{E}_1 \cos^2 \theta \qquad (3.37)$$

θ, the angle between the beam axis and the normal to the vane surface, equals 45° in this case. Therefore, for $\cos \theta = 1/\sqrt{2}$, $F = \bar{E}$ and the system has a sensitivity equal to that of a perfect absorber of cross-section equal to the reflectors projected surface area in the plane of the beam axis.

3.9 OPTICAL METHODS

Optical methods are capable of the absolute measurement of sound pressures and intensities at ultrasonic frequencies and have the advantage

77

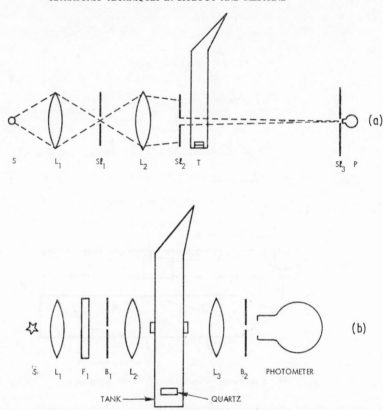

Fig. 3.19. (a) *Optical arrangement for ultrasonic pressure amplitude measurement by the diffraction method.* (b) *Optical arrangement for ultrasonic pressure amplitude measurement by the refraction method*

over all other methods of avoiding any disturbance of the field by the presence of a measuring device. Two measurement principles are involved; diffraction or refraction of a beam of light by the ultrasonic waves. The diffraction method measures the relative light intensity in the various orders of a diffraction pattern whereas the refraction method is based on observing the periodic variation in the gradient of the refractive index. The discovery that the image of a slit is broadened in the presence of sound and the relationship between image broadening, for images short compared with the ultrasonic wavelength have been made by Lucas.[29] Huter and Pohlman[30] were among the first to apply this method for ultrasonic waves in liquids whereas Loeber and Heidemann[31] developed an indirect method in that they measured the light intensity within, rather than the broadening of, the slit image. All three systems measure the integrated optical effects due to the action of the sound field on a light beam during its passage through the field and should be least influenced by pressure variations in the Fresnel field of the transducer. These optical methods measure the total pressure or intensity in a plane normal to the axis of sound propagation but give no indication as to the intensity distribution within this portion of the field.

The optical arrangements for the three methods are very similar; typical arrangements are illustrated in Figs. 3.19(a) and (b).

3.9.1 DIFFRACTION METHOD

Power measurement by the diffraction method was first put forward as a practical possibility by Raman and Nath.[32] In their experiment the continuous ultrasound beam forms a moving diffraction grating due to the periodic changes in refractive index within the transport medium. As the light passes through a plane progressive wave at normal incidence, the light is diffracted at angles θ given by the Bragg diffraction law:

$$\sin \theta = -n\lambda/\lambda_m \tag{3.38}$$

where n is an integer having zero, positive and negative values, λ is the light wavelength λ_m the wavelength of ultrasound in the medium and θ is the angle formed by the incident and transmitted light. For sinusoidal waves, the light intensity in the nth order is given by:

$$I_n = J_n{}^2(\nu)$$

and
$$\nu = 2\pi\Delta\mu L/\lambda \tag{3.39}$$

where $\Delta\mu$ is the maximum change in refractive index and L is the path length of light through the ultrasound. This development is however only an approximation and can only be applied when the sound beam is narrow and the sound intensity is low enough so that the light rays are not curved unduly when passing through the ultrasonic beam. The necessary conditions for this are:

$$2\pi L\lambda\nu/\mu_0\lambda_m{}^2 < N \tag{3.40}$$

Values for N between one and two have been suggested.[33] On this basis, $L\nu f^2 < 37$ for most liquids. Where L is expressed in centimetres and f is the ultrasonic frequency in Mc/s. In practice higher values have been used and the results compensated for curvature effects by noting that for non-normal incidence ($\phi_i \neq 0$) the light diffracted into a particular order will diminish according to,[33]

$$I_n = J_n{}^2(K\nu)$$

where
$$K = \sin\left[\pi L \tan\left(\phi_i/\lambda_m\right)\right]/\left[\pi L \tan\left(\phi_i/\lambda_m\right)\right] \tag{3.41}$$

The need for this correction is the main reason why quantitative studies of ultrasonic beam intensities are so difficult, presupposing a knowledge of those regions in the beam where ϕ_i is not zero. However for many practical measurements, observations of the ratios of the light intensities in the zero and first order diffraction patterns can lead to useful results. A plot of I_0 and I_1 as a function of ν is illustrated in Fig. 3.20. Greatest

79

precision is obtained with this method when L and $\Delta\mu$ are large enough so that the relative value of I_1, will always lie in the region of increasing intensity (i.e. ν less than 0·2). Both I_1 and I_0 are directly related to the same sound pressure and as such their evaluation can lead to an absolute pressure measurement. Their ratio also provides a means of determining whether the measurement has been made under the correct conditions. In fact I_1, I_0 or their ratio can be measured and a value of ν determined

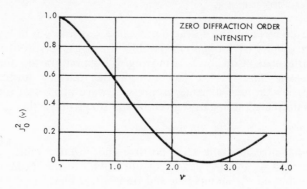

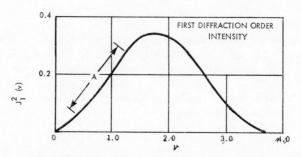

Fig. 3.20. Intensity of zero and first diffraction orders

for the particular measurement by referring to graphs of $J_0^2(\nu)$, $J_1^2(\nu)$ where J_n is the nth order Bessel function. From this value of ν the pressure can be calculated. Willard[33] has summarized the procedure for sinusoidal waves and has shown that pressure and ν are related by the following expression

$$p = c^2\lambda\rho\nu/(\sqrt{2\pi}\mu'L) \tag{3.42}$$

and

$$\mu' = (\mu_0 - 1)(\mu_0^2 + 1\cdot4\mu_0 + 0\cdot4)/(\mu_0^2 + 0\cdot8\mu_0 + 1) \tag{3.43}$$

where p is the r.m.s. value of the pressure amplitude. For ultrasonic waves in water the relationship between pressure and ν reduces to:

$$p = 0\cdot5\nu/L \tag{3.44}$$

80

Multiple reflections and high intensities are responsible for the same types of errors with this method as with any other power measuring system. In particular, the theory presupposes a plane wave front, and a free or standing wave field. As the frequency decreases the divergence of the beam increases so that the method is not suitable for frequencies less than 5 Mc/s in water. In addition higher order images are excited at the higher intensities and some light may be diffracted back into the main beam. Observation of the light intensity in the first two orders and their comparison with the expected theoretical ratio is a possible means of minimizing errors due to both these effects. Alignment too is particularly important, the light beam must be narrow and accurately perpendicular to the sound beam. Low intensities and narrow light beams result in greatly reduced sensitivities but improvements in the general technique using mono-chromatic light sources and electron multiplier detectors have made it possible to develop very serviceable instruments.[34]

3.9.2 REFRACTION METHODS

The optical arrangement used for the measurement of power by the refraction method is illustrated in Fig. 3.19(*b*). A slit source of light is transmitted through the ultrasound and either photographed for line broadening measurements or measured using a photomultiplier microphotometer for line intensity measurements.

Line broadening method

The theory relating line broadening and pressure is due to Huter and Pohlman.[30] Using geometrical optics they have shown that the relationship between the r.m.s. pressure amplitude p and the optical properties of the irradiated medium is given by the expression,

$$p = \gamma\lambda/\mu'\delta\sqrt{2} \qquad (3.45)$$

where γ is the angle of maximum deviation of the light beam, λ the light wavelength, K is a constant involving the compressibility and the refractive index of the liquid and δ is the length of the light path in the ultrasound beam. In deriving this equation they have made the necessary assumption that the width of the light beam is small compared with the ultrasonic wavelength. In practice, however, it is often convenient to make the slit width approach the ultrasonic wavelength. Sharper photographic images are obtained and this increases the accuracy with which the photographed images may be measured. Alternatively the light intensity distribution along the broadened slit image can be recorded using a recording micro-photometer. This method has the additional advantage that values of the angle γ are most accurately obtained by measurement of the distance between the half-maximum points on the recorded waveform. Errors increase, particularly at low pressures when the distance between the

81

extremes of the broadened image are used. Experiment too has shown that the light beam passing through the ultrasound field can be assumed small compared with the ultrasonic wavelength for beam widths less than $\lambda/3$. Beam widths equal to $\lambda/4$ are most commonly used.

Line intensity method

The theory relating the decrease in the intensity of a broadened image and the ultrasound pressure amplitude in a stationary wave has been developed by Loeber and Heidemann.[31] Basically the measurement involves the determination of the ratio of the light passing through the

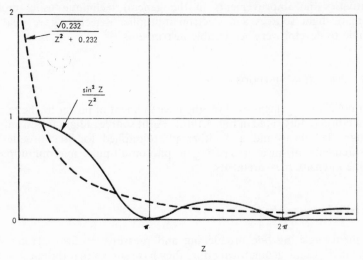

Fig. 3.21. Plot of the functions $(0\cdot232)^{\frac{1}{2}}/(Z^2 + 0\cdot232)$ and $(\sin^2 Z)/Z^2$

system with the ultrasound on and off. This ratio R has been related to the pressure amplitude in a plane progressive wave by the expression:

$$p = r\lambda\lambda_m(R^{-2} - 0\cdot232)^{1/2}/(2\sqrt{2\pi^2ag\delta\mu'}) \qquad (3.46)$$

Where r is the distance between the two image forming slits, g is the width of the final slit, a is the distance from the middle of the sound beam to the recording photometer, δ is the width of the sound beam. For standing wave fields with total internal reflection the coefficient of the radical differs from this case only by a factor two. In deriving this expression the authors have used the approximation that the function

$$(0\cdot232)^{1/2}/(Z^2 + 0\cdot232)$$

may be replaced by the function $\sin^2 Z/Z$ for R values less than $0\cdot3$. This imposes a lower limit on the pressure values which can be measured. Referring to Fig. 3.21 it is evident that for single measurements the limitation $R < 0\cdot3$ must be observed.

All three methods of power measurement by optical effects are theoretically well established and have been widely applied in practice. In general measurements have been carried out in the Fresnel field of particular transducers. Results obtained have been in all cases lower than that to be theoretically expected when treating the transducer as an ideal piston-source. This is not a serious limitation because it is well known that few transducers act as perfect sources. In general the agreement between these three optical methods is good and results may be obtained to within ±5 per cent. Few controlled experiments have however been made comparing these methods with other forms of power measurement in an attempt to assess the absolute accuracies attainable.

3.10 FILM METHOD

Various types of photographic and other films are sensitive to ultrasonic radiation and some of these have been used, after suitable calibration, to measure the intensity distribution within a transducers field. The mechanism by which ultrasound accelerates the development of an image is not fully understood, but Bennett[35] suggests a transport phenomenon may be involved. Particularly so when the starch/iodine blue stain reaction is used to obtain the field distribution in front of a transducer.

In this method, a thin starch film is deposited onto an ultrasonically transparent polyethylene sheet some 0·003 in thick. An anechoic tank is used, filled with degassed water and an iodine solution prepared in the ratio: 4 g of iodine with 6 g of potassium iodide dissolved into 100 cm^3 of water. Adequate sensitivity and good linearity are obtained when 40 cm^3 of this solution is added to 10 l of water. The film and transducer are mounted directly parallel, in this solution, and the transducer activated. In general it takes between 5 and 100 sec for an image to form, which image can be photographed and photographic densities read from it. The photographic density of this film has after calibration against a radiometric intensity meter, been found to be directly proportional to intensity and so the intensity distribution can be obtained using standard densiometric techniques. The accuracies attainable with this method are very sensitive to the control exercised in preparing the starch film. Particular care has to be taken to obtain a good bond between the starch film and the polyethylene support membrane. Wetting the polyethylene surface with a solution of 20 mg of carboxy-methyl-cellulose and 10 mg of sodium-lauryle-sulphate in about 20 cm^3 of warm water ensures a good bond when the starch film is deposited. Various starch paste formulae have been proposed of which the most successful has been; 12 g of good quality potato starch dissolved in 20 cm^3 of water and mixed with 10 cm^3 of commercial starch to which 14 gm of 40 per cent polyvinyl acetate has been added. This starch paste is then dissolved in 100 cm^3 of boiling water to which has been added 1 g of gelatine. This mixture is deposited hot onto the polyethylene sheet and spread thinly and evenly over the surface. During the dehydration which follows the starch film should shrink to less than 0·003 in thick. Ageing is allowed for one day prior to usage. Aged the film can withstand water temperatures up to 40°C and when exposed the pattern stays permanently on the film but tends to fade after about the first 30 min. It is for this reason that the image should be photographed immediately after exposure. Accuracies attainable are said to be of the order of ±15 per cent in the range 0·1 to 2 W/cm² where the film has a linear characteristic. Above 2 W/cm² cavitation effects tend to break up the film and below 0·3 W/cm² the starch/iodine reaction is not always reliably initiated. Although the intensity range in which this method may be applied is limited the frequency range in which the measurements have been made is wide ranging from 600 kc/s to 40 Mc/s for waterborne ultrasound. Results however have only proved truly reliable and reproducible when both the starch film and support film have been thin compared with the wavelength of the ultrasound being measured. Very thin Melinex films have been invaluable as support membranes in the higher megacycle range.

Other chemical reactions which ultrasonics have been observed to accelerate include the preferential development of a latent optical image on photographic plate. In this method Ernst and Hoffman[36] amongst others, expose a photo-sensitive film to light for a controlled period and then place it in the field of a transducer. The medium in which measurements are made contains a developing agent, which develops the latent image preferentially at regions of highest intensity. Various possible mechanisms for this preferential development have been put forward including mass-transport, local thermal action and the preferential agitation of developer in high intensity regions. The main disadvantage with these photographic plate methods is that rather high intensities are required for activation, exposure times are long, the plates used are difficult to prepare and dark-room conditions are necessary throughout the measurement. It is widely acknowledged that the starch plate method is both to be preferred and capable of the greater accuracy.

3.11 ULTRASONIC VIBRATION POTENTIALS

When a liquid is subject to ultrasonic waves, free field or standing-wave, alternating potentials developed within the medium have been observed. This effect was first predicted for electrolytes by Debye[37] and studied by a number of authors.[38,39] Their results are often in disagreement with predictions based on Debyes' formulae, and potentials have also been observed in some pure liquids.

In general these potentials have been detected using single platinum probes less than 0·025 cm in diameter sealed into soft glass tubing of 0·6 cm outside diameter with 1·0 cm length of wire exposed. This is then mounted in a small, thin walled spherical glass vessel, filled with the test liquid. The outside of the vessel is covered with silver paint and maintained at ground potential. The potential developed at the probe is then amplified using a low noise high gain system for measurement. Physically this arrangement could provide a very versatile probe assembly for intensity measurements. However, the system is electrically not very sensitive, subject to electrical interference from the source and theoretically the origin of the observed potential has not been satisfactorally established.

One possible contribution to the observed signal could be the condenser microphone action of the section of tubing in which the platinum wire is sealed. The platinum-glass seal acting as one surface of the microphone and the glass-liquid interface as the other. If this concept is true, a response should be obtained even if the wire is totally enclosed in glass and prevented from contacting the liquid. Such an effect for contact and non-contact probes in distilled water has been demonstrated by Yeager et al.[40] This a.c. response, associated with the glass-tubing, is characterized by a high internal impedance whereas at reasonable ionic concentrations, the signal due to the ionic vibration potentials should be generated at a much lower impedance. Exploiting this property Yeager et al. have resolved these two signal contributions and have shown that in 0·01 N KCl the observed potentials are characteristic of the ionic vibration potentials and not false effects due to their method of detection. Recently Weinmann[41] has shown that even in pure polar liquids, the alignment of molecular dipoles, due to density gradients is the most probable cause for the observed potentials. Although there are more areas of disagreement than agreement with regard to the possible causes of this effect, all authors are in agreement that the signal due to ionic-vibration potentials is a direct measure of the velocity amplitude within the medium or,

$$\phi_{max} \text{ is proportional to } u/c \tag{3.47}$$

Probe microphones are available for the direct measurement of the particle pressure within a small test volume and now a better knowledge of the origins of ultrasonic potentials could lead to direct particle velocity measurements. An instrument containing these two facilities could be invaluable in measuring the relative magnitudes of p and v as well as the phase angle between them. By means such as this it should prove possible in the future to define fully the characteristics of any field generated by an ultrasonic transducer.

REFERENCES

1. HUETER, T. F. and BOLT, R. H., *Ultrasonics*. 67, Wiley, New York (1960).
2. WILLIAMS, A. O., *J. Acoust. Soc. Am.*, **16**, 231 (1945), **17**, 219 (1946).
3. CADY, W. G., *Contract N.6. O.N.R.—262 Task Order 1*, November 20, (1950).
4. LANGEVIN, R. A., *J. Acoust. Soc. Am.*, **26**, 421 (1954).
5. CARSTENSEN, E. L., *J. Acoust. Soc. Am.*, **19**, 961 (1947).
6. FRY, W. J. and FRY, R. B., *J. Acoust. Soc. Am.*, **26**, 294, (1954).
7. DUNN, F. and FRY, W. J., *I.R.E., Trans. Ultrasonic Eng.*, **5**, 59 (1957).
8. SPROULE, D. O. and BOYLE, R. W., *Can. J. Res.*, **2**, 1 (1930).
9. BIQUARD, P., *Compt. Rend.*, **188**, 1230 (1929).
10. WIEDERHIELM, C. A., *Rev. Sci. Instr.*, **27**, 7, 540 (1956).
11. MIKHAILOV, I. G., *Ultrasonics*, 129, July–September (1964).
12. WOOD, A. B., *Proc. Phys. Soc.*, **47**, 262 (1935).
13. KING, L. V., *Proc. Phys. Soc.*, **153**, 17 (1935).
14. HARTMANN, J. and MORTENSEN, T., *Phil. Mag.*, **39**, 377 (1948).

15. BEYER, R. T., *Am. J. Phys.*, **18**, 25 (1950).
16. *J. Acoust. Soc. Am.*, **25**, 546 (1953), **25**, 892 (1953).
17. HENRY, G. E., *I.R.E. Trans. Ultrasonic Eng.*, **6**, 17 (1957).
18. KOSSOFF, G., *Acustica*, **12**, 84 (1962).
19. KLEIN, E., *J. Acoust. Soc. Am.*, **10**, 109 (1938).
20. CADY, W. G. and GITTINGS, C. E., *J. Acoust. Soc. Am.*, **25**, 892 (1953).
21. BOYLE, R. W. and TAYLOR, G. B., *Trans. Roy. Soc. Can. Sect.*, **20**, 245 (1926).
22. WELLS, P. N. T., *et al.*, *Ultrasonics*, 124, July–September (1964).
23. KING, L. V., *Proc. Roy. Soc.*, **A153**, 1 (1935), **A147**, 212 (1934).
24. EMBLETON, T. E., *Can. J. Phys.*, **34**, 276 (1956).
25. FOX, F. E., *J. Acoust. Soc. Am.*, **12**, 147 (1940).
26. WELLS, P. N. T., *et al.*, *Ultrasonics*, 1 (1963).
27. KOSSOFF, G., *J. Acoust. Soc. Am.* (to be published).
28. NEWELL, J. A., *Phys. Med. Biol.*, **8**, 215, 241 (1963).
29. LUCAS, R., *Compt. Rend.*, **199**, 1107 (1934).
30. HUTER, T. and POHLMAN, R., *Z. Angew. Phys.*, **1**, 405 (1949).
31. LOEBER, A. and HIEDEMANN, E., *J. Acoust. Soc. Am.*, **28**, 27 (1956).
32. RAMAN, C. V. and NATH, N. S., *Proc. Indian Acad. Sci.*, **A2**, 406 (1935), **A3**, 75 (1936).
33. WILLARD, G. W., *J. Acoust. Soc. Am.*, **21**, 101 (1949).
34. SANDERS, F. H., *Can. J. Res.*, **A14**, 158 (1936).
35. BENNETT, G., *J. Acoust. Soc. Am.*, **24**, 470 (1952).
36. ERNST, P. J. and HOFFMAN, C. W., *J. Acoust. Soc. Am.*, **24**, 207 (1952).
37. DEBYE, P., *J. Chem. Phys.*, **1**, 13 (1933).
38. HUNTER, A., *Proc. Phys. Soc.*, **71**, 847 (1958).
39. RUTGERS, A., *Trans. Faraday Soc.*, **54**, 13 (1958).
40. YEAGER, E., *et al.*, *Proc. Phys. Soc.*, **472**, 690 (1959).
41. WEINMANN, A., *Proc. Phys. Soc.*, **481**, 102 (1960).

4

PULSE TECHNIQUES

G. L. Gooberman, B.Sc., Ph.D., A.Inst.P., A.R.C.S., D.I.C.

4.1 INTRODUCTION

Pulse techniques provide a convenient method for obtaining a visual presentation of some of the ultrasonic properties of the interior of a body. If these ultrasonic properties can be correlated with other physical properties in which we are primarily interested we can build up a meaningful picture of the interior of the body. This is exactly similar to radar in which an electromagnetic discontinuity is interpreted, for example, as representing an aircraft.

Basically, we generate a train of short duration pulses of ultrasonic waves which travel at a finite speed away from the transmitting transducer. When a pulse meets a boundary separating two media of differing specific acoustic impedances part of the pulse energy is scattered and if this scattered energy can be detected we can:

(*a*) postulate the presence of a discontinuity,

(*b*) determine the time taken for any one pulse to travel from the transmitter to the receiver via the discontinuity and hence the distance involved if we know the velocity and

(*c*) assess either the magnitude of the discontinuity, or, if the scattering body is small and its acoustic properties known, then assess its physical size.

Furthermore, if the dimensions of the pulses are small and we scan over the interior of the body we can build up a picture of a cross section through the body in the same way that a radar map is made.

87

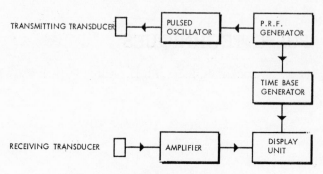

Fig. 4.1. Block diagram of pulse system

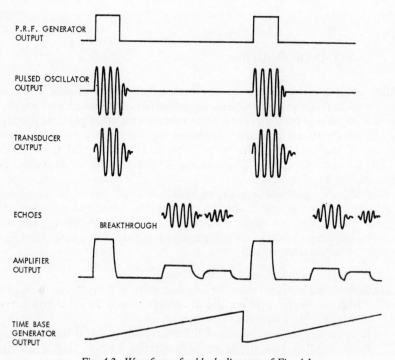

Fig. 4.2. Waveforms for block diagram of Fig. 4.1.

4.2 ELEMENTS OF A PULSE SYSTEM

Any pulse system will contain the following units:

1. a pulsed oscillator
2. a transmitting transducer
3. a receiving transducer
4. a pulse repetition frequency generator
5. a time base generator
6. an amplifier
7. a display unit.

These seven units are interconnected in the manner shown in Fig. 4.1 and the waveforms occurring at various points in the block diagram of Fig. 4.1 are shown in Fig. 4.2. While two transducers are shown it is more common in practice to use the same one for both transmitting and receiving since the echoes to be detected arrive at the transducer at times when it is not transmitting.

The pulsed oscillator generates a train of radio frequency pulses at a suitable repetition frequency (p.r.f.), determined by the p.r.f. generator, which are converted by the transmitting transducer into corresponding

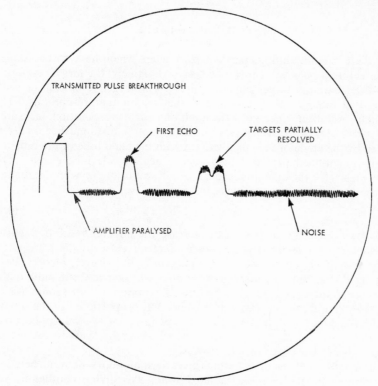

Fig. 4.3. Typical A scan display

89

7

pulses of ultrasonic waves. The echoes from the discontinuity, or target, to use radar terminology, are picked up by the receiving transducer, amplified by the amplifier and converted into a suitable form to appear on the display unit which is usually a cathode ray tube. There are several types of display in common use, but, for the moment we will consider the simplest type which is known as an A scan and which is illustrated in Fig. 4.3. In this type of display the demodulated pulses are applied to the vertical deflection or Y plates of the cathode ray tube. At the same time a linearly rising voltage, generated by the time base generator, is applied to the horizontal or X plates in order to sweep the trace horizontally across the face of the tube. If this horizontal motion starts when the transmitter radiates a pulse, the position of the echoes along the trace will be proportional to the time taken for a pulse to travel from the transmitter to the target and back again. Hence if we know the velocity of the ultrasonic waves and also the speed at which the trace moves horizontally across the face of the tube we can find the distance of the target from the transmitter provided that the transmitting and receiving transducers are side by side, or, preferably, if the same transducer is used for both functions. Just before the oscillator generates another pulse the trace is deflected rapidly back to its starting point and the cycle recommences.

4.3 PULSE SYSTEM PARAMETERS

There are two mutually dependent parameters which have to be decided upon before a pulse system can be designed, namely, the target resolution and the maximum target range required. The target resolution depends upon two factors; the angular and the longitudinal resolutions. The angular resolution which gives the minimum angular separation, measured at the receiver, below which two targets cannot be distinguished, is determined by the angle of the cone within which the main lobe of the radiated energy is confined provided that we can neglect side lobe effects. The cone angle θ for the main lobe from a piston source of diameter d radiating ultrasonic waves with a wavelength λ is given by:

$$\sin \theta/2 = 1 \cdot 2(\lambda/d) \tag{4.1}$$

Thus by decreasing (λ/d) we can increase the angular resolution but if we do this by increasing d the beam diameter close to the transmitter increases and may counteract the reduction in θ. If, however, λ is decreased, keeping d constant, the angular resolution will increase but only at the expense of maximum range since the absorption of ultrasonic waves increases with frequency (linearly in solids but proportional to the square of the frequency in liquids). Thus except in a few special applications some compromise has to be reached which generally leads to the use of frequencies in the range of 1 to 5 Mc/s.

The longitudinal resolution, which gives the minimum separation between two targets situated on the radiated beam axis giving contiguous yet distinguishable echoes, is determined by the pulse duration. Thus in order to resolve two targets, separated by a distance l, the trailing edge of the first echo must occur just before the leading edge of the second echo, that is:

$$\text{pulse duration} \leqslant 2l/c \qquad (4.2)$$

where c denotes the ultrasonic wave velocity. For example, in order to resolve two targets situated 1 mm apart in water the pulse duration must not exceed $1 \cdot 3$ μsec. Eqn. 4.2 has to be slightly modified in practice since although the pulsed oscillator may produce a pulse with sharp leading and trailing edges, these edges are distorted by the rest of the system, particularly the transducers. It does, however, give an adequate design figure.

The maximum required target range controls the choice of peak transmitted power, pulse duration and pulse repetition frequency. Any amplifier generates a certain amount of randomly fluctuating voltages in its component resistances which may be regarded as a 'noise' signal appearing at the amplifier input. Unless very sophisticated techniques are used no signal smaller than this noise signal can be detected.

We consider a transducer radiating a power of P W and which has a maximum gain along the beam axis of G, then the intensity I at a distance of r m from the transducer, along the axis and in a medium of absorption coefficient denoted by α, is given by:

$$I = (GP/4\pi r^2)\, e^{-2\alpha r}\ \text{W/m}^2 \qquad (4.3)$$

A target situated at a distance r will scatter some of this incident energy such that the intensity, I_r, of the echo at the transducer, now acting as the receiver, is given by:

$$I_r = (GP\sigma/16\pi^2 r^4)\, e^{-4\alpha r}\ \text{W/m}^2 \qquad (4.4)$$

where σ denotes the effective scattering cross section of the target in the direction of the receiver. The receiver absorbs this incident intensity I_r over an area of A m^2 so that the condition that the signal power exceeds the noise power P_n at the amplifier input, assuming that the transducer converts all the incident ultrasonic energy into electrical energy, is:

$$I_r A > P_n\ \text{(W)} \qquad (4.5)$$

We can take our analysis one stage further by considering P_n in greater detail. The noise power P_n at the input to an amplifier is given by[1]:

$$P_n = n\mathbf{k}T\Delta f \qquad (4.6)$$

where $\mathbf{k}$ denotes Boltzmann's constant, $1 \cdot 374 \times 10^{-23}$ W/deg/c/s., T the absolute temperature of the noise source, Δf the bandwidth of the receiver and n the amplifiers 'noise figure' which ranges from about 3 to 100, depending upon the design of the amplifier. The optimum bandwidth[2] for the maximum ratio of signal to noise power is approximately equal to $1/d$, where d denotes the pulse width, hence, combining Eqns. 4.4, 4.5 and 4.6 we obtain:

$$(PdGA\sigma/16\pi^2 r^4)\, e^{-4\alpha r} > n\mathbf{k}T \qquad (4.7)$$

91

We can draw at least three important conclusions from Eqn. 4.7. Firstly, we have the obvious conclusion that all other things being equal, the maximum range in a highly absorbing medium is less than in a slightly absorbing medium. Secondly, if we neglect absorption for the moment, the maximum range is proportional to Pd rather than P alone, and thirdly if we again neglect absorption Pd has to be increased sixteen times in order to double the maximum range.

There are two limits to the magnitude of Pd. Firstly, the peak power available from the transducer will be limited by the maximum voltage it will withstand without breaking down and, secondly, since Pd is proportional to the average power output from the transducer, this may be limited on medical grounds. If necessary Pd can be increased but only by reducing the pulse repetition frequency so that the average power remains constant. If the pulse duration is long the possibility of cavitation forming at high peak powers must be considered.

Apart from the average power considerations of the previous paragraph, another factor influences the choice of the pulse repetition frequency. Suppose that an echo appears on the A scan at a time t_1 after the start of the trace. The actual time taken, t_1', for a pulse to travel to the target and back is given by:

$$t_1' = t_1 + mT \tag{4.8}$$

where T denotes the period of the pulse repetition frequency and $m = 0, 1, 2, 3, 4, \ldots$. There is no way of finding the value of m unless T is made sufficiently large, that is the p.r.f. sufficiently low, that from considerations of the maximum possible range or the dimensions of the body being investigated, $m = 0$ is the only possible solution.

4.4 MATHEMATICS OF PULSES

Before we can study in detail each of the blocks shown in Fig. 4.1 we must first consider the mathematics of pulses and, in particular, repetitive pulses.

Fourier's theorem states that any waveform may be represented by a sum of sinusoidal and cosinusoidal waves each with its appropriate amplitude. For a repetitive waveform, denoted by $F(t)$, we have:

$$F(t) = B_0 + \sum_{k=1}^{\infty} [A_k \sin (k2\pi ft) + B_k \cos (k2\pi ft)] \tag{4.9}$$

where k is an integer and f the repetition frequency of $F(t)$. The coefficients B_0, A_k and B_k are given by:

$$B_0 = f \int_{-1/2f}^{1/2f} F(t) \, dt \tag{4.10a}$$

$$A_k = 2f \int_{-1/2f}^{1/2f} F(t) \sin (k2\pi ft) \, dt \tag{4.10b}$$

$$B_k = 2f \int_{-1/2f}^{1/2f} F(t) \cos{(k2\pi ft)} \, dt \qquad (4.10c)$$

In the form given in Eqn. 4.9, each kth harmonic is represented as the sum of a sinusoidal and cosinusoidal wave. These can be combined to give:

$$A_k \sin{(k2\pi ft)} + B_k \sin{(k2\pi ft)} = C_k \sin{(k2\pi ft + \theta_k)} \qquad (4.11)$$

where
$$C_k = A_k^2 + B_k^2 \qquad (4.12a)$$

$$\theta_k = \tan^{-1}{(B_k/A_k)} \qquad (4.12b)$$

We can now plot the pulse spectra of typical waveforms encountered in pulse techniques and these are show in Fig. 4.4. These spectra illustrate the important point that for a repetitive waveform, such as a rectangular pulse as shown in part 1 of Fig. 4.4, the spectrum consists of lines, separated by the frequency f, with frequencies up to several times the reciprocal of the pulse duration. The spectrum for a rectangular pulse modulated radio frequency waveform is similar to that for the modulating waveform except that the frequencies are all increased by the radio frequency and the spectral envelope is now symmetrical about the carrier frequency. In order to reproduce the waveforms with good fidelity a network must be capable of passing a wide range of frequencies with little or no amplitude or phase distortion. If we compare the waveforms of parts 1 and 3 of

WAVEFORM   SPECTRUM

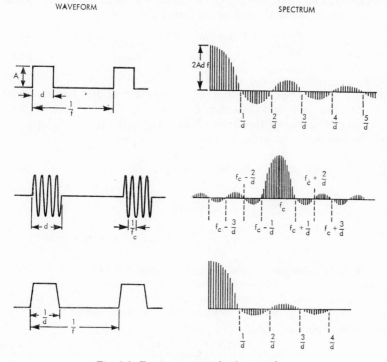

Fig. 4.4. Fourier spectra of pulse waveforms

93

Fig. 4.4 we see that the steeper the edges of the waveform the more important the high frequency spectral components become.

In the case of non-repetitive waveforms the pulse repetition frequency has sunk effectively to zero so that the spectral lines all merge into each other and the spectral distribution becomes continuous. Expressed mathematically this means that the summation sign in Eqn. 4.9 now becomes an integral. One important non-repetitive waveform consists of a step of amplitude H occurring at $t = 0$. The Fourier expansion for this waveform is:

$$F(t) = \frac{H}{2} + \frac{H}{2} \int_0^\infty \frac{\sin(\omega t)}{\omega} \, d\omega \qquad (4.13)$$

We shall require this expression in the next section.

4.5 MODIFICATION OF PULSES BY ELECTRICAL NETWORKS

Pulses do not exist in isolation but have to be passed through electrical networks, an amplifier for example, which will inevitably modify them. This modification can be conveniently represented by the network's 'transfer function' which is defined as the ratio of the network's output voltage, v_0, to its input voltage v_i. Because of Fourier's theorem we need consider only sinusoidal waveforms, thus we may write:

$$v_i = V_i \sin(\omega t) \qquad (4.14a)$$

$$v_0 = |Z(\omega)| V_i \sin[\omega t - \phi(\omega)] \qquad (4.14b)$$

where the quantities $Z(\omega)$ and $\phi(\omega)$ are the two parts of the transfer function; the former governing the magnitude of the output voltage relative to the input and the latter its phase.

If now the input to the network is a repetitive pulse of some sort, Eqn. 4.9 enables us to write the following expressions for v_i and v_0:

$$v_i = \sum_{k=1}^\infty [A_k \sin(k\omega t) + B_k \cos(k\omega t)] \qquad (4.15a)$$

$$v_0 = \sum_{k=1}^\infty \Big[A_k |Z(k\omega)| \sin[k\omega t - \phi(k\omega)] \\ + B_k |Z(k\omega)| \cos[k\omega t - \phi(k\omega)] \Big] \qquad (4.15b)$$

In both these equations we have neglected the constant term B_0 since as far as studying the distortion produced by the network is concerned, it is irrelevant, since it is simply a d.c. level. From Eqn. 4.15b we have that for the output of the network to be of identical shape but different magnitude to the input:

$$Z(k\omega) = \text{constant} \qquad (4.16a)$$

$$\phi(k\omega) = k\omega t_1 + n\pi \qquad (4.16b)$$

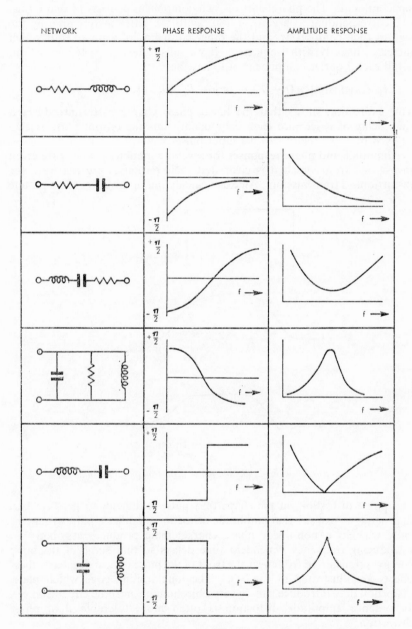

Fig. 4.5. Amplitude and phase responses for various passive networks

where t_1 is a constant and $n = 0, 1, 2, 3, \ldots$ Thus we have that the amplitude of each Fourier component is increased or decreased by the same amount. The phase shift of each component consists of two terms, one corresponding to a zero or 180° shift, the latter merely altering the sign of each component, and the other consisting of a phase shift which increases linearly with frequency. If we substitute Eqn. 4.16b into Eqn. 4.15b each Fourier component of v_0 has the form:

$$A_k |Z(k\omega)| \sin [k\omega(t - t_1) - n\pi] + B_k |Z(k\omega)| [\cos k(t - t_1) - n\pi]$$

This expression shows that the linear phase characteristic introduces a time delay of t_1 sec into each component, thus the output pulse is also delayed by t_1 sec relative to the input pulse.

Amplitude and phase responses for several common networks are given in Fig. 4.5 from which it is clear that their responses are not ideal for distortionless transmission. An exact calculation of the effect of amplitude

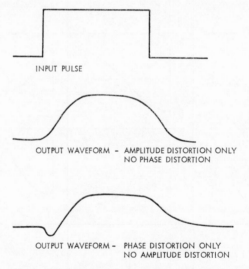

INPUT PULSE

OUTPUT WAVEFORM – AMPLITUDE DISTORTION ONLY
NO PHASE DISTORTION

OUTPUT WAVEFORM – PHASE DISTORTION ONLY
NO AMPLITUDE DISTORTION

Fig. 4.6. Effects of amplitude and phase distortion on rectangular pulse

and phase distortion on the shape of a pulse is difficult to perform but, in general, we can say that amplitude distortion modifies a pulse symmetrically whereas a non-linear phase characteristic produces assymetry by introducing frequency dependent time delays so that some of the pulse energy is transferred from near the front of the pulse to near the rear—these effects are illustrated in Fig. 4.6. The long trailing edge which phase distortion may introduce can be very objectionable in some circumstances. In practice amplitude distortion is often more tolerable than phase distortion.

While space does not permit a thorough analysis of pulse transmission through physically realizable networks, we can illustrate the salient points by considering the passage of a pulse through a perfect low pass filter

96

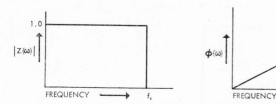

Fig. 4.7. Idealized low pass filter characteristics

which has the idealized characteristics illustrated in Fig. 4.7. To do this we apply a step input to the filter and compute the output by summing all the Fourier components which the filter passes. The spectrum of the step, of amplitude H, is given by Eqn. 4.13. The filter output is obtained by replacing the upper integration limit of infinity by the maximum frequency passed by the filter, ω_1, and inserting a time delay t_1. Thus the output $F_0(t)$ becomes:

$$F_0(t) = \frac{H}{2} + \frac{H}{2} \int_0^{\omega_1} \frac{\sin \omega(t - t_1)}{\omega} \, d\omega \qquad (4.17)$$

The form taken by $F_0(t)$ is shown in Fig. 4.8. The first point to notice about this waveform is that it indicates a response before the step is applied but as this is physically impossible the characteristics which we have assumed for the filter must be physically unrealizable. In practice the characteristics of the low pass filter must be such as to eliminate this premature response. We can, however, still obtain useful information from Eqn. 4.17. For example the time, t_r, required for the output to reach H is given approximately by[3]:

$$t_r - \pi/\omega_1 = 1/2f_1 \qquad (4.18)$$

The second point to notice is that the top of the output step contains a ripple whose period is given by the time interval between the zeros of the integrand in Eqn. 4.17, that is the period $= 2\pi/\omega_1 = 1/f_1$.

We can find the response at the rear end of the pulse in exactly the same way as for the front edge by considering the filter response to a negative going step which will simply be the response of Fig. 4.8 inverted. Thus the response to a pulse of a low pass filter, after correcting the ideal

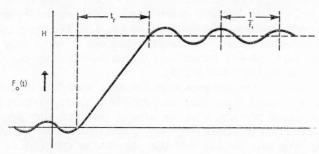

Fig. 4.8. Reproduction of step function by idealized low pass filter

97

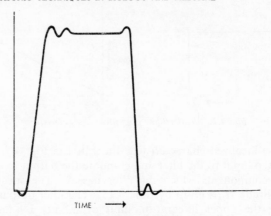

TIME ⟶

Fig. 4.9. Reproduction of rectangular pulse by physically realizable low pass filter with sharp cut off

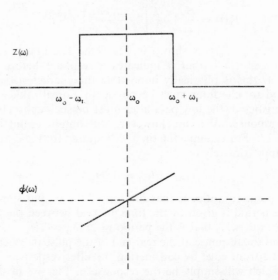

Fig. 4.10. Response of ideal band pass filter

characteristics to those more nearly approaching physically realizable ones, becomes similar to that illustrated in Fig. 4.9. The ripple appearing in the filter response may be undesirable and can be reduced by sloping the sides of the amplitude characteristic so that the high frequency response falls off gradually instead of sharply.

Our analysis of the low pass filter can be extended to deal with the response of a band pass filter transmitting a pulse modulated radio frequency signal provided that we assume that the filter response is symmetrical about its centre frequency f_0 and that the carrier frequency is also f_0. We have already seen that the Fourier spectrum of a pulse modulated signal consists of spectral lines symmetrically disposed about

98

the carrier frequency. This being so and with a filter with a symmetrical response, each spectral line situated f cycles above f_0 will receive the same treatment as one situated f cycles below f_0 (Fig. 4.10). We should there-fore, be able to predict the filter response to our signal by considering only that part of the filter response to frequencies f_0 and above. Provided now that we keep the filter response unchanged in terms of $f - f_0$, we can choose any value we like for f_0, that is we can make f_0 equal to zero. In other words the envelope of the filter output now becomes the output of a low pass filter whose input is the modulating envelope of the actual filter input. Thus the output of a symmetrical bandpass filter becomes that shown in Fig. 4.11.

One particular circuit which is of special importance and which behaves very similarly to a band pass filter is the parallel tuned circuit shown in Fig. 4.12. In order to find its equivalent low pass filter we consider a very long radio frequency current pulse to be applied to the circuit. Eventually the voltage across the circuit will settle down to its steady

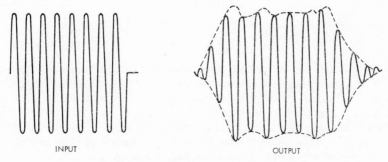

INPUT   OUTPUT

Fig. 4.11. Reproduction of pulse modulated R.F. signal by idealized band pass filter

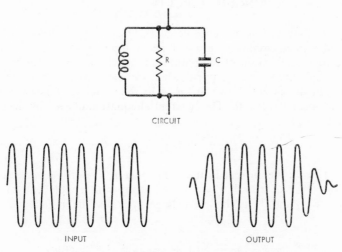

CIRCUIT

INPUT   OUTPUT

Fig. 4.12. Parallel tuned circuit—circuit and response

99

state conditions. If now we move the circuit's resonant frequency to zero we must make either L or C infinite. If L is infinite and we force the current step through it the voltage across the circuit will rise to an infinite value after which it will fall to zero when the current is no longer varying. This does not correspond to the operation of the tuned circuit. If we make C infinite no steady state voltage can appear across the circuit since a finite current flowing for a finite time into an infinite capacity will not cause a voltage to appear across the capacitor. The only way we can get a steady state voltage across the zero frequency equivalent circuit is to represent the tuned circuit by a parallel resistance-capacity network. The condition for the voltage across the low pass filter to be 3 dB down on its very low frequency value is:

$$2\pi f = 1/CR \tag{4.19}$$

For the tuned circuit the frequency deviation from resonance for the 3 dB down point is:

$$f = f_0/2Q \tag{4.20}$$

where $Q = R/2\pi f_0 L$. Equating Eqns. 4.19 and 4.20 we obtain:

$$CR = 2Q/2\pi f_0 \tag{4.21}$$

The voltage across the low pass equivalent circuit rises exponentially with time a constant CR. Hence the envelope of the waveform appearing across the tuned circuit will also rise exponentially with a time constant of $Q/\pi f_0$. Expressed in another way the envelope has risen to 63 per cent of its final value after Q/π cycles of the carrier wave. Thus we can draw the important conclusion that for faithful reproduction of pulse modulated carrier waves any tuned circuit must have a low Q.

4.6 THE RINGING CIRCUIT

In the previous section we considered the response of filters, including the parallel tuned circuit, to various types of input signals. There remains however one application of the parallel tuned circuit which we must still consider and that is what happens when we suddenly apply or remove a current. In the circuit shown in Fig. 4.13 the switch S, which is initially closed, is opened at $t = 0$. The differential equation obeyed by the circuit for $t \geqslant 0$ is:

$$LRC\frac{\mathrm{d}^2 i}{\mathrm{d}t^2} + L\frac{\mathrm{d}i}{\mathrm{d}t} + Ri = 0 \tag{4.22}$$

where i denotes the current in the inductance L. Inserting the boundary conditions that at $t = 0$, $i = E/r$ and $\mathrm{d}i/\mathrm{d}t = 0$, enables us to solve Eqn. 4.22 for i and thence for the voltage E_L across the inductance. Thus we find:

$$E_L = L\frac{\mathrm{d}i}{\mathrm{d}t} = -\frac{E}{r}\left[1 + \frac{1}{4Q^2}\right]\omega L\, e^{-\frac{\omega t}{2Q}}\sin(\omega t) \tag{4.23}$$

where
$$\omega = \frac{1}{\sqrt{(LC)}} \left[1 - \frac{1}{4Q^2} \right]^{1/2} \tag{4.24}$$

If instead of suddenly removing the current from the circuit at $t = 0$ we were to apply a current step we would obtain the same equation as Eqn. 4.23 except that we should have to take into account the shunting effect on R of the current generator's output resistance. We notice that Eqn. 4.23 shows that the voltage across the circuit is a damped sine wave of frequency equal to the circuit's resonant frequency. The rate at which the voltage oscillations decay depends upon the circuit Q. Since $\omega t/2Q = \pi n/Q$ where n denotes the number of cycles since the start of the

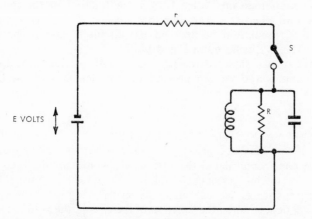

Fig. 4.13. Circuit for analysis of ringing circuit

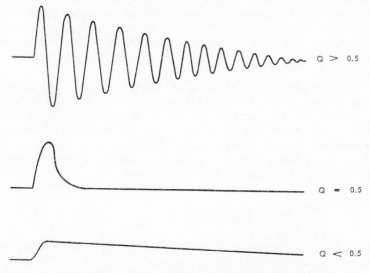

Fig. 4.14. Voltages across ringing circuit for differing values of Q

101

oscillation or ringing, the condition for the amplitude to have fallen by p per cent is given by:

$$e^{-\frac{\pi n}{Q}} = 1 - p/100$$

whence $\hspace{4cm} n = Qp/100\pi \hspace{4cm}$ (4.25)

Taking a typical value for Q of 100, the oscillations will take about 16 cycles to fall to 50 per cent of their initial amplitude. The time constant governing the exponential decay is the same as that derived for the modulation envelope in the previous section.

If the circuit Q is reduced, the number of cycles required before the oscillation amplitude has fallen to a given fraction of the initial value decreases until when Q reaches 0·5, that is when $R = \frac{1}{2}\sqrt{(L/C)}$, only one half cycle of oscillation occurs and the circuit is said to be critically damped. This is illustrated in Fig. 4.14.

We have now completed the necessary mathematical introduction to pulse techniques and we can proceed to consider each of the blocks in Fig. 4.1 in detail.

4.7 VALVES OR TRANSISTORS?

Before we consider in detail the various electronic circuits used in pulse work it is worthwhile pausing to look into the question of whether to use valves or transistors. No definitive answer can be given to this question since all will depend upon the function of the circuit, the voltages involved, and the state of transistor technology at the time, but, as a rough guide, we can say that where miniaturization and reliability are concerned transistors are probably superior, where minimum power consumption is paramount transistors are definitely superior but where large voltages are involved valves are probably better although transistors capable of withstanding up to 500 V between collector and emitter are becoming available. Where low noise is important valves are generally better than transistors.

There is no reason why hybrid circuits using both valves and transistors cannot be used provided that care is taken to ensure that no high voltage surges from the valve supplies can reach the transistors since, while a transistor will operate happily almost indefinitely under its correct operating conditions, a momentary surge of voltage or current can easily destroy it. In the following sections both valve and transistor circuits will be given and the reader left to take his pick.

4.8 PULSED OSCILLATORS

The transmitting transducer has to be driven by a pulse modulated radio frequency signal derived from an oscillator which must have adequate frequency and amplitude stability. We could use a continuously running

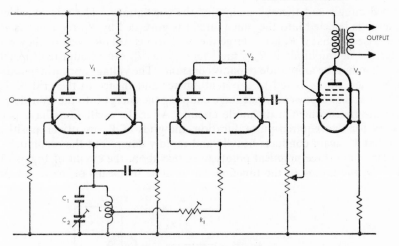

Fig. 4.15. Pulsed oscillator

oscillator whose output is passed through a gating circuit which only transmits the oscillator output during the required pulse duration. This technique, however, is rarely used since some of the oscillator output inevitably leaks to the receiver where it can easily mask the echo signals. Instead a pulsed oscillator is used, that is an oscillator which is switched on for the pulse duration only.

A pulsed oscillator consists essentially of a shock excited tuned circuit. Normally the oscillations will decay exponentially according to the equations of Sect. 4.6 with the rate of decay dependent upon the amount of damping present. If this decay is objectionable it can be eliminated by reducing the damping to such a low value that the oscillation amplitude changes by a negligible amount during the required pulse duration at the end of which the damping is suddenly raised to such a high value that the oscillations die away extremely fast. The typical tuned circuit Q of about 100 is too small for a reasonably constant amplitude output if the pulse lasts more than a few cycles so that if we require a constant amplitude pulse we have to replace the energy being dissipated in the circuit resistance. One way of doing this is shown in Fig. 4.15 which gives the circuit of a useful pulsed oscillator capable of generating pulses of any width from about one microsecond upwards. In this circuit L, C_1 and C_2 form the tuned circuit which resonates at the required frequency. In the absence of any input the grids of V_1 are at the same potential as the cathodes so that V_1 is conducting heavily thereby heavily damping the tuned circuit so that oscillations are impossible. If now the grids of V_1 are driven sufficiently negative that the valve is cut off the rapid change in current through L induces the tuned circuit to ring. Normally the oscillations would decay, however, part of the voltage across the tuned circuit appears between the grid and cathode of V_2 thereby causing an oscillatory current to flow through V_2 and hence through the bottom section of L. This current is in the correct phase to inject energy into the

103

tuned circuit and thereby maintains the oscillations. The rate at which energy is injected into the tuned circuit is governed by R_1, reducing as R_1 increases so that if R_1 is too large the oscillations will die away or they will increase in amplitude if R_1 is too small. Thus R_1 can be adjusted to such a value that the amplitude remains constant. The voltage appearing across the tuned circuit is fed to a potentiometer and thence to the grid of V_3 which acts as a power output stage coupling the energy into the transducer via the transformer in its anode circuit. After the oscillations have persisted for the required pulse duration, the grids of V_1 are driven positive so that V_1 again conducts heavily and rapidly damps out the oscillations.

There are three practical points to notice about the circuit of Fig. 4.15. Firstly, the tuning of the tuned circuit is done by means of the trimming

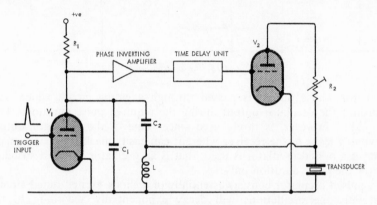

Fig. 4.16. Circuit for shock excitation of ringing circuit (after F.A. Firestone. U.S. Pat. 2,280226)

capacitor C_2. Secondly, the negative voltage applied to the grids of V_1 must be greater than the amplitude of the oscillatory voltage across the tuned circuit so that when the cathodes of V_1 reach their maximum negative voltage there is no possibility of V_1 starting to conduct. Finally, since the oscillatory voltage may be large, care must be taken to ensure that the cathode to heater potential of V_1 never exceeds the maximum value quoted by the valve manufacturer.

An alternative technique which is particularly useful at high frequencies, when a very rapid change in current through a small inductance is required in order to get a high output voltage, uses the discharge of a thyratron to initiate oscillations. One such circuit is shown in Fig. 4.16. Normally both thyratrons are non-conducting so that C_1 charges through the resistor R_1 to the H.T. potential. If now a positive pulse is applied to the grid of V_1 it will fire and rapidly discharge C_1. This rapid voltage change induces the tuned circuit formed by L and C_2 to ring. The negative going voltage step at the anode of V_1 is inverted by the amplifier, delayed by the desired pulse length and then applied to the grid of the second thyratron V_2. This then fires and since it is across the tuned circuit it rapidly dampens out the oscillations. The resistor R_2 serves to both limit

104

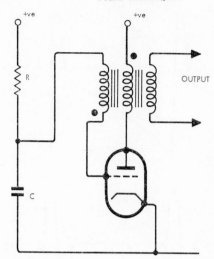

*Fig. 4.17. Valve blocking
oscillator*

the surge current through V_2 and to control the rate of decay of the oscillations at the end of the pulse. While this technique cannot generate a
flat topped pulse it can generate high power short duration pulses. The
thyratrons should be hydrogen filled in order to get fast operation.

4.9 PULSE REPETITION FREQUENCY GENERATORS

The pulsed oscillator requires to be driven by a train of steep sided pulses,
each a few microseconds long, occurring at frequencies from a few cycles
per second up to the order of 20 kc/s. There are two standard techniques
available for generating this type of waveform: blocking oscillators and
multivibrators. While the blocking oscillator is convenient, in that it use
fewer components than the multivibrator, it has the disadvantage of
requiring a pulse transformer in addition to which the pulse duration is
not variable.

The circuit of a typical free running valve blocking oscillator is shown in
Fig. 4.17 and the important waveforms in Fig. 4.18. We assume, initially,
that the valve is cut off by a suitably large negative voltage developed
across the capacitor C. This voltage decays as C discharges through R
and eventually the valve begins to conduct. The resultant slight rise in
anode current induces a voltage in the grid connected winding of the
transformer which is so arranged that this voltage takes the grid in a
positive direction so that the valve conducts slightly more. As this process
is regenerative, the anode current rises extremely fast until the transformer
core becomes saturated when the grid voltage will start to fall, reducing
the anode current and thereby driving the grid negative. As before, this
process is regenerative so that the valve is rapidly switched off. While
the grid is positive a heavy grid current will flow into the capacitor C
charging it up to the voltage which we postulated initially.

105

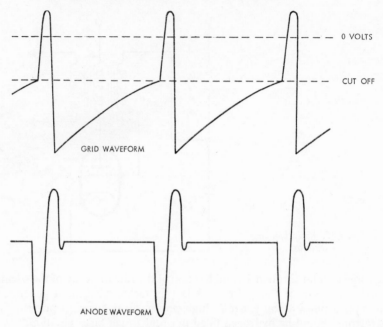

Fig. 4.18. Valve blocking oscillator waveforms

The rate of rise of the pulse is limited by the leakage inductance and stray capacitance of the transformer windings since a blocking oscillator is essentially a shock excited oscillator producing only one cycle of oscillation whose frequency is determined by the effective inductance and capacitance of the transformer regarded as a tuned circuit. Thus these quantities control the pulse width. The transformer should be sufficiently damped either by having adequate core loss or, alternatively, by connecting a resistor across one winding, otherwise even though the valve has been cut-off at the end of the pulse the transformer will continue to ring and produce a damped oscillatory output.

The p.r.f. of this circuit will depend upon the time taken for the voltage across C to fall to such a value that the valve begins to conduct, that is, upon the product CR. Thus while the pulse duration is fixed by the transformer characteristics the p.r.f. is controllable by changing CR.

The transistor equivalent of this circuit is shown in Fig. 4.19. This works in an analogous manner to the valve circuit except that the p.r.f. control is now situated in the emitter circuit. The diode and resistor placed in series across the transformer primary serve to shunt out any overswing in voltage arising from the transformer ringing.

In some circumstances it is convenient to have the blocking oscillator generate a pulse only when triggered from an external source. This can be managed by biassing the valve, or transistor, so that it is not conducting until a pulse of suitable magnitude and polarity is injected into the grid or base circuit.

106

A multivibrator consists essentially of two amplifiers, A and B, cross connected so that the output of A is the input to B and the output of B is the input to A. Depending upon the type of coupling between the amplifiers and the static biassing arrangements, this type of circuit will generate a free running almost rectangular waveform (astable operation), a rectangular pulse of fixed duration initiated by a trigger pulse (mono-stable operation) or be a two state device which changes its state upon application of a trigger pulse (bistable operation). We shall consider only the first two types here since the bistable multivibrator rarely occurs in pulse circuitry associated with ultrasonic systems.

Circuit diagrams for typical multivibrators are given in Fig. 4.20 and the associated waveforms are given in Fig. 4.21. Except during transition, one valve or transistor is conducting heavily so that its anode or collector

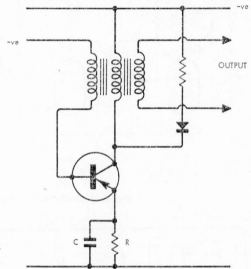

Fig. 4.19. Transistor blocking oscillator

is at a very low potential relative to earth while the other is cut off so that its anode or collector is at a high potential. After transistion this state of affairs is reversed so that, for example, the valve which was conducting is now cut off. For clarity we will consider transistor circuits only—valve circuits behave in an analogous manner.

We assume that transistor T_1 of the astable multivibrator is cut off and T_2 conducting. For this state of affairs to have arisen from the circuit's previous state in which the conducting conditions of the transistors were reversed, the collector of T_2 must have changed from a high to a low nega-tive potential, that is, the collector potential has moved in a positive direction. This change in potential will have been transmitted through the coupling capacitor C_1 to the base of T_1. Previously the base potential of T_1 had been about -0.6 V (assuming silicon transistors) so that now the base of T_1 is positive relative to its emitter. Hence T_1 will be cut off. C_1 will now start to charge, taking the base of T_1 towards $-E_{v1}$ V. After

107

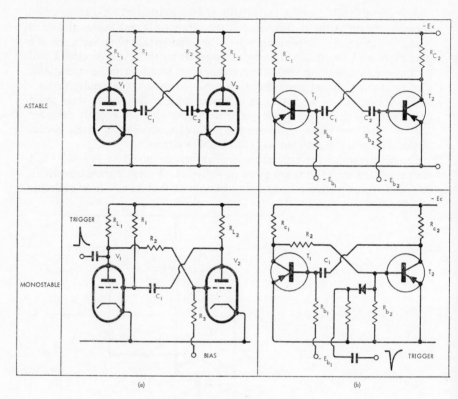

(a)   (b)

Fig. 4.20. Multivibrator circuits

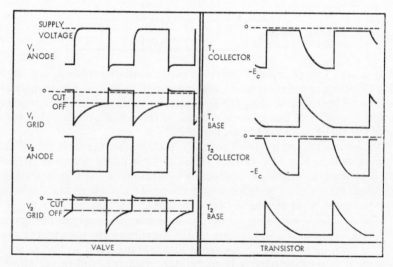

Fig. 4.21. Astable multivibrator waveforms

a time dependent upon the time constant associated with C_1, the base of T_1 will become slightly negative thereby causing T_1 to start conducting slightly so that its collector potential becomes slightly less negative, that is it moves in a positive direction. This positive potential movement is coupled by C_2 to the base of T_2 which thus conducts slightly less than before so that its collector potential moves negatively causing the base of T_1 to become more negative, T_1 conducts a little more and so on. This process builds very fast so that after a very short time interval T_1 is conducting heavily and T_2 is cut off. This process now repeats itself as transition will again occur when the base of T_2 falls from its positive value to a slightly negative one. Provided that the time constants $C_1 R_{c2}$ and $C_2 R_{c1}$ are small compared with $C_2 R_{b2}$ and $C_1 R_{b1}$ respectively, the times τ_1 and τ_2 for which T_1 and T_2 respectively are cut off are given by the following approximate expressions:

$$\tau_1 \approx C_1 R_{b1} \log_e \left[1 + \frac{E_c}{E_{b1}} \right] \tag{4.26a}$$

$$\tau_2 \approx C_2 R_{b2} \log_e \left[1 + \frac{E_c}{E_{b2}} \right] \tag{4.26b}$$

These equations also assume that each transistor conducts when its base to emitter potential is zero and that the collector bottoming potential is also zero. Neither of these assumptions is correct but, provided that E_c and E_b are several volts these equations are sufficiently accurate for most applications. The corresponding equation for the valve astable multivibrator is of the form:

$$\tau_1 \approx R_1 C_1 \log_e \left[\frac{E_u + E_i}{E_u + E_c} \right] \tag{4.27}$$

where E_u denotes the voltage to which R_1 is returned, $-E_i$ the voltage from which the grid must rise and which is approximately equal to the voltage drop across the corresponding anode load resistor when its associated valve has zero grid bias, and E_c the cut off voltage of the valve with its anode voltage equal to the supply voltage.

The monostable circuit is very similar except that one transistor (or valve) is always cut off and the other conducting until a trigger pulse is injected to cause transition. For example, in the transistor circuit of Fig. 4.20(b), T_1 conducts and T_2 is cut off until the injected trigger causes T_1 to conduct. When this happens regeneration occurs until T_1 is cut off thereby maintaining T_2 conducting until the base potential of T_1 is such that it recommences conducting when regeneration again occurs until T_2 is cut off and T_1 conducting heavily. This state of affairs will persist until another trigger is injected. The duration of the pulse produced by this circuit is given by Eqn. 4.26(a) with a similar one holding for the valve circuit.

Trigger pulses should preferably be injected via a diode so arranged that, just after the trigger has been injected and the circuit starts to switch over, the diode becomes reverse biassed and thereby disconnects the triggering source from the multivibrator. This avoids the possibility of the trigger source loading the multivibrator and modifying its operation.

The sharpness of the transition between states for either of these circuit depends, for valves, upon the stray capacitances connected to the valve electrodes. Stray capacitances are not so important for transistors since the collector load resistances are less than those used in the anode circuits of valves. However the voltage rises at the collectors depend upon the time constants CR_c and the transistor switching times. Transition times of much less than a microsecond can be achieved by suitable design.

There is one practical point which should be noted for transistor circuits. At some point in the cycle the base emitter junction of each transistor becomes reverse biassed and care must be taken to ensure that this reverse bias is less than the maximum which the transistor will withstand. Planar transistors rarely withstand more than about 4 V but alloy junction types can withstand up to as much as 50 V, depending upon the type used.

In describing multivibrators we have somewhat digressed from p.r.f. generators in that the monostable multivibrators are not p.r.f. generators although they follow logically from the astable types. We could use an astable multivibrator as our p.r.f. generator using one timing circuit to control the p.r.f. and the other to control the pulse width. Usually the resulting highly asymmetrical multivibrator which this approach calls for is unsatisfactory and it is better practice to use one astable unit to generate a train of pulses with the required p.r.f., differentiate these to obtain spikes occurring at the beginning and end of each pulse, and inject these via a diode into a monostable multivibrator which generates a pulse of the required width to modulate the oscillator.

4.10 AMPLIFIERS

The function of the amplifier is to receive the small electrical echo signals from the receiving transducer, amplify them and convert them into a form suitable for presentation to a human observer via the display unit. Since the electrical echo signal from the receiving transducer may be as small as a few microvolts and as the display unit requires signals of the order of tens of volts, the amplifier gain may need to be of the order of one million. With such a large gain any large input signal can cause paralysis, that is, the signal somewhere within the amplifier becomes so large that an amplifying stage becomes non-linear and the signal is rectified causing capacitors to charge up. When the signal is removed the voltages across these capacitors may bias off the stage so that it no longer amplifies until the capacitors have discharged. This danger is particularly likely during the time immediately following the emission of the transmitted pulse since with the single transducer system the amplifier is effectively connected across the transmitter. Even with two transducers sufficient signal may be picked up by the amplifier to cause paralysis since it is not possible to screen the amplifier input completely from the transmitter. This paralysis danger can be reduced by keeping all capacitors as small as possible so that their time constants are small and also by using direct coupling in the video amplifier if this is possible. Alternatively the video amplifier must be designed to have a very wide dynamic range. Since weak signals will usually be those from distant targets provision is sometimes made for the amplifier gain to increase exponentially with time so that signals displayed on an A scan tend to appear with roughly equal heights irrespective of target distance.

The amplifier should distort the signal as little as possible so its amplitude response should be reasonably flat and its phase response reasonably linear over the range of frequencies in the signal's Fourier spectrum. This usually means that the overall bandwidth should be in the region of 1 or 2 Mc/s. If weak echoes are to be detected the amplifier noise should be small.

The design of amplifiers is an art in itself and a considerable literature is available to assist the designer. In the space available here we can do little more than outline the salient points and skim through the techniques currently employed.

4.11 NOISE

When discussing the parameters controlling the maximum range from which echoes could be detected we introduced the concept of noise arising from random fluctuations of current in either a resistor, valve or transistor. A convenient parameter for describing the noise properties of an amplifier is the 'noise figure,' n, which is defined as the ratio of the signal to noise power ratio of an ideal noiseless amplifier to the actual signal to noise power ratio at the output of the practical amplifier. The noise output from the ideal amplifier arises from the noise generated in the source resistance, which, in our case will be the radiation resistance of the transducer. The noise figure is expressed either as a number or, more commonly in decibels. In order to give an idea of the minimum detectable signal we consider an amplifier with a noise figure of 10 and a bandwidth of 1 Mc/s, in which case the noise power, referred to the input is $4 \cdot 10^{-14}$ W. Doubling the bandwidth would double the noise power.

The noise generated by valves tends to be less than that by transistors and the more grids a valve has the noisier it is. Transistor noise decreases with decreasing collector current. It is also frequency dependent with a minimum around several hundred kilocycles (this depends upon the transistor type) and rising at both low and high frequencies. Valve noise, however, is uniformly distributed over the frequency spectrum.

Each stage of amplification generates noise but as far as signal to noise ratio is concerned only the first stage is important, unless its gain is very low, since once the signal has been lifted to a magnitude well above the input noise level of a stage the noise contributed by that stage becomes negligible.

111

4.12 AMPLIFIER DESIGN

The information carried by the echo signals is contained in the envelope modulating the carrier frequency but before this can be retrieved by a detector and possibly further amplified by the video amplifier, the signal must be amplified up to about 1 V in amplitude since detectors work most satisfactorily at this signal level. The radio frequency amplifier used for this purpose can be either a straight type with a suitable pass band centred on the carrier frequency or a superheterodyne amplifier in which the carrier frequency is changed to a different value and the signal then amplified. In this latter type of amplifier the input signal, at a carrier frequency f_1, is fed into a frequency changer which is also supplied with a signal at a frequency f_2. The output of the frequency changer, or mixer, contains signals with frequencies of $f_1, f_2, f_1 + f_2$ and $f_1 - f_2$. One of these latter two frequencies is chosen to be amplified by a fixed tuned intermediate frequency amplifier. Mixers tend to be noisier than amplifiers so it is good practice to precede the mixer by at least one stage of amplification to lift the signal above the mixer noise level. The output from the last stage of the intermediate frequency amplifier is fed into a detector whose output consists of the modulating waveform with the carrier removed. This signal is then amplified further by the video amplifier until it is sufficient to operate the display unit. A block diagram of a typical amplifier system is given in Fig. 4.22.

The two basic parameters, which have to be decided upon before the amplifier can be designed, are the overall gain and bandwidth. These have already been discussed but there is one other factor, apart from pulse distortion, which affects the choice of bandwidth. While increasing the bandwidth reduces pulse distortion it also increases the noise power. If the signal consists of rectangular pulses of width τ μsec, the maximum signal noise ratio occurs with a bandwidth of about $1 \cdot 2/\tau$ Mc/s. Below this the pulse is clipped and above this the noise increases. If however the pulse rise times are important, and the noise permits, a wider bandwidth may have to be used.

4.13 RADIO FREQUENCY AMPLIFIERS

Circuit diagrams for both valve and transistor r.f. amplifiers are given in Fig. 4.23. The valve type can be easier to construct since the transistor

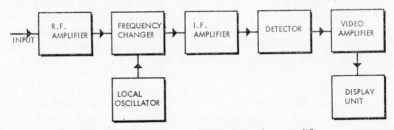

Fig. 4.22. Block diagram of superheterodyne amplifier

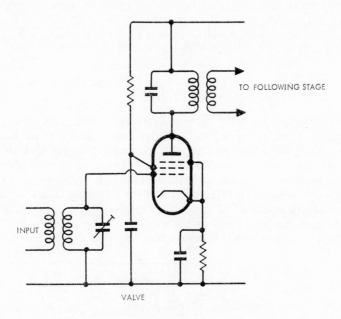

TO FOLLOWING STAGE

INPUT

VALVE

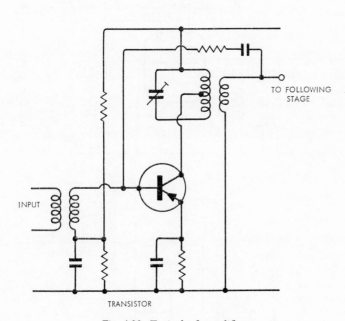

TO FOLLOWING
STAGE

INPUT

TRANSISTOR

Fig. 4.23. Typical r.f. amplifiers

version may require neutralization. Otherwise both types are very similar in that a signal applied to the input appears in an amplified form across the output transformer which couples it to the next stage. The Q of the tuned circuit must be chosen with the overall bandwidth in mind.

4.14 FREQUENCY CHANGERS

Circuit diagrams for both valve and transistor frequency changers (or mixers) are given in Fig. 4.24. The valve version uses a triode hexode in which the hexode section performs the frequency changing while the triode operates as a tuned grid oscillator. The double tuned transformer in the hexode anode circuit is tuned to the intermediate frequency and couples the hexode output at this frequency into the following i.f. amplifier.

The transistor circuit is somewhat different in that one transistor is used both as the mixer and as the oscillator. The collector load of the transistor considered as a common base amplifier is tuned to the inter-

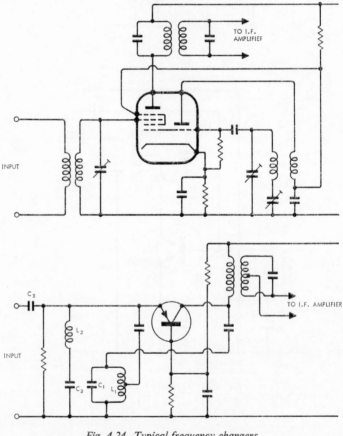

Fig. 4.24. Typical frequency changers

114

mediate frequency, as also is the series tuned filter circuit formed by L_2 and C_2. The parallel tuned circuit L_1, C_1, controls the frequency of oscillation of the transistor regarded as a Hartley oscillator. While this circuit is economical and works satisfactorily, the input and oscillator circuits are not isolated from each other and this may result in the oscillator frequency being pulled towards the input signal's frequency if their frequency separation is small. This can be cured by using a separate oscillator.

4.15 INTERMEDIATE FREQUENCY AMPLIFIERS

The signals at the intermediate frequency entering the i.f. amplifier will have amplitudes ranging from below a millivolt to possibly a hundred millivolts or more. In order to drive the detector with a signal of the order of 1 V the i.f. amplifier must have a gain of the order of 1000 if the smaller echo signals are to be adequately detected. This may mean that the i.f. amplifier paralyses with much larger echo signals, thus all time constants associated with capacitors which may charge up on large signals must be kept small. Gain control is usually applied to the i.f. amplifier rather than the r.f. amplifier since the latter's gain should be as high as possible in order to raise the input signal level to well above the mixer noise level. This may be done, with valves, by varying the bias on the control grid of the first and possibly other valves, if variable mu valves are used. With transistors, gain control is usually achieved by varying the quiescent collector current, increasing the current increases the gain. Manual gain control is usual but in certain cases swept gain control as mentioned in Sect. 4.10 can be applied.

The i.f. amplifier consists essentially of several r.f. stages, tuned to a fixed frequency, connected in cascade. The intermediate frequency chosen for pulse work is usually several megacycles in order to facilitate obtaining the required bandwidth. Each amplifying stage must have a wider bandwidth than the required overall bandwidth since, for example, if the amplifier consists of n identical single tuned stages the overall bandwidth is given by:

$$\text{overall bandwidth} = \frac{\text{single stage bandwidth}}{1 \cdot 2 \sqrt{(n)}} \qquad (4.28)$$

Double tuned transformers are often used instead of single tuned stages in which case the overall bandwidth is given by:

$$\text{overall bandwidth} = \frac{\text{single stage bandwidth}}{1 \cdot 1 \sqrt[4]{(n)}} \qquad (4.29)$$

A third technique, which is probably the simplest to design and adjust when wide bandwidths are required, uses stagger tuned amplifiers. In its commonest form, this technique employs three amplifiers, each of which is a single tuned stage but each stage is tuned to a different frequency, so chosen, that the resultant response approaches the required

115

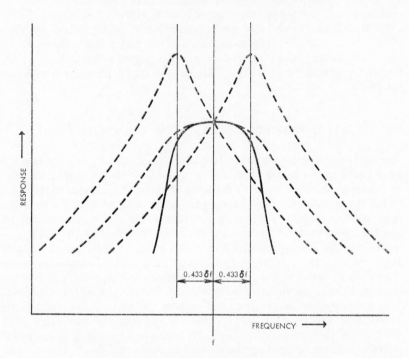

Fig. 4.25. Response curves for stagger tuned triple

overall response. This is illustrated in the responses plotted in Fig. 4.25. If the overall bandwidth is to be δf, centred on a frequency f_0, one stage whose coil has a Q given by $f_0/\delta f$ is tuned to f_0 while the other two stages, with coils of Q given by $2f_0/\delta f$, are tuned to $\pm 0\cdot 433\,\delta f$ cycles away from f_0.

Circuits of typical i.f. amplifiers are given in Fig. 4.26. For these circuits to work satisfactorily, care must be taken in the circuit layout and with screening in order to minimize coupling between stages which could lead to instability. Earth loops are a common source of instability and it is advisable to connect all the earth connections of any one stage to one point only.

4.16 DETECTOR

The function of the detector is to rectify the output from the i.f. amplifier, remove the intermediate frequency component and leave an output which faithfully follows the carrier modulation. A typical detector circuit is shown in Fig. 4.27. The diode charges the capacitor C to the peak value of the signal arriving from the i.f. amplifier. At the same time some

116

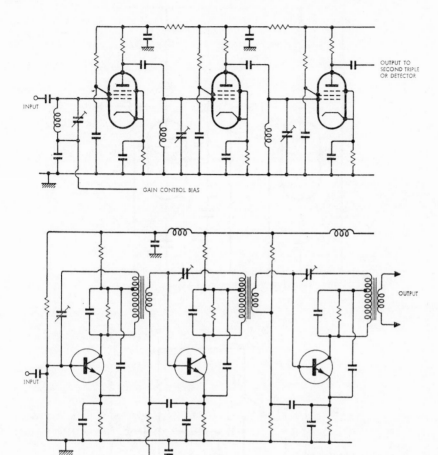

Fig. 4.26. Typical i.f. amplifiers. (*Courtesy Fairchild Semiconductors*)

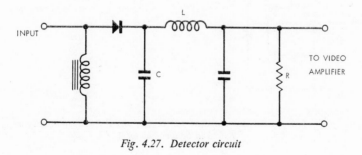

Fig. 4.27. Detector circuit

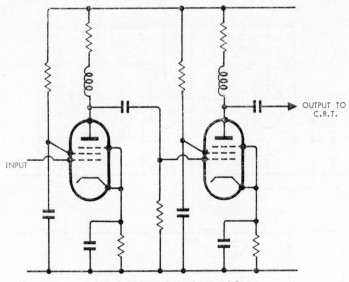

Fig. 4.28. Valve video amplifier

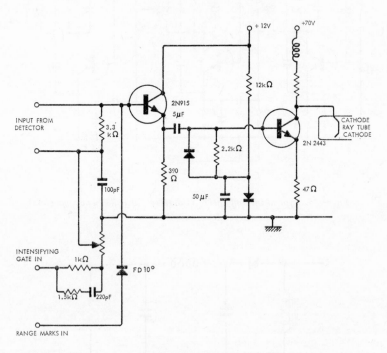

Fig. 4.29. Transistor video amplifier for B scan and P.P.I. systems (Courtesy Fairchild Semiconductors)

charge leaks away through the resistor R. Provided that the time constant CR is correctly chosen the change in potential across the capacitor during one period of the intermediate frequency will be very small yet this potential will still be able to follow the modulation. In order that the potential across the capacitor is not attenuated excessively the value of C should be several times the diode capacitance. Since the voltage across C may vary to some extent at the intermediate frequency, particularly if C is made small in order to follow fast edged modulation pulses, the inductance L is sometimes incorporated to add additional filtering at the intermediate frequency.

4.17 VIDEO AMPLIFIERS

The output from the detector is typically of the order of 1V but the cathode ray tube invariably used to display the echo signals requires a voltage drive of about 40 V. Thus the amplifier interposed between the detector and display unit has to provide a gain of about 40, have good transient response with little overshoot and not paralyze easily.

The commonest type of video amplifier is the resistance-capacity-coupled type, circuits of which are shown in Figs. 4.28 and 4.29. The valve circuit of Fig. 4.28 differs slightly from the standard resistance-capacity-coupled amplifier in that an inductance is connected in series with the anode load. This inductance serves to extend the high frequency response of the amplifier. Normally, the anode load consists of the load resistance shunted by the capacitances connected to the anode arising from the output capacitance of the valve, the input capacitance of the following stage plus wiring capacitances. Since the reactance of this shunting capacitance decreases with increasing frequency the amplifier gain falls as the frequency rises, such that the amplifier gain is 3 dB down on its gain at lower frequencies at a frequency f_h given by:

$$f_h = \frac{1}{2\pi RC} \qquad (4.30)$$

where R and C denote the anode load and associated capacitance respectively. The inductance L resonates with C at f_h thereby neutralizing its effect over a particular frequency range. The value of L is defined by[4]:

$$L = QR^2C \qquad (4.31)$$

in which the parameter Q can be given various values depending upon the frequency response required. With $Q = 0$ we get the normal response of an uncompensated amplifier and as Q increases the bandwidth increases until when $Q = 0.414$ the bandwidth is 1.73 times as wide as for the uncompensated case. Increasing Q further increases the bandwidth still further, although not by much, although at the expense of introducing a peak in the response at a frequency just below f_h. Provided that only one or two stages of amplification are used it is convenient to take $Q = 0.5$

119

as a design figure. If we require minimal phase distortion rather than maximum bandwidth the optimum value for Q is 0·34. Other types of compensation can be used but apart from exceptional cases these hardly justify the design effort involved.

As well as obtaining a fast rise time for the amplified pulses we also require that the pulse top should not decay during the pulse duration. This decay (sag or droop) arises from the finite values of coupling and bypassing capacitors used but because of the relative narrowness of the pulses employed in ultrasonic techniques we rarely require to incorporate sag correcting networks.[5]

Transistorized video amplifiers are similar to valve types and are becoming more common with the arrival of high voltage transistors capable of driving cathode ray tubes. The circuit of one typical video amplifier is given in Fig. 4.29.

4.18 DISPLAY UNITS

The function of the display unit is to present information to an observer about the distance, orientation and possibly size of the target or targets. Three types of display unit are used; the cathode ray tube, chart recorder and neon tube illuminated rotating disc but, of these, only the first is relevent to medical applications since it gives the clearest presentation as well as being the fastest acting. The others are only suitable for indicating echoes from distant targets such as arise in depth sounding or fish location.

Cathode ray tube displays can be divided into three types: A scan, B scan and the plan position indicator (P.P.I.). The A scan has already been discussed in Sect. 4.2 (Fig. 4.3). This type of scan gives one dimensional information only since it indicates the range but not the bearing of the target. It does, however, also indicate the magnitude of the target if by magnitude we mean a combination of physical size and reflecting properties. If two dimensional information is required, that is both range and bearing, we have to use either of the other two display systems.

The type of picture obtained from a B scan is shown in Fig. 4.30. The output from the video amplifier is applied to the control grid of the cathode ray tube which is normally biassed so that no electrons reach the phosphor screen. When an echo is received it appears as a spot of light on the screen whose vertical coordinate is proportional to the target's range and whose horizontal coordinate is proportional to the target's angular bearing relative to some reference bearing. The main use of this type of display, which gives a distorted target map, is to present easily measurable information about the range and bearing of any target.

The plan position indicator type of display, illustrated in Fig. 4.31, is similar to the B scan in that it uses intensity modulation of the electron beam but differs in that the bearing of the target is now given by the angular position of the light spot on the face of the tube. Thus the P.P.I. display gives a correct map with the transducer sited at the tube centre. In medical work a modified form of P.P.I., known as a sector scan, is

120

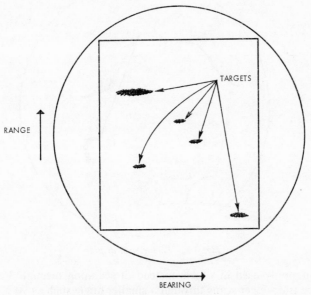

Fig. 4.30. B scan display

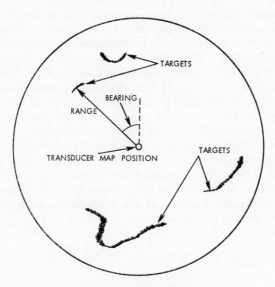

Fig. 4.31. P.P.I. display

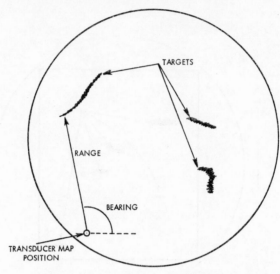

Fig. 4.32. Sector scan display

more commonly used in which, instead of scanning through 360° in one plane, the transducer scans through a smaller angle such as 90°. In sector scan there is no need for the apparent position of the transducer to be in the centre of the display and it can be offset to any desired position as shown in Fig. 4.32. A further modification of sector scan is sometimes used in medical work. The echo received from a target will depend considerably on the surface presented to the incident ultrasonic pulse by the target. It is thus advisable to illuminate the target from as many directions as possible. This can be done in suitable circumstances by arranging for the transducer to execute one sector scan, then to move a short distance over the surface of the body being scanned, execute a further sector scan, move on to a third position and so on. With this system information about the position of the transducer is fed into the display unit to position the transducer site on the display accordingly.

All types of display require some means for deflecting the electron beam linearly with the time in order to represent range. In addition, types B and P.P.I. displays require some means for coordinating the direction of travel of the electron beam across the face of the cathode ray tube with the angular position of the transducer. Both problems are dealt with in the next two sections.

4.19 TIME BASES

We consider first the techniques available for deflecting the electron beam linearly across the face of the cathode ray tube. The electrical signals required are usually referred to as time bases or sweeps. Deflection of the electron beam can be achieved by either an electrostatic or magnetic field;

122

the former requires a linearly increasing voltage applied between a pair of deflecting plates while the latter requires a linearly increasing current flowing through a deflection coil situated outside the cathode ray tube. Rapid deflection of the electron beam is not possible with the magnetic system because of the coil's inductance so electrostatic deflection is invariably used with A scan. Magnetic deflection, however, allows greater deflections than does the electrostatic technique, so that while the latter is suitable for both A and B scans in view of the smaller size of tube face which is acceptable, the former is better for P.P.I. displays in which larger tubes are often used. In addition magnetic tubes provide better focussing of the intense light spots required for P.P.I. and B scan displays than do the electrostatic types.

We can divide time base generators into two types depending upon whether they are to drive electrostatic or magnetic tubes. For electrostatic tubes we require a voltage which rises linearly with time to a maximum value of about 300 V followed by a rapid fall to zero at which the voltage remains until a further trigger pulse is applied to initiate the linear rise again. Although high voltage transistors are now available they are more expensive than valves which are still, perhaps only marginally, the better elements to use. Thus we will consider only a valve time base generator such as the Miller circuit shown in Fig. 4.33. Initially V_1 is conducting heavily so that its anode is at a low potential, V_{2b} is conducting heavily also so that the cathode of V_{2a} will be at a high potential almost sufficient to cut off V_{2a}. In order to initiate the time base, the grid of V_1 is driven negative thereby cutting off V_1 whose anode starts to rise towards the H.T. potential E_p. This rise in voltage causes V_{2a} to conduct more, its anode voltage drops, and this drop is coupled back to the grid of V_{2a}. The conflict at the grid of V_{2a} arising from its attempt to rise being opposed by the voltage fed back from the anode leads to a linear fall in voltage occurring at the anode. This linear voltage fall forms one output, with

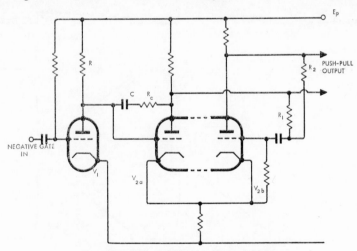

Fig. 4.33. Valve Miller time base generator

123

another, in opposing phase, being derived from the anode of V_{2b} whose grid is fed from the junction of two equal resistors R_1 and R_2. Provided that the gain of V_{2b} is sufficiently large, the voltage at the anode of V_{2b} moves in such a direction as to keep the voltage at the junction of R_1 and R_2 almost constant, that is the anode voltage of V_{2b} must move in almost exact opposition to that at the anode of V_{2a}. This circuit generates a push pull output with an amplitude approaching the supply voltage E_p which can be of the order of 400 V. The resistor R_c is inserted to minimize the step which appears at the start of the sweep due to the sudden increase in conduction of V_{2a}. Minimum step is obtained when $R_c = 1/g_m$ where g_m denotes the mutual conductance of V_{2a}. The slope of the sweep is given by E_p/RC V/sec. When the sweep has lasted long enough for the anode of V_{2a} to bottom no further change in voltage is possible until the negative input to V_1 is removed when the circuit reverts to its initial state. Many modifications of this circuit have been developed and can be found in the literature.[6]

For magnetic tubes we require that the current through the deflection coil rises linearly with time. The deflection coil possesses both inductance and resistance and since, with a linearly increasing current, the voltage across the inductance will be constant and the voltage across the resistance a linearly rising one, the actual voltage required to drive the desired current

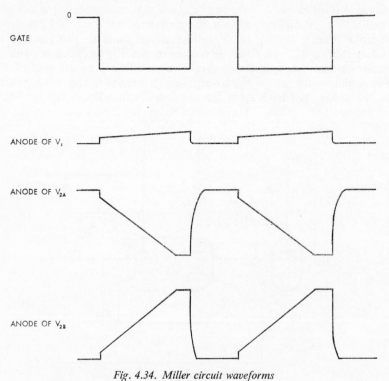

GATE

ANODE OF V_1

ANODE OF V_{2A}

ANODE OF V_{2B}

Fig. 4.34. Miller circuit waveforms

124

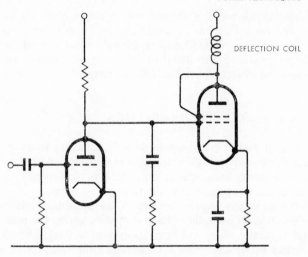

Fig. 4.35. Trapezoidal voltage generator for magnetic tube deflection

through the coil will be a trapezoid. One way of achieving this waveform is to make use of the step at the start of the Miller circuit output which one normally attempts to suppress with electrostatic tube driving waveforms. Alternatively the desired current waveform may be driven through the coil by using a source of sufficiently high impedance that the reaction of the coil upon the driving source is negligibly small. This may be achieved by using a pentode whose control grid is driven from a linear sweep generator. Alternatively a transistor in the common base configuration can be used. As well as inductance and resistance a deflection coil will also possess some capacitance arising from both the self capacitance of the coil winding and stray wiring capacitances. At the end of the sweep, when the current falls rapidly to zero, the coil will behave like a ringing circuit. This may be undesirable in which case the coil can either be shunted by a damping resistor or by a diode which conducts on the overswing thereby absorbing the coil energy and damping out the oscillation. Circuit diagrams for magnetic deflection systems are shown in Fig. 4.35.

In both electrostatic and magnetic deflection systems the rapid return of the trace at the end of the sweep should be suppressed. One way is to arrange that the electron beam is cut off for all times except during the period of the rectangular gating pulse driving the time base generator.

Although time bases can be made extremely linear, measuring the range of a target by measuring the position of its echo on the display with a scale may not be sufficiently accurate. Greater accuracy can be obtained through the use of range markers. There are several ways of deriving these but one of the commonest consists in generating a precision linear voltage sweep which is applied to a comparator. This device, which may be a Schmitt trigger, generates a fast rising pulse when its input voltage reaches a predetermined level which may be set up accurately on a precision potentiometer. If the precision sweep starts when the transmitter fires

125

and the comparator pulse is aligned with a target echo, either as a step in the A scan trace or as a brightening pulse on the other displays, the comparator triggering voltage will be directly proportional to the target range, hence provided the ultrasonic velocity is known the precision potentiometer can be calibrated directly in range.

4.20 BEARING COORDINATION

In both B scan and P.P.I. displays some means has to be provided to coordinate the display with the transducer bearing. As far as B scan is concerned one simple technique is to couple a potentiometer mechanically to the transducer housing so that the position of the potentiometer wiper arm is governed by the angular bearing of the transducer relative to some reference bearing. If a steady voltage is applied across the potentiometer, the voltage from the wiper will be proportional to the bearing and can be used to deflect the B scan trace horizontally either directly or after some amplification.

For the P.P.I. display a resolver is required. This often takes the form of a sine-cosine potentiometer which is merely a potentiometer with two outputs one being proportional to the sine of the arm deflection and the other proportional to the cosine. If now instead of applying a constant voltage across the potentiometer we apply a linear voltage sweep and feed the potentiometer outputs to two deflection coil driver units driving two coils at right angles to each other, the angular direction of the trace across

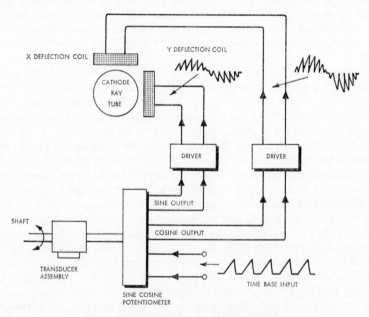

Fig. 4.36. P.P.I. trace coordination system

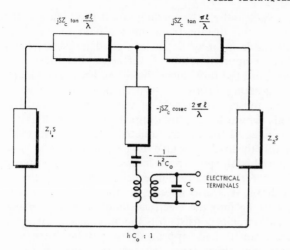

Fig. 4.37. Equivalent circuit of transducer. (s = surface area of one plane surface, h = piezoelectric constant, l = transducer thickness, λ = ultrasonic wavelength in transducer)

the face of the cathode ray tube will correspond to the transducer bearing. This system is illustrated in Fig. 4.36. Instead of using a sine-cosine potentiometer, a magnetic resolver is sometimes used. This has the advantage that as it does not possess a wiper arm to cause the wear which is inevitable with a resistive potentiometer.

4.21 TRANSDUCERS

In the previous sections we outlined techniques for generating, amplifying detecting and displaying flat topped rectangular pulses with fast edges. While it is possible to design and build circuits with magnificent pulse response, the overall response of any network is only as good as that of the poorest unit, which, in ultrasonic work is usually the transducer. The equivalent circuit[7] for a disc shaped piezoelectric transducer, valid for all frequencies, but assuming that only the thickness mode of vibration exists, is given in Fig. 4.37. This circuit contains several components which are highly frequency dependent, implying that we cannot expect its transient response to be particularly satisfactory unless special precautions are taken. For example, if we denote the specific acoustic impedances of the media on either side of the transducer by Z_1 and Z_2 and that of the transducer material by Z_c, the mechanical Q of the transducer, defined as the mechanical resonant frequency divided by the difference between the two frequencies at which the radiated power has fallen to one half that at resonance under constant drive conditions apart from frequency, is given by:

$$Q = \frac{\pi}{2}\left[\frac{Z_c}{Z_1 + Z_2}\right] \tag{4.32}$$

127

Eqn. 4.32 is valid only if the loading is not too high and the half power frequencies not too distant from the resonant frequency. Normally a low Q is desirable in order to achieve good transient response so while Eqn. 4.32 is an approximation, nevertheless it indicates that for good transient response the transducer should be heavily loaded. The loading on the front radiating surface will be determined by the medium into which the ultrasonic pulses are to be sent but we have control over the rear surface. This should have a high impedance and be highly absorbing so that little or none of the energy radiated into it returns to the transducer to either modify the loading or give rise to spurious echos. One satisfactory loading material is an epoxy resin loaded with tungsten powder.[8]

As well as the transient response being affected by the mechanical Q of the transducer, it is also affected by the electrical Q of the circuit as seen when looking into the electrical input terminals of the transducer. The electrical circuit consists of the mechanical circuit, transformed through the transformer, appearing in parallel with the transducer capacitance which arises from the fact that the transducer electrodes look like a parallel plate capacitor. We can reduce the effect of this capacitance by shunting it with an inductance so that the parallel tuned circuit so formed resonates at the transducer resonant frequency. This inductance may require shunting by a resistance in order to reduce its Q.

Finally we should consider the shape of the radiated pulse. We saw in Sect. 4.3 that the energy radiated by a piston transducer is mainly confined within a cone. This confinement arises from interference effects which may not have time to establish themselves during the lifetime of a pulse. Fortunately the radiation pattern at a point sets itself up within a time of less than one period of the ultrasonic waves so that with a pulse lasting several cycles the radiation pattern will be that expected for continuous waves.[9]

REFERENCES

1. BELL, D. A., *Electrical Noise*, 312, Van Nostrand (1960).
2. LAWSON, J. L. and UHLENBECK, G. E., *Threshold Signals*, 211, McGraw-Hill (1949).
3. FINK, D. G., *Radar Engineering*, 121, McGraw-Hill (1947).
4. VALLEY, G. E. and WALLMAN, H., *Vacuum Tube Amplifiers*, 73, McGraw-Hill (1948).
5. LANDEE, R. W. *et al.*, *Electronic Designers Handbook*, 3.48, McGraw-Hill (1957).
6. CHANCE, B., *et al.*, *Waveforms*, Chap. 5, McGraw-Hill (1949).
7. MASON, W. P., *Physical Acoustics and the Properties of Solids*, 61 Van Nostrand (1958).
8. LUTSCH, A., *J. Acoust. Soc. Am.*, **34**, 131 (1962).
9. FILIPCZYNSKI, L., *Proc. 2nd. Conf. Ultrasonics*, *Polish Acad. Sci.*, **29**, (1956).

BIBLIOGRAPHY

In addition to the books mentioned above, the following books contain useful information.

FRANK, E., *Pulsed Linear Networks*, McGraw-Hill (1945).
RIDENOUR, L. N., *et al.*, *Radar System Engineering*, McGraw-Hill (1947).
REINTJES, J. F. and COATE, G. T., *Principles of Radar*, McGraw-Hill (1952).
SCHWARTZ, S., *et al.*, *Selected Semiconductor Circuits Handbook*, John Wiley and Sons.
FITCHEN, F. C., *Transistor Circuit Analysis and Design*, Van Nostrand (1960).

In addition useful application reports are published by the transistor manufacturers.

5

THE USE OF ULTRASOUND IN DIAGNOSIS

D. Gordon, M.B., D.M.R., D.M.R.D., Sen.M.I.E.E.E.

5.1 THE ACOUSTIC CHARACTERISTICS OF THE HUMAN BODY

Published lists of specific acoustic impedances for a wide variety of materials tend to give a very simplified picture of the world as if it were composed of large blocks of homogeneous matter such as are used in laboratory experiments. A moment's thought will show that the world of nature is conspicuously lacking in large blocks of homogeneous matter. Even the sea which comes nearest to the ideal, in fact contains significant variations whether in the obvious form of fish or whales or in the less obvious forms of varying amounts of dissolved gas and solids.

The human or animal body is in quite a different category, the one thing hardest to find being a homogeneous tissue mass large enough to be studied acoustically with any accuracy. Furthermore the obvious method of meeting the difficulty, the separation of one type of tissue from another and the measurement of artificially assembled blocks of a single tissue, is quite invalid. There can be no doubt that the mere presence or absence of life in the tissues alters their acoustic characteristics.

The tables already mentioned usually give the velocity in one or more modes, the temperature of measurement, the density and the specific acoustic impedance. In the case of piezoelectric materials numerous other constants are given such as dielectric constant, volume resistivity, coefficient of coupling and expansion and the Curie point. The one thing that never appears in published tables but is the most important from the biological point of view is the attenuation of ultrasound by the material.

There is some excuse for this in that the attenuation does not follow a straightforward mathematical function. It varies even in truly homogeneous matter with both temperature and frequency and its very nature must be defined with precision or it will have variable values according to the technique used in medicine.

Let us now consider the simple case of a large flat crystal of quartz energized at 1 Mc/s and applied with good acoustic coupling to the skin of the thigh over the femur (Fig. 5.1)· Over a substantial proportion of the surface the intensity level is reasonably constant and the approximation to plane waves will be good.

At 1 Mc/s the wavelength in water will be 1·5 mm. Most soft tissues of the body do not depart far from water in their velocity or their density but such is the effect of the law of acoustical reflection that quite a significant proportion of energy is reflected back even when the acoustical mismatch is slight. At the site chosen and over-simplifying the situation, one can

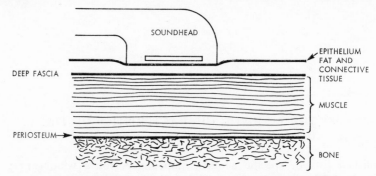

Fig. 5.1. Diagram of the use of ultrasound in physical medicine

assume that the ultrasound will travel first through two to three wavelengths of epithelium, (the outer layer of the skin, a carpet of cells with no separation between them but varying from dry flattened dead cells on the surface to cuboidal actively growing cells with free electrolyte exchange in the deeper layers). Then it passes through a variable thickness of connective tissue which in its deeper parts is heavily loaded with fatty material.

The thickness of this layer varies from one or two wavelengths in the emaciated to perhaps twenty wavelengths in the obese. Scattered through this layer will be found the veins that often are visible through the skin. These of course contain blood and are able to carry away a certain amount of heat. Arteries are very small in the skin and may be ignored from the acoustic point of view.

The next structure to be considered, the deep fascia, is very thin in all people being constructed of a sheet of fibrous tissue. It is approximately flat. It acts therefore like a membrane, which indeed it is, and may well have a considerable significance acoustically in spite of the fact that it is only a fraction of a wavelength thick. The acoustic characteristics cannot be investigated experimentally but judging by the observations made of fibrous tissue when it occurs in larger masses, tendons and scars, it is probable that the velocity is higher than in softer tissue and its density is also greater.

130

The presumption is that a fairly large amount of energy is reflected back at the interface in spite of the thinness of the layer. This is supported by the observations of ultrasonic tomography described later. The fibrous tissue is the sheath of the muscle and immediately below it is the mass of muscle tissue. Here again the thickness of the layer varies greatly from the Olympic athlete to the bedridden patient. Something of the order of twenty to forty wavelengths will be in muscle.

Muscle tissue consists of a multitude of fine fibres all disposed in parallel and in practice ultrasound almost always passes through muscle at right angles to the axes of the fibres. The fibres themselves are striated very finely but this is much finer structure than the ultrasound can be expected to detect. Very little fibrous tissue occurs in a healthy muscle but, when a muscle is torn, healing occurs by the formation of fibrous tissue. The far side of the muscle has a similar fibrous tissue membrane to the near side. There is then a layer of perhaps a wavelength of soft connective tissue between the muscle capsule and the periosteum.

The periosteum is again a layer of fibrous tissue but it is the outer covering of the bone to which it is very closely applied. Its importance in ultrasonic applications is due to the fact that it contains nerve fibres that give sensory perception. The bone itself is without sensory nerves. Acoustically the periosteum itself is no different from the muscle sheath but its proximity to the bone makes a big difference.

Bone is obviously in quite a different class from all the other tissues acoustically. It is for example sufficiently solid to be able to transmit shear waves which cannot be transmitted by the soft tissues. Its density and the velocity of sound in it are both much higher than those of soft tissue so the proportion of energy reflected back at the surface is very large.

Once the ultrasound has entered bone it is attenuated very rapidly because of the high hysteresis. It is a poor conductor of heat so in fact the ultrasound affects only the most superficial part of the bone and the immediate effect is to heat up the periosteum that is so closely applied to its surface. The natural result is for the nerves to be stimulated and a dull pain is felt if the temperature rises seriously.

It is perhaps advisable at this point to digress somewhat to describe the way in which the body detects temperature. Sensory nerves are of several types, more types than the traditional five senses would suggest. Setting aside sight, hearing, taste, smell and the vestibular function discussed later in this book, more than the sensation of touch is recorded by the skin.

There are many fine nerve fibres in the skin that record true touch but there are also nerve endings like strain gauges that record pressure in the muscles and a vibration sense in the bone that responds to audio frequencies but not directly to ultrasonic frequencies.

Pain is more complex than most. It is detected by a network of nerve fibres in the skin that have no other function but most sensory nerves if overstimulated produce a sensation of pain. In addition to touch and pain nerves, the skin contains temperature-sensing nerve endings but these are capable of functioning only through the normal temperature range of

131

the skin. As is well known, too cold a temperature makes the skin numb or anaesthetic while too high a temperature produces a sense of pain and an immediate withdrawal reaction of the muscles. The sensation of temperature rise only occurs after the finger has left the soldering-iron!

Now let us go back to the crystal radiating ultrasonic power into the thigh of a normal patient. What is going to happen to the energy as it passes through this over-simplified series of layers? Clearly there is going to be a great deal of reflection back of energy at each of a number of interfaces. The energy reflected back into the crystal will of course not be absorbed by it but will be reflected back again.

Eventually all the energy fed into the transducer will be converted into heat. Only a small amount will be turned into heat by the quartz, the rest will be turned into heat by the tissues. It is assumed here that the crystal remains stationary though this is not the usual clinical procedure in physical medicine.

There is now a big defect in our knowledge to consider. We do not know what factor is responsible for the biological effect of ultrasound. It has been suggested that it was a cavitation phenomenon but this has been clearly disproved, most notably by Fry[1], who showed that mice subjected to several atmospheres of pressure were as susceptible as those at normal pressure. If cavitation were responsible raised pressure would abolish the cavitation and hence the biological effect.

In some contexts heat generated in the tissues is clearly the major factor but in other contexts biological effects are produced at power levels so low that there can be no significant rise of temperature. This is discussed in Chapter 7. Suffice it now that we do not know if particle velocity or pressure is crucial.

In a plane wave propagation in an infinite homogeneous medium, the particle velocity and the pressure are proportional but where there is a standing wave situation there will be zero particle velocity at the nodes but double particle velocity at the antinodes. Pressure will however be highest at the nodes where the peaks of pressure coming from both sides are in exact antiphase. No direct experimental work intended to elucidate this point is known though experiments have been suggested.

The way in which the heat is distributed in the tissues will be greatly affected by the frequency. With very high frequencies of the order of 10 Mc/s and upwards, the hysteresis of the tissues is sufficient to absorb virtually all the energy in a centimetre or two, even in soft tissues. At lower frequencies than 1 Mc/s the hysteresis is much lower and little energy will be absorbed until bone is struck.

The situation that arises with multiple partially reflecting surfaces normal to the beam is clearly quite impossible to forecast as the interference effect will differ according to whether the path between two such surfaces is an even or an odd number of quarter wavelengths. If reflection were total at a flat surface and in the crystal, clearly the whole of the energy would have to turn into heat between the two surfaces. Irrespective of the number of wavelengths, if multiple reverberations were taking place, the amount of power absorbed while travelling one way would be virtually the same as that absorbed while travelling in the opposite direction. The two would add to give approximately consistent energy absorption per unit of volume between the two surfaces.

Between multiple partly reflecting surfaces it would work out that the dose absorption would go down in steps each compartment showing a lower dose level than the previous but a uniform power level within it.

Now imagine absolutely loss-less water between crystal and bone. No matter how often the energy reverberated between the crystal and the bone surface no energy would pass into the water (this is of course an exaggeration). The ultrasound would end by entering the bone and being converted into heat in the first few millimetres whence the heat would pass slowly by conduction into the deeper part of the bone and the water.

Add these two pictures together and one has what in fact appears to be the case in practice, the majority of the heat appearing in the superficial part of the bone and passing by conduction to the periosteum, heating it up and causing pain while the rest is distributed in layers depending on the hysteresis of that particular block of tissue. Biological experiments published by the writer[2] tend to support this (Plate 5.1). There is a thin layer of undamaged tissue in close approximation to the cavity of the ventricle though this surface is not normal to the beam path. This suggests that all the tissue has a uniform dose but the convection cooling of the thin layer by cerebro-spinal fluid removes heat fast enough to bring it below the danger threshold.

The effect of frequency change is to cause much more energy to be absorbed in the superficial layers relative to the bone and this is in agreement with the clinical observations in ultrasonic therapy. High frequency ultrasound produces relatively little periosteal pain if the bone is covered by a good thickness of soft tissue but low frequency will produce pain very readily.

The very simple anatomical situation described does not cover the whole picture. Suppose the rays passed through the thigh missing the bone. The energy would then be reflected back totally on reaching the far skin surface. As this would normally not be exactly parallel with the transducer the energy would be scattered through the soft tissues and eventually all would appear as heat. It would be unlikely that this scattered energy would rise to a level where it would produce clinical effects. However the main beam would probably have a considerable effect even after travelling many centimetres. A beam too weak to cause periosteal pain in the femur at 5 cms might damage a sciatic nerve at 10 cms.

As will be seen later, nerve tissue is particularly susceptible to ultrasound and it must be stressed that damage to nerves may produce muscle weakness and anaesthesia which are not obvious to the patient. Such effects, if slight, are transient but, if severe, they can be permanent.

Where there are tissues containing air or gas such as the lung or the intestine, the acoustical mismatch is enormous and for all practical purposes the reflection is total. With parts of the body like the chest wall this may confine the energy to a very small volume of tissue with consequently enhanced effect.

133

Cartilage is almost as attenuating as bone and shows a large acoustic mismatch. The tendons and ligaments are rather less attenuating. The abdominal organs and tumour masses vary with their physical characteristics as one would expect. The liver, if healthy, is so uniform and fine in structure that it behaves as if homogeneous. A tumour containing a cystic space shows usually a large acoustic mismatch at each surface of the cyst with naturally low attenuation in the fluid. The variation in tumour tissue attenuation is of diagnostic importance.[3]

The earliest attempt to use ultrasound in medical diagnosis was that of Dussik.[4] He employed a technique very comparable to that of X-rays, in each case the reduction in intensity of the radiation as it passes through the whole thickness of the body is measured and recorded as a form of picture. Unfortunately Dussik attempted to examine the brain and found that the contribution of the skull to the absorption was overwhelmingly large compared with the effect of the difference between brain and fluid.

5.2 ECHO TECHNIQUES IN DIAGNOSIS

The first clinically valuable work in ultrasonic diagnosis was an application of the industrial flaw-detector as described in the previous chapter. Howry[5] and Wild[6] in the U.S.A. and the physicists of the Royal Cancer Hospital, London (now the Royal Marsden Hospital)[7] were the earliest workers to produce evidence of clinical value.

The acoustic characteristics described above adequately explain the variable results obtained. The majority of the early work was concentrated on the brain, about as difficult a target as could be found. It was with very great difficulty that any echoes at all could be obtained from brain through about 5 mm of bone which of course attenuates in both directions.

The reason why the brain was given early attention was because the brain itself is normally not visible on a routine X-ray of the skull. To make the brain visible an operative procedure is necessary and these carry a significant risk and involve considerable discomfort for the patient. The brain and the cerebro-spinal fluid in which it floats are identical to X-rays. The first practical technique was the replacement of cerebro-spinal fluid by air which has a lower X-ray density than the fluid which it replaces. This fluid occupies the ventricles, the cavities within the brain, as well as forming a layer between brain and skull. Air may be introduced by drilling a small hole in the skull and passing a hollow needle into the ventricle or by passing a hollow needle between the lumbar vertebrae and bubbling the air up from below. The latter technique (pneumo-encephalography) carries a higher risk than the former (ventriculography).

In recent years the injection of air has been supplemented by the injection of an oily synthetic material (pantopaque or myodil) which has a much higher opacity to X-rays as it contains iodine. This is particularly valuable in showing very small passages between ventricles.

The other recent introduction is angiography, the injection of a watery solution of an iodine compound into one of the arteries supplying the brain. As these arteries contain blood at high pressure travelling rapidly, it is necessary to make the injection very rapidly, using a very concentrated solution and to take a series of pictures in a matter of 3 to 5 sec. This not only involves a team activity that can only be compared to a smash-and-grab, but the passage of the concentrated solution through the capillaries, the smallest of the blood-vessels, causes the patient very considerable pain for a few seconds.

Either of these procedures involves not merely an element of risk but also considerable time which in the case of an acute head injury, may be more than the patient can afford. In such cases all the surgeon needs to

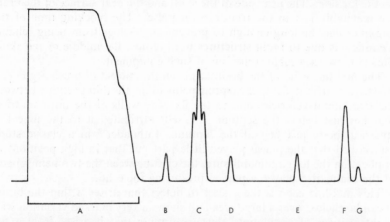

Fig. 5.2. Diagram of echoes obtained during echo-encephalography: A. Complex due to transmission pulse and reverberation in skull and other superficial layers; B. Lateral wall of lateral ventricle on near side; C. Three echoes close together probably the two walls of the third ventricle plus the septum pellucidum; D. Lateral wall of lateral ventricle of far side; E. Temporal horn, an offshoot of the lateral ventricle. Seldom identifiable on the near side; F. Inner surface of skull on far side; G. Skin surface on far side

know is whether the brain is in the normal position, displaced to the right or displaced to the left. If the brain is displaced the haemorrhage causing the displacement must be controlled by immediate operation.

Ultrasound will give this information in a matter of a minute with no risk to the patient. X-ray examination may take an hour and though the pictures give more information this is valueless to a dead patient.

The investigation is in some centres deputed to a technician but this is strongly condemned by the more experienced workers. 'An echo is an echo is an echo is an echo . . .' is an aphorism that should not be forgotten. Every echo signal observed is basically the same and the most characteristic echo patterns to be found in the skull can more easily be reproduced by using a water tank than by examining a patient!

It must never be forgotten that the normality of the beam to the reflecting surface is of far greater importance than the size of the surface or its nature. Very slight variations in the angle of the beam relative to the skull will cause the pattern to change very widely. Therefore the value of the examination depends on the whole period of investigation with the inter-pretation based on knowledge of the point on the skull to which the probe is applied and the direction in which the beam is directed.

The technique is therefore essentially one to be used by a doctor with a good knowledge of intra-cranial anatomy at least and preferably a considerable experience of the technique. It must be frankly admitted that with a sufficiently sensitive amplifier and enough perseverance a determined operator can obtain an echo at almost any distance he chooses. This is however not a reason for abandoning the technique (Fig. 5.2).

The easiest echo to elicit is almost always the inner surface of the skull on the far side. The near side of the skull and the near surface of the brain are inevitably lost in the transmission pulse. The blocking time of the amplifier may be long enough to prevent any echoes from being reliably identified as due to brain structures until almost the middle of the skull. This is however a major criticism of such equipment.

The mid-line echo of the brain has been the subject of much argument. The writer attributed it to the septum pellucidum, the thin partition between the two lateral ventricles and to the flat side walls of the third ventricle that lies just below the septum. Leksell[9] attributed it to the pineal, a spherical body just behind the septum. Lithander[10] in a classic study established that the pineal played little part but that in high positions of application the longitudinal fissure, the cleft between the two hemispheres of the brain, also played a part in producing the echo.

This mid-line echo is the easiest to detect that arises within the brain. It can be elicited over a large area and shows a very marked variation with slight changes of angulation, thus confirming that it arises from a flat surface.

In the normal brain these mid-line surfaces are parallel with the flat areas of bone near the ear. With a head injury the bleeding pushes the brain to one side or the other but the brain retains a normal shape. The echoes from the mid-line structures are therefore easily obtained but show different distances from the probe when the probe is placed first on one side and then on the other.

When however a tumour grows in the brain over a long period of time often years in length, the anatomy of the brain becomes much altered and there is usually considerable tilting as well as displacement of the ventricles. This makes it much easier to diagnose that the brain is abnormal than it is to decide on which side the tumour lies. Again this does not invalidate the technique. If it establishes that an abnormality is present, it has shown the need for full X-ray examination from which an accurate diagnosis may be made. Its value is to detect those cases where there is a brain abnormality present but not enough clinical evidence to justify submitting the patient to possibly dangerous examinations. Such patients are commonly sent home and may not have the diagnosis made until too late.

The only other technique to achieve early acceptance in clinical diagnosis using the hand-held probe and the simple A scan is that of Oksala[11] in the examination of the eye. Here the probe is applied direct to the cornea, the transparent covering of the iris and pupil, local anaesthesia

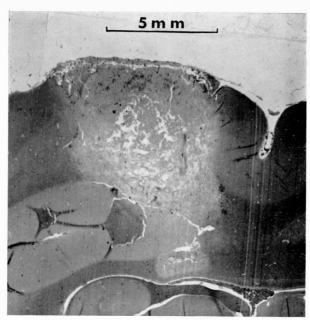

Plate 5.1. *Irradiation of cat brain by collimating transducer 8 mm in diameter. 20 W/cm² for 10 min. Note sharpness of edges and greater sensitivity of white matter than grey. Deepest penetration stops just short of surface of lateral ventricle*

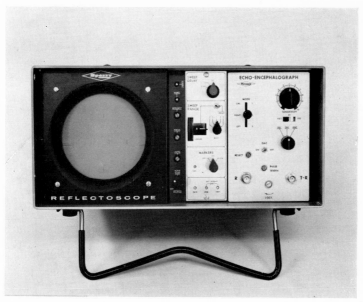

Plate 5.2. *The Sperry Reflectoscope*

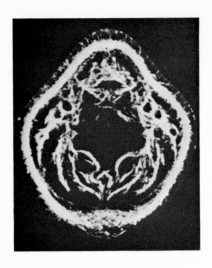

Plate 5.3. Ultrasonic tomogram of the neck (Howry)

Plate 5.4. Ultrasonic tomograms of breasts: (a) Low sensitivity to show carcinoma invading breast tissue that produces no echoes

(b) High sensitivity shows normal breast tissue but no echoes come from cyst containing fluid (vertical line due to screen burn) (Howry)

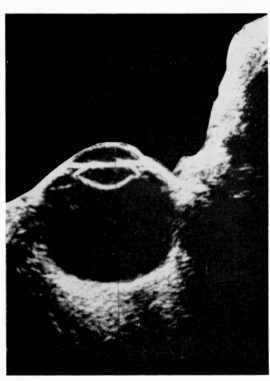

Plate 5.5. Ultrasonic tomogram of eye and orbit (Baum)

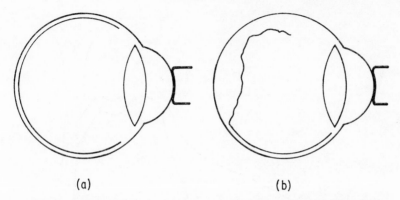

(a)   (b)

Fig. 5.3. Diagram of the eye with probe applied to centre of the cornea. (a) Normal eye with retina close to the outer wall, (b) Detachment of the retina

being of course necessary (Fig. 5.3). In the majority of cases the interior of the eye can be examined directly with the ophthalmoscope and it is only in the small proportion of patients when there is opacity to light of structures normally transparent that ultrasound has any advantage. Occasionally it helps in the diagnosis of bulges of the retina, the membrane of nerve cells that provides the sensation of sight. If the membrane becomes detached from the outer wall of the eye, the sclera, there is fluid between retina and sclera which produces no echo. If however the retina is pushed forwards by a solid tumour there is no empty zone behind the retina.

Recently a third application has become accepted in ophthalmology. This is the measurement of the size of the eye and of the position of the lens within it. The procedure is very similar to that used by Oksala but naturally in biometry, as the technique is called, it is essential to establish the accuracy of the time-base calibration much more rigidly than is needed in most other applications.

A limited amount of work has been done with the hand-held probe in other parts of the body. Gall-stones normally composed of a waxy material, cholesterol, with a variable amount of mineral salts, present no surgical problem when occupying the gall-bladder, as the whole gall-bladder is removed with the contents. When however a gall-stone escapes down the cystic duct from the gall-bladder it lodges in the common bile duct which runs from the hepatic duct to a small orifice in the duodenum often too small to let it pass (Fig. 5.4).

At operation the surgeon has good access only to the place where the three ducts meet. Attempts to remove a common duct stone may be tedious as the stone can pass readily from the normal site at the lower end right up into the liver as a result of the pressure of the surgeon's finger. The need to identify a wandering stone during the course of an operation occasionally arises at short notice. X-ray examination under such circumstances is not merely inconvenient but often futile. A stone made only of cholesterol casts no shadow in a routine X-ray. It has a to be shown

137

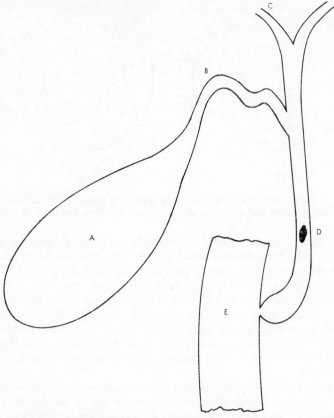

Fig. 5.4. Diagram of gall-stones: A. Gall-bladder; B. Cystic duct; C. Hepatic ducts; D. Gall-stone in common bile duct; E. Duodenum

up by making the liver excrete bile containing iodine compounds that make the less opaque stone appear as a bubble. This takes hours and is impossible during an operation.

Under these conditions some help has been obtained by passing a probe along the course of a duct relying on the stone to produce a larger echo than any of the soft tissue structures. It should however not be forgotten that a bubble of air can easily be introduced during the course of the operation and this would given an even larger echo. The major practical difficulty is that the probe has to be introduced into the operation field. Few probes will withstand sterilization, even fewer sterilization at 120°C in an autoclave. The probe has in practice to be inserted into a sterile rubber glove and the examination made with an extra thickness of rubber interposed. The consequent problems of coupling and reverberation must be overcome.

Other techniques such as identifying the presence of a pericardial effusion, a pleural effusion, the lower pole of the kidney, or abscess in the liver are the forerunners of a wide field of clinical research but none has yet become generally used. The remaining technique using a hand-held probe that has been accepted fairly widely is in the examination of the heart. Edler of Lund[12] introduced this technique and showed its value particularly in mitral stenosis.

Mitral stenosis is a narrowing of the mitral valve which lies between the thin walled left atrium or auricle and the thick-walled left ventricle, the main pumping chamber of the heart. The valve, as its name implies, resembles a mitre having two cusps, flaps of strong fibrous tissue which are attached at their edges. Pressure between the cusps, acting like the bishop's head, converts them to a cylinder giving free passage to the blood while pressure on the outside brings them together giving a blood-tight seal (Fig. 5.5).

The valve lies near the centre of the heart inclined at an angle as the left atrium lies above and behind the left ventricle. Every time the heart beats there is a four stage sequence of events rather reminiscent of the four-stroke internal combustion engine. It should be realized that both the atrium and ventricle have other valves to control the direction of blood flow.

Tracing the blood round the left side of the heart, it is simplest to begin with the opening of the valves that permit blood to enter the left atrium as its wall relaxes. Blood enters the left atrium from the large veins of the lungs but none can pass the mitral valve which is held closed by high pressure in the ventricle. The atrium fills up with blood so that as soon

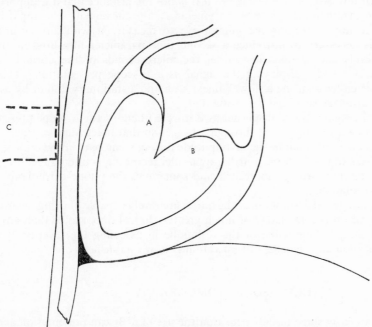

Fig. 5.5. Diagram of the mitral valve technique: A. Anterior cusp of mitral valve at times of closure; B. Posterior cusp; C. Probe applied to skin over sternum

as the left ventricle relaxes, the mitral valve is subjected to a push-pull effect, the left atrium contracting to raise the atrial pressure while the dilation of the left ventricle causes a rapid fall in ventricular pressure.

Naturally enough the valve passes from fully closed to fully open very rapidly indeed, the most rapid movement of the four. During the dilation of the left ventricle the mitral valve narrows slightly as the rate of filling falls off. The ventricle then begins to contract and immediately the mitral valve closes fully and remains closed while the blood in the left ventricle is pumped out into the aorta, the main artery supplying the whole body. When the contraction ends, the aortic valve closes leaving the left ventricle empty so that the mitral valve opens as soon as the pressure drops thus restarting the sequence.

In mitral stenosis the cusps become thickened and less pliable and the edges become adherent thus limiting the extent to which the valve can open. When this reduces the circulation seriously, it is possible to operate and cut through the adherent parts leaving a valve that at least has its normal size when open, though it cannot recover its original flexibility.

The probe can only be applied usefully to that part of the chest wall where there is no lung between the skin and the heart. This virtually restricts it to a small area over the sternum or breast-bone and to its left. From this 'bare area' the beam passes through the mitral valve at an angle, the nearer cusp being much nearer normal to the beam than the further and therefore easier to detect.

In this case, unlike in the brain, it is not the distance that it is important to measure, it is the rate of movement. As the movement is so rapid it is quite impossible for the human eye to measure it with any accuracy. It is necessary to introduce a second time parameter measured in milli-seconds and seconds instead of the microseconds of the normal flaw-detector while displaying the signal as a B-scope presentation. This is done either by using a slow Y linear scan and a stationary film or by using a stationary scan and a moving film.

The signal can be displayed as if it were intended for A-scope presenta-tion or it can be passed through a trigger so that much sharper traces are obtained but a fall in signal amplitude during some part of the cycle gives a discontinuous trace. Further a parallel recording is often added to give the electro-cardiogram record and sometimes the phono-cardiograph as well (Plate 5.2).

Though valves other than the mitral are rarely capable of being recorded, the mitral is fortunately of much greater clinical importance than any of the others. The value of the technique in assessing the severity of the condition and the effect of operation is now established.

5.3 ULTRASONIC TOMOGRAPHY

At an early stage in flaw-detection the use of a B-scan presentation and a linear probe movement linked to a linear trace movement was used to dis-play as a photograph the cross-sectional features of masses of metal.

140

Wild at a very early date[6] utilized this system to examine the female breast. The patient lay supported above a tank of water into which the breast hung. A probe travelled horizontally through the water under the breast with the beam directed upwards. The display was naturally a B-scope system with the trace moving proportionally to the probe movement and the timebase set to make actual distances on X and Y axes equal on the tube face which was photographed during a complete scan to integrate the results.

Howry[5] at a very early stage realized that such a simple scanning system could only detect such surfaces as were normal to the rays, each reflecting object furthermore tending to appear to be as broad as the beam. Howry

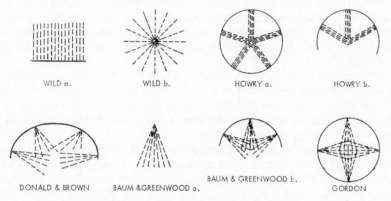

WILD a. WILD b. HOWRY a. HOWRY b.

DONALD & BROWN BAUM &GREENWOOD a. BAUM & GREENWOOD b. GORDON

Fig. 5.6. Scan patterns in tomography

therefore invented the compound scan system, developing two devices one of which involved immersion of the patient above the level being examined.

Donald and Brown, Baum and the writer developed comparable compound scan systems (Fig. 5.6). The essence of these systems is that every point in the tissue plane being examined is reached by a beam from several probe positions. They are fully described elsewhere.[13]

In recent years many scanning systems have been tried out most being intended for scanning the brain. Unfortunately the physical principles that are the basis of ultrasound have not changed over the years! The results are as unsatisfactory as in Howry's earliest attempt many years ago. Though echoes are obtained it is only when the rays are directed with the plane of the crystal tangential to the skull. This makes true compound scanning impossible and the standard of accuracy falls far below the acceptable.

The place where ultrasonic tomography, as this type of P.P.I. display is known, has its assured future is in the investigation of soft tissues uncomplicated by bone. Tomography means 'writing a cutting' and first came to be used in X-radiology. By causing an X-ray tube and an X-ray film to move in opposite directions on either side of the patient only those structures that lay in a single plane of the patient appeared sharp on the

141

film, the remainder being so blurred as to be undetectable. Multiple 'cuts' are taken at different levels in the body but in practice these are nearly always taken parallel to the long axis of the body, either antero-posterior or lateral projections. Special equipment was devised many years ago for horizontal cuts but these have never proved their worth.

The ultrasonic tomogram however is nearly always in the transverse plane of the body but it too gives a 'cut' through a single plane of the body. The more important difference comes in what the two methods will demonstrate. The most striking difference is perhaps in the neck (Plate 5.3). The horizontal section resembles what the neck would look like after a visit to the guillotine! While in an X-ray tomogram of the neck the only structures to be distinguished are the cervical vertebrae, the skin surface, the air in the throat and windpipe, the cartilages of the larynx, if calcified, and any glands that may contain calcium, in the ultrasonic tomogram the bone is seen only as a silhouette surrounded by a maze of complicated patterns.

Any structure showing a significantly different acoustic impedance from its surroundings is outlined, so the sheaths of the muscles, the walls of the major blood-vessels and the skin surface are well outlined. As the muscle sheaths are visible the size of the muscle is indicated, though the muscle itself generates no echoes.

Structures like the thyroid gland are outlined for the same reason and obviously it is only the interpreter's knowledge of anatomy that indicates which space is filled by gland and which by muscle. Similarly the identification of blood-vessels is primarily by their position though the thicker wall of an artery may be demonstrated and help to distinguish it from the thin-walled veins.

Where special structures like the breast and eye are concerned special considerations arise. Breast tissue consists of a mixture of elements, glands, ducts, vessels and fat. Some of these are sufficiently fibrous to produce some mismatch. If therefore the amplifier gain is high the whole of the breast tissue will appear as a network of small structures but if it is low it will only be the skin over the surface and the muscle sheath behind that are demonstrated (Plate 5.4).

The breast is subject to a variety of conditions. Most cancerous growths are more fibrous than the normal tissue, hence their description as 'lumps in the breast.' These show up when the gain is low and they can be detected before they can be felt by the surgeon's fingers. If however a cyst full of watery fluid develops in the breast it may show a cyst wall echo at normal gain but shows up better when the normal breast tissue is demonstrated leaving the cyst cavity as a blank area in the network.

The eye has a special problem in that it contains a lens which differs considerably from water acoustically though not as much as it does optically. Furthermore it has a spherical wall that is sunk deep into a bony orbit so that it cannot be scanned through more than 60 degrees of arc. Nevertheless Baum's compound scan technique has produced a remarkably good result[14] (Plate 5.5). The total distance to be penetrated is very small in the eye and not much greater in the breast. It is therefore possible to

142

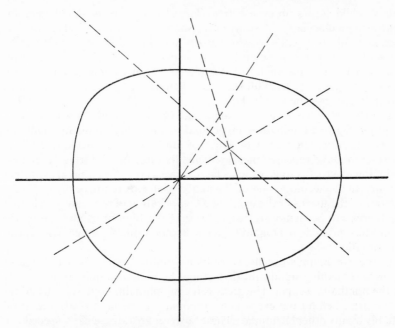

Fig. 5.7. Diagram of the foetal skull. It will be seen that only the continuous lines representing the longitudinal and transverse axes of the skull pass through the bone perpendicularly

employ very high frequencies and swept gain and obtain echoes from all depths of interest. The use of high frequencies, 10 to 15 Mc/s, permits narrow directional beams from small crystals. Furthermore with very short wavelengths practically any irregularity in a tissue surface will act as a point source and direct some energy back to the transducer. Normality of the rays is thus less important for the detection of a structure.

The other factor that must not be forgotten is that angulation occurs in two planes. With a structure like the neck which is roughly cylindrical and contains structures nearly all parallel with its long axis, there are few structures likely to be missed with a compound scan tomogram. In the case of the eye however the cuts at the level of the cornea being near the equator will be recorded much better than those above and below where the rays will be largely deflected upwards or downwards and will miss the transducer.

Thin bones like the ribs are not much of an obstacle but the edge of the lung comes down over much of the liver and acts as a very considerable barrier even when thin. Similarly gas in the bowel may pass in front of the liver from below and again act as a major obstacle. Tumours of the ovary and uterus, once they reach any size, push the intestine away and they can then be examined quite readily. A solid tumour behaves very much as breast in that one can obtain echoes from fibrous elements but attenuation is high. A cyst can be demonstrated readily and the thin bone of the

143

unborn child shows up even better. Foetal skull bone is thin enough not to absorb much energy. A study of the shape of the foetal skull shows that there are only two paths by which the beam can traverse the skull and be perpendicular to the bone surface twice over, the long axis of the skull and the path at right angles to this that traverses the maximum breadth of the skull (Fig. 5.7). Willocks has achieved a very high accuracy with this in measuring the foetal skull.

The clinical value is very considerable. There is a well known objection to using X-ray examination in pregnancy and measurements made by X-rays do not compare with those of ultrasound for accuracy. It is possible to make repeated measurements by ultrasound during pregnancy and allow the foetus to grow to as large a size as is compatible with normal labour. In gynaecology one of the major problems is the occurrence of a tumour of the uterus or the ovary as a complication of pregnancy. Though the foetus can be demonstrated by X-rays the tumour cannot and ultrasound has proved in Donald's hands a very valuable diagnostic aid in this situation.[3]

In the eye Baum's excellent results are unfortunately only rarely able to show something significant that cannot be examined quite satisfactorily by the ophthalmoscope. The great value in ophthalmology is in structures in the orbit behind the eye which cannot at present be investigated at all reliably by any other technique. These however are rare even in a specialized hospital.

REFERENCES

1. FRY, W. L., 'Intense ultrasound in investigations of the central nervous system, *Advances in Biological and Medical Physics*, **6**, 281–348 (Ed. Lawrence, J. H. and Tobias, C. A.) Academic Press, New York (1958).
2. GORDON, D., 'Studies in the measurement of ultrasonic energy and its effect on nerve tissue,' *Acta oto-laryngol. Suppl.*, **192**, 175–182 (1963).
3. DONALD, I. and BROWN, T. G., 'Demonstration of tissue interfaces within the body by ultrasonic echo sounding,' *Brit. J. Radiol.*, **34**, 539–545 (1961).
4. DUSSIK, K. T., 'Uber die Moglichkeit hochfrequente mechanische Schwingungen als diagnostisches Hilfsmittel zu verwenden,' *Z. Neurol.*, **174**, 153 (1942).
5. HOWRY, D. H. and BLISS, W. R., 'Ultrasonic visualization of soft tissue structures of the body,' *J. Lab. Clin. Med.*, **40**, 589–592 (1952).
6. WILD, J. J., 'Use of ultrasonic pulses for measurement of biologic tissues and detection of tissue density changes,' *Surgery*, **47**, 183–188 (1950).
7. *Handbook of Scientific Instruments and Apparatus*, 182, Physical Society, London (1955).
8. GORDON, D., 'Echo-encephalography. Ultrasonic rays in diagnostic radiology,' *Brit. Med. J.*, **1**, 1500–1504 (1959).
9. LEKSELL, L., 'Echo-encephalography: detection of intracranial complications following head injury,' *Acta. Chir. Scand.*, **115**, 255–259 (1956).
10. LITHANDER, B., 'Clinical and experimental studies in echo-encephalography,' *Acta. Psychiat. Scand. Suppl.*, **159**, 1–53 (1961).
11. OKSALA, A. and LEHTINEN, A., 'Diagnostics of detachment of the retina by means of ultrasound,' *Acta Ophthalmol.*, **35**, 461–467 (1957).
12. EDLER, I., 'The diagnostic uses of ultrasound in heart disease,' *Acta med. Scand. Suppl.*, **308**, 32–36 (1955).
13. GORDON, D., *Ultrasound as a Diagnostic and Surgical Tool*, 103–123, Livingstone Edinburgh (1964).
14. BAUM, G., *Ultrasound as a Diagnostic and Surgical Tool*, (Ed. Gordon, D.) 176–184 Livingstone, Edinburgh (1964).

6

DIAGNOSIS EQUIPMENT AND TECHNIQUES

D. Samain, M.Sc.

6.1 INTRODUCTION

Ultrasonic flaw detectors are now widely used in industry. A crack or cavity invisible to the eye can cause the catastrophic failure of, for example, a turbine or a high pressure chemical plant. Inspection by ultrasound reveals these faults before they can cause serious trouble.

In most cases the commercial equipment available for medical diagnosis is based on industrial flaw detectors. Ultrasound is much more widely used for flaw detection than for medical diagnosis and there is therefore a wider range of industrial than medical equipment. It should be noted that while longitudinal waves will pass through liquids and human tissue shear waves will only pass through solids. Some flaw detector transducers generate shear waves and these are unsuitable for medical work. Most equipment uses the pulse-echo technique with an A-scan presentation on a cathode ray tube. In most cases the medical equipment has simpler controls than the corresponding industrial equipment because the hospital user is interested primarily in the patient and not the equipment.

For a specific purpose such as midline detection the medical equipment designed for the purpose is most suitable but for some medical research purposes the industrial flaw detector with special probes may prove more suitable if it offers facilities not offered by the medical equipment.

The layout of a typical ultrasonic pulse echo measuring device is shown in block diagram form in Fig. 6.1. One transducer only is shown although some equipment uses two transducers for certain purposes.

The pulse repetition frequency generator which may be a multivibrator produces a train of pulses which control the sequence of events in the rest of the equipment. A pulse from the p.r.f. generator triggers the thyratron in the transmitter and thus discharges a capacitor into the transducer

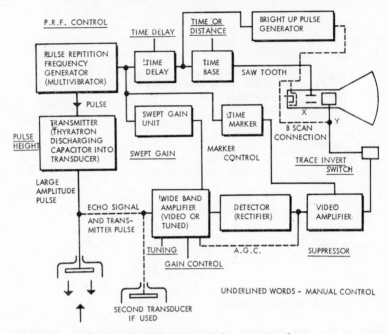

Fig. 6.1. Typical ultrasonic echo measuring device

producing the ultrasonic signal. At the same time a pulse is fed into the time delay unit and either immediately or after a short delay into the swept gain unit, the marker unit, the bright-up pulse generator and the time base. There is a wide band amplifier (the receiver) across the transducer to amplify the returning echo signal. In a flaw detector and in some medical equipment this may be a very wide band amplifier, wide enough to permit the use of any transducer on one of several different frequencies. This has the advantage that the operating frequency is determined by the transducer only and changing this changes the operating frequency.

Because tissue attenuates high frequencies much more rapidly than low, the very wideband pulse which this arrangement produces will suffer frequency distortion. An improved signal to noise ratio is obtained with a narrower band amplifier tuned to the transducer frequency. This is more complicated and less convenient because the amplifier frequency must be switched when the transducer frequency is changed. The bandwidth is about half the midband frequency. The gain is of the order of 10,000 times (80 dB) before detection and 10 to 100 times (20 to 40 dB) in the video amplifier.

Generally, near echoes will be very much larger than distant echoes but both must be displayed on the cathode ray tube. In some equipment there is only a manual gain control which must be adjusted to make the particular echo of interest a reasonable size on the cathode ray tube. In other equipment there is a swept gain unit. The unit which is triggered

146

by the p.r.f. generator feeds a shaped waveform into the wide band amplifier. By this means the amplifier gain is first reduced and then increased steadily as more distant echoes come in. It is also possible to use a fast acting automatic gain control system (A.G.C.) as in the Smith ultrasonic diasonograph.

After rectification the echo signal is amplified by the video amplifier and fed to the Y plates of the cathode ray tube. Echoes from small discontinuities and amplifier noise will produce a blurred base line (the •grass' of a radar set) and may distract the operator. A suppressor control is sometimes fitted to the video amplifier to cut off all small signals and leave only large echoes displayed on the tube.

The time delay unit is only required for special purposes. Usually the time base will begin to move the spot across the screen at the same moment as the thyratron is fired. If desired the start can be delayed by the time delay unit and then the trace can be expanded to permit better examination of a distant echo.

The p.r.f. is set by the operator and is adjustable from about 50 c/s to about 1 kc/s or so. For a large part of the cycle of operations the cathode ray tube spot will be off the screen, only being visible when brightened by the bright-up pulse during the forwards can. Increasing the p.r.f. will brighten the trace but care must be taken to see that all echoes from one transmitted pulse have died away before the next is sent out. If this is not so spurious echoes will appear on the trace. These spurious echoes can easily be detected because they will move when the p.r.f. is changed whereas true echoes will be unaffected.

For A scan the cathode-ray tube always has electrostatic deflection. It is now usual to use Post-Deflection Acceleration (P.D.A.). The electrons are accelerated by a relatively low voltage in passing through the electron gun assembly and then deflected by the deflection plates. They are then accelerated by the main accelerating potential. The cathode of the tube will be negative with respect to earth by a suitable amount, perhaps 1 or 2 kV. The deflecting plates will be near earth potential, probably at video anode potential, say $+100$ V and the final anode will be positive perhaps 4 to 8 kV giving a total E.H.T. of 5 to 10 kV. This arrangement gives a very bright trace because the total E.H.T. is high and requires lower deflecting voltages than tubes of older design.

The time marker produces pulses a known time apart and therefore corresponding to a known distance apart in human tissues. There may be a train of pulses a fixed time apart or the time may be varied by a calibrated control. In the block diagram they are fed into the video amplifier and hence to the Y plates. As an alternative they could be connected to the tube grid to produce a brightness change.

6.2 USE OF TRANSISTORS

Most commercial equipment is mains operated and not intended to be especially portable. Valves are used generally but transistors are now used

147

in some equipment. Unless the equipment is required for battery operation, transistors do not offer any special advantages although there may be small advantages in long term reliability. The reduced power consumption and hence heat production reduces the need for ventilation and permits the use of a case without louvres. The introduction of Post-Deflection Acceleration cathode ray tubes has made the design of transistor equipment easier and it is likely that with the rapid development of transistors capable of standing higher voltages more transistorized equipment will appear on the market. A similar situation exists with television and oscilloscope equipment and for the same reasons.

6.3 ECHOENCEPHALOGRAPHY

Several firms offer equipment for general medical diagnosis and in particular for Echoencephalography. The problem is to determine whether the middle of the brain is in the centre of the skull or not. There is no need to measure the actual size of the head or the actual distance to the midline, only its displacement from the centre-line.

The Sperry Reflectoscope and the Ultrasonoscope Mark 3 CM use the following method of measurement. Initially two probes are used, one

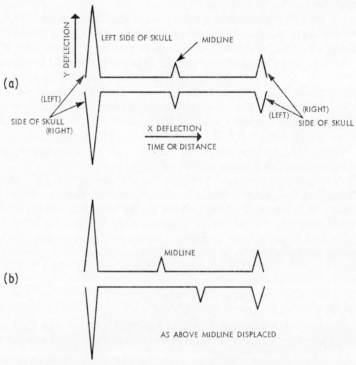

Fig. 6.2. Echoencephalograph of (a) normal head (b) with midline displaced

148

as a transmitter and one as a receiver, one on each side of the head. The ultrasonic signal will pass straight through the head to the receiving probe. The received signal will be delayed by a time corresponding to the distance between the probes and therefore the width of the head. After adjustment of the time base control to bring this signal to a suitable point on the screen the operation mode switch is changed over so that one probe is disconnected and the other used as transmitter and receiver. If the midline is correctly placed the distance from one probe to the midline and back to the same probe is the same as the distance right through and so the echo signal is in the same position on the screen as the direct transmission signal.

A different method is used in the Kelvin Ultrasonic Diasonograph, the Siemens Krautkramer Echoencephalograph, and the Smith-Kline equipment. Here one probe is used first on one side of the head and then on the other. When applied to the side of the head, there will be three main signals visible on the cathode ray tube. First there will be a very large echo from the skull on the same side as the transducer merging with the transmitted pulse, then the midline echo and then a large echo from the far side of the skull. The midline echo may be difficult to detect at first but a small movement of the transducer which is hand held should show it. As before the time base is adjusted and then the probe is applied to the other side of the head to produce a similar picture but in this case the trace is inverted by reversing the Y plate connections. The two midline echoes should appear one above the other as shown in the upper drawing Fig. 6.2. The lower drawing shows the result when the midline is displaced.

These are detail differences between the different makes. Most of them can be used with separate probes for transmission and reception as well as using one probe for both.

The method of switching from one side of the head to the other varies according to make. In some cases a foot switch is used to invert the trace.

Assuming a head to be 150 mm wide and the velocity of sound to be $1 \cdot 5$ mm/μsec the time of transmission will be 100 μsec and the echo signal will take 200 μsec as shown in Fig. 6.2. If the P.R.F. is 1 kc/s then the spot will be on the screen for 200 μsec and off for 800 μsec, which means that the screen will only be illuminated for 20 per cent of the time and less for lower P.R.Fs.

6.4 ULTRASONIC DIAGNOSTIC EQUIPMENT FOR GYNAECOLOGY

In Glasgow ultrasonic equipment is now used for gynaecological purposes. This has been developed by Kelvin Instruments (formerly Smith Industrial Division) in cooperation with Professor Donald. The equipment produces a two dimensional picture of a cross section of the abdomen (Tomography). Basically the equipment is similar to the pulse echo system previously described. Unlike other equipment in which the probe is hand held, the two dimensional picture (P.P.I. display, see Chapter 4) requires that

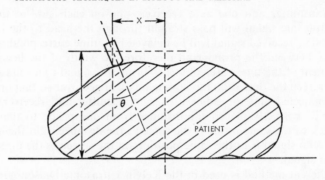

Fig. 6.3. Cross-section of patient showing scanning process used in tomography

both the probe position and the direction in which it is pointing should be accurately known during use and that the patient should not move.

As explained previously (Chapter 5) a large echo signal is only obtained when the ultrasonic beam strikes a surface normally and the probe must therefore be moved so that it looks at the patient from all possible positions and angles to produce a complete picture.

Fig. 6.3 shows the probe in contact with the abdomen. The beam position must be known and so the coordinates X and Y and the angle θ must be measured. The probe is partly rotated on its axis varying the angle θ and scanning right across the abdomen. Large echoes will be received from a small part of the surface of the internal organ, that part at right angles to the beam. After moving the probe bodily it is again rocked on its axis this time receiving echoes from a different part of the organ.

To produce a complete picture of the internal organ the separate pictures from each probe position must be added together. This is done continuously on the cathode ray tube and photographed. The spot must move across the tube in the same direction as the ultrasonic beam is crossing the patient and it must start from a point corresponding to the probe position. This is done by means of co-ordinate potentiometers and sine/cosine potentiometers which are mechanically fixed to the probe and give an electrical output which controls the position and direction of travel of the spot. In addition the spot must travel across the tube at the correct speed corresponding to the scale of the picture. If this is not so the various parts of the picture will not fit together.

The transducer output is amplified, in this case by a tuned amplifier, and fed to the grid of the cathode ray tube producing a bright spot whenever there is an echo.

In the latest equipment the probes which are not in use are stored in an interlocked rack. To free a probe for use on a particular frequency the frequency selector switch on the amplifier has to be changed to that frequency. This ensures that the correct amplifier is always used.

The equipment in Plate 6.1 is fully automatic, the probe being motor driven in three dimensions. It is controlled from a small movable unit which can seen in front of the operator. Plate 6.2 shows slightly simpler equipment with manual scanning. There are coordinate and sine/cosine potentiometers as before but the probe has to be moved directly by the operator. This may be preferable because a nervous patient will be less distressed by a machine which is seen to be under human control.

The description given above only mentions the surface of an internal organ. The ultrasonic beam will also penetrate the organ and be reflected from any discontinuities inside it and it will be attenuated by tissue and little affected by a clear liquid. The equipment is primarily intended for gynaecological use and so the organ examined is most likely to be the uterus. The picture produced by a normal pregnant uterus will differ from, for example, a case of hyditidiform mole because the contents of the uterus will reflect ultrasound in a different way in these two cases. A large tumour will give a different picture from a similar size liquid filled cyst because the small attenuation of the latter will mean that the far wall of the cyst will show almost as clearly as the near wall, whereas the tumour will so attenuate the signal that the far wall will be fainter or invisible.

One advantage of the equipment is that it gives a cross-sectional picture which bears a direct resemblance to the picture in a medical textbook, while its interpretation needs skill and training its significance is probably more readily appreciated than the A scan pictures.

In the case of the A scan the width of the ultrasonic beam is not of primary importance because only distance is being measured. The P.P.I. display depends on the measurement of distance and angle and so transducer design is especially important. The resolution of fine detail requires as narrow a beam as possible which in turn means as high a frequency as possible. Because high frequencies are heavily attenuated several probes are provided working in the 1 to 5 Mc/s range.

This equipment can be used to produce pictures of any of a number of different planes. The automatic equipment in Plate 6.1 is shown taking a longitudinal section down the patients midline. The manual equipment is shown in Plate 6.2 set up to take a transverse section.

6.5 ECHO-CARDIOGRAPHY

Movement of the mitral value in the heart can be detected by pulse echo technique (see Chapter 5). A special display unit is made by Sperry Products for this purpose. Two forms of display are needed, an A scan to locate the desired echo signals and an intensity modulated display to show how the valve is moving. After location the display is changed so that there is a bright spot on the screen at the point where the echo was previously seen. This spot will move backwards and forwards as the mitral valve moves. By slowly sweeping the whole trace with a second time base at right angles to the first the movement of the valve can be made clearly visible. The electro-cardiograph trace can be displayed at the same time if desired.

Instead of the slow time base a moving film camera can be used to produce a permanent record. An alternative method has been developed by Edler[1].

6.6 PROBES FOR SPECIAL PURPOSES

Ultrasonoscope have made special probes for the detection of gallstones[2] at operation (See Chapter 5). A 3·5 mm transducer operating at 2·5 Mc/s is mounted at the end of a 12 in metal tube of 4 mm diameter and connected to the flaw detector by a screened cable. The probe and cable can be sterilized in a cabinet.

The same firm have also made a 5 Mc/s probe for measurements on the eye.[3] To make contact with the eye the probe has a plastic extension filled with distilled water. The measurements are done with local anaesthesia. Two special probes are marketed by Smith Kline for the location

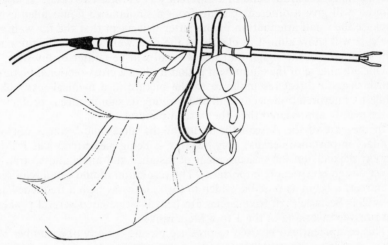

Fig. 6.4. The Bronson foreign body locator and extractor

and removal of a foreign body in the eye. The first probe is used before operation to locate the object and decide on the correct approach at operation. The second probe, the Bronson foreign body locator and extractor is a combination of forceps and ultrasonic transducer (Fig. 6.4). The echo signal from the forceps, the foreign body and the far wall of the eye can be seen simultaneously on the cathode ray tube, thus reducing the possibility of accidental damage to the retina.

The probe is used with the Ekoline ultrasonic equipment which is now fully transistorized. In addition to the main cathode ray tube there is a small tube in a movable display unit which can be sterilized and held in the view of the surgeon.

6.7 SAFETY

In most cases there is no special safety problem associated with ultrasonic diagnostic equipment. There are two points which should be checked before equipment is used in an operating theatre.

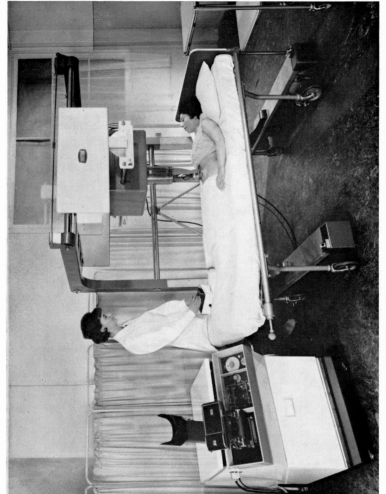

Plate 6.1. *Fully automatic scan at Western Infirmary, Glasgow*

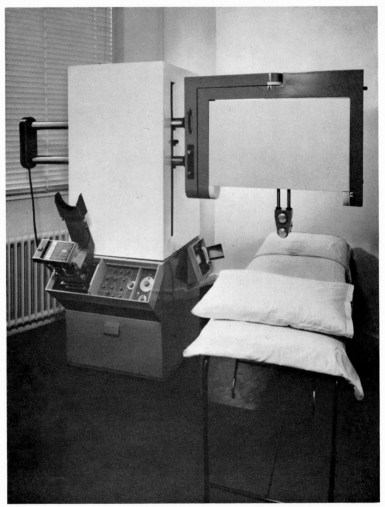

Plate 6.2. Manual scanning at Queen Mother Hospital, Glasgow

Commercial probes commonly use barium titanate transducers which will be depolarized if heated just above 100°C and which will deteriorate if stored above 70°C. These probes cannot therefore be heat sterilized. For most work this is not important because the probe is applied to unbroken skin.

There are high voltages within the equipment, in particular on the cathode ray tube and on the thyratron and hence on the transducer. This is all perfectly safe in normal use but can ignite gases. Non-inflammable anaesthetics should be used and where a probe is introduced at an operation it should be of the lead-zirconate-titanate type or be cold sterilized.

REFERENCES

1. EDLER, E., *Ultrasound as a Diagnostic and Surgical Tool*, (Ed. Gordon, D.), 124–144, Livingstone, Edinburgh (1964).
2. KNIGHT, P. R. and NEWELL, J. D., 'Operative use of Ultrasonics in Cholelithiasis,' *Lancet*, 1023, May 11 (1963).
3. LEARY, G. A., SORSBY, A., RICHARDS, M. J. and CHASTON, J., 'Ultrasonographic measurements of the components of ocular refraction in life,' *Vision Research*, 3, 487 (1963).

II

7

BIOLOGICAL EFFECTS BELOW CAVITATION LEVEL

D. Gordon, M.B., D.M.R., D.M.R.D., Sen.M.I.E.E.E.

7.1 INTRODUCTION

In Chapter 5 the acoustic characteristics of the body tissues have been described particularly in so far as the tissues produce attenuation and acoustic mismatches. It is now necessary to consider how this energy affects the tissues through which it passes.

At the frequencies at which these examinations are performed it is necessary to attain an intensity measured in kilowatts per square centimetre before cavitation occurs. Even in the surgical techniques described in the next chapter these intensities do not appear to produce cavitation at the focus though it has been repeatedly elicited inside the velocity transformer of the Royal Ear Hospital Transducer when tested at power levels far above those usable at operation. The cavitation effects are therefore discussed separately in Chapter 11.

7.2 HEAT

Eventually all the energy entering the tissues becomes converted into heat. This of course is distributed in accordance with the rate of attenuation. As bone has the highest attenuation of all the body tissues, most of the heat effects are noted in or close to the bone. If sufficient heat is produced to raise the tissue temperature to a lethal level, the heat will pass by conduction to adjacent tissues that may not have received any ultrasonic irradiation but which may nevertheless be killed by the conducted heat.

It should not be forgotten that the body is fitted with what must be one of the most elaborate and effective heat regulating systems to be found

154

anywhere. This is capable of maintaining the temperature of the interior of the body at a remarkably constant temperature in spite of very large variations in the ambient temperature, in the physical work being performed and in the nature and quantity of fuel (food) being taken in.

This is a function of the blood circulation that is often ignored. Blood is thought of as carrying oxygen to the tissues, carbon dioxide from the tissues to the lungs, white cells to any site of infection, waste products to the kidneys, sugar to the liver for storage as glycogen and in disease as a carrier of bacteria and blood clots. The blood is however mainly water which has a large specific heat and it travels at such a speed that it can transfer large amounts of heat from one part of the body to another.

As an example the volume of blood passing through brain tissue is so large that every gram of brain tissue has its own weight of blood passing through it in two minutes. In other parts of the body the circulation is much more variable in its rate. The brain never has its blood supply restricted as of course it has to continue to function even in the deepest sleep. Elsewhere the blood supply is automatically adjusted to the current needs of the tissues by the autonomic nervous system, the sympathetic and para-sympathetic nerves.

When food is being digested the arteries to the abdominal viscera appropriate most of the available blood leaving little for the muscles and skin. This accounts for the inadvisability of swimming in cold water just after a meal. During active exercise the muscles have their blood supply increased at the expense of the viscera.

The normal source of the body heat is the oxidation of food constituents mainly glucose, when work is being done. The majority of the heat is therefore produced in the muscles. Everyone knows that one takes exercise to get warm. This heat is transferred to the rest of the body by the blood so that the body temperature tends to rise and immediately the regulating mechanism comes into play. During exercise the respiration becomes deeper. This not only increases the oxygen supply it also increases the amount of evaporation of water from the lungs and this of course has a cooling effect. Larger amounts of exercise provoke the next stage in the cooling mechanism, the increase in heat loss from the skin by evaporation of sweat. This is matched by a greater blood flow to the skin so that radiation as well is increased.

With cold conditions the blood supply to the skin is reduced so that its temperature falls and it is able to give up less heat to the surroundings. When the temperature falls too low, shivering occurs, i.e. muscular contractions to provide the needed heat.

Viewing the effect of ultrasonic heating in the light of the above, it will be realized that it is not merely a matter of calculating the number of joules, converting them into calories and determining from this the temperature rise of a given weight of tissue. This is a calculation more like carrying water in a bucket with a hole in it. It all depends on how large a hole there is in the bucket how much water will be carried each journey. In the brain it is unlikely that the heat removed will vary much in health though it certainly would be less if the circulation were impaired by disease.

In the muscles however the circulation is very unpredictable and the same is true of the skin.

It will be found that the intensities of ultrasound used in physical medicine when allowance is made for pulsing and the normal procedure of moving the transducer continuously over a considerable area, produces so few calories that even if the circulation were cut off completely the temperature rise would be insignificant in the soft tissues at any distance from bone. It is only when the high attenuation of bone is present that temperature rises to a point capable of stimulating the periosteal nerves.

At the other end of the range in ultrasonic neuro-surgery the exposures are of the order of a fraction of a second to a few seconds. Here the amount of heat that can be removed during the actual exposure is unimportant and the circulation merely affects the rate at which the irradiated tissue falls to that of the surroundings.

Many workers have assumed that all the effects of ultrasound on tissue are attributable to heat either directly or indirectly. As has been argued elsewhere[1] this seems improbable. However some heat production is certain to occur and should never be forgotten.

Similarly some have assumed that all biological effects are due to cavitation. This was a tenable view when only low frequencies were used but the high threshold of cavitation at frequencies above a megacycle per second makes it impossible to accept this view.

7.3 THE DISRUPTION OF CELLS

This was one of the earliest biological effects described but at high frequency it seems reasonably certain that no direct rupture of cell-membranes is produced by ultrasound under clinical conditions. Where cells have been overheated their membranes will rupture but this is an indirect effect. Ackerman[2] has shown rupture of the membranes of blood cells in vitro but though he employed frequencies up to a megacycle per second he used very high intensities and comparable conditions would not occur *in vivo*.

7.4 CELL NECROSIS

There can be no doubt from many animal experiments that cells which immediately after ultrasonic irradiation are normal to histological examination are in fact doomed to die. At least 24 hours should be allowed to elapse if even the most skilled pathologist is to be able to identify which cells are dying. For preference the interval should be extended to a week. It is almost impossible to believe that heat alone would have such a delayed action. There is a comparable latent period after a dose of one of the ionizing radiations. In both cases it is assumed that some damage has been done to the internal structure of the cell too small to produce changes visible to the eye with a conventional microscope.

Recent work by El'piner in Moscow has shown that the mitochondria are ruptured immediately after irradiation. This can only be demonstrated by the electron miscroscope and it is to be hoped that the full mechanism of biological effect will eventually be demonstrated in this way.

7.5 REVERSIBLE LESIONS

This is one of the most contentious subjects in ultrasonic surgery. It would be a great help surgically if it were possible to give a dose of ultrasound sufficient to produce a temporary paralysis of a part of the brain which would pass off completely leaving no damage. If such a reversible lesion were produced and showed relief of a symptom but no unwanted complication it would then be a simple matter to give a second larger dose capable of producing a permanent destruction.

Some experiments have been described which appeared to produce such effects but unfortunately they have not been numerous and have not been repeated elsewhere.[3] The writer considers that the evidence so far available makes it probable that such lesions occur but improbable that they can be produced of a large enough and certain enough size to make their use on patients likely to become an accepted procedure. This is one of those occasions where one hopes very much to be proved wrong by subsequent experiments.

7.6 CHEMICAL EFFECTS

Physical medicine specialists have claimed that absorption through the skin of drugs and the metabolism of cells can be accelerated by ultrasound. No convincing evidence has been produced that any such effect is a true ultrasonic action and not the result of the mechanical massaging of the transducer on the skin or the increased blood supply induced.

There can however be no doubt that chemical reactions are much accelerated by ultrasound and there is no reason to doubt that the same would apply to bio-chemical reactions. The practical problem is that the reactions that one wants to accelerate normally take place over the whole mass of the liver or kidneys and not in some small accessible structure. It would be tempting to suggest that muscle metabolism could be accelerated by ultrasound so that a man could run a mile in three minutes. It would indeed be a miracle of technology to produce a system for irradiating the leg muscles with a miniaturized set of transducers which would improve muscle function enough to offset the restraints they would impose!

7.7 RADIATION PRESSURE

The minute forces produced by absorbed radiation are unlikely to have any physiological effects of their own. However the possibility that streaming, which is a radiation pressure effect, occurring within the cell plays an important part in the cell necrosis mentioned earlier, has been suggested by the writer[1] as a result of observing Dyer's botanical observations.[4]

7.8 ACTION ON NERVES

This too is a contentious subject. In physical medicine it has been claimed that ultrasound relieves spasm, stimulates, 'soothes,' improves tissue nutrition, inhibits the sympathetic, dilates the vessels and indeed does practically anything the user wants it to do.

There can be no doubt that nerve tissue is more susceptible to ultrasound than any other tissue. Laboratory experiments have shown that ultrasound can produce a blocking of nerve impulses along nerve fibres and that this effect is transient. Whether there is complete long term recovery is less certain. No direct stimulating action of ultrasound has been described which cannot be explained on the basis of stimulation by heat produced by the ultrasound.

An open mind must be kept as to the way in which the ultrasound used in physical medicine produces its effects. There can be little doubt that much can be explained as due to suggestion. Some of the claims made are clearly untenable such as the irradiation of the inter-vertebral discs through the skin of the back and the bone of the neural arches. Apart from the periosteal nerves it is on the available evidence unlikely that any nerve irradiated with an unfocused transducer receives a dose capable of causing more than a transient interruption of function.

REFERENCES

1. GORDON, D., *Ultrasound as a Diagnostic and Surgical Tool*, 31, Livingstone, Edinburgh (1964).
2. ACKERMAN, E., 'Surface Modes of Resonance of Biological Cells in Ultrasonic Fields,' *Proc. 3rd. Int. Conf. Med. Electronics*, 437, I.E.E. London (1961).
3. FRY, F. J., ADES, H. W. and FRY, W. J., 'Production of reversible changes in the central nervous system by Ultrasound,' *Science*, **127**, 83 (1958).
4. DYER, H. J. and NYBORG, W. L., 'Characteristics of Intracellular Motion induced by Ultrasound,' *Proc. 3rd. Inst. Conf. Med. Electronics*, 445, I.E.E. London (1961).

8

THE USE OF ULTRASOUND IN SURGERY

D. Gordon, M.B., D.M.R., D.M.R.D., Sen.M.I.E.E.E.

8.1 INTRODUCTION

The first and probably still the most widely used application of ultrasound in surgery was the so-called Ultrasonic Massage introduced in Germany before the War. This was introduced as a substitute for the hands of the masseur in patients who had suffered from fractures and similar injuries. Rubbing movements are capable of improving the circulation very considerably and help also to break down adhesions between muscles and their sheaths which limit the range of movement.

It was thought that the same effects would be obtained by the mechanical movement of the tissues with plane wave ultrasonic irradiation. This was generated by flat quartz crystals the earthed surface of which could be applied directly to the skin. The operating frequency was usually 800 to 900 kc/s but over a considerable period this has tended to rise and several machines are now marketed that operate at 3 Mc/s. It did not take long for the view that this was a form of massage to become obsolete. It was realized that it approximated much more closely to medical diathermy and short wave therapy both of which produce heat deep in the tissues. Just as the tissues in which heat was produced differed with the higher frequency of short wave therapy from that obtained with the lower frequency of medical diathermy, so ultrasound showed a variable heat distribution.

8.2 PRODUCTION IN TISSUES

Most of the tissues of the body are composed of water and therefore show relatively little absorption effect on ultrasound per centimetre of path through the tissue. The almost perfect elasticity of the weak saline that constitutes the cerebro-spinal fluid gives virtually no absorption effect. As tissues depart more and more from the watery consistency of, for example, brain tissue, the rate of absorption rises with increasing hysteresis.

Muscle and fibrous tissue show considerable absorption but they are very greatly surpassed by cartilage and bone. Various figures have been published for the different tissues and wide discrepancies will be found between the authors.

The most obvious explanation of this is the least likely to be correct. With increasing frequency the attenuation must rise but in fact nearly all the published papers cover frequencies close to 1 Mc/s. The absorption differs much more with the method of measurement. If an echo technique, is used, the attenuation will appear much higher than if a transmission technique using plane waves is used. The scattering and refracting effect of the tissue is added to the true absorption in the echo technique as the reduction in the power returning to the probe is due to all three phenomena. Further if only the pulse height is measured this further invalidates the result. A short transmission pulse may return as a long relatively flat top echo through reverberation between close parallel surfaces.

There is one further source of discrepancy that is often completely ignored. This is the difference between tissues measured live and dead. For obvious reasons it is much easier to measure velocities in prepared uniform specimens made of excised tissue than to make an examination in living animals or in man when it is seldom possible to separate any useful mass of one tissue from other types of tissue.

All workers in echo techniques who have used isolated organs floating in tanks of water or saline have discovered how much easier it is to obtain echoes from such specimens than from the same structure at operation. This only indicates a greater amount of reflection at the first interface in living tissue but there can be little doubt that the attenuation is also affected by the immediate loss of intra-cellular tension immediately cells lose their normal circulation even though they may still respond to stimuli.

However with cartilage and bone the effect of death or loss of blood supply is unlikely to be so great, as the cells constitute only a very small part of the tissue and it is the inorganic deposit of calcium salts in bone that provides the largest factor by far in attenuating the ultrasound. Both show much higher attenuation rates than other tissues and bone in particular has the highest rate.

Bone is however a very variable tissue that can be a soft spongy mass containing a low proportion of calcium relative to fibrous tissue especially in such bone diseases as osteitis deformans, while in some parts of the body it is a dense marble-like material of high density. Even more difficult from the acoustic point of view, it often has an outer layer of dense bone and of fairly smooth surface, an inner layer of dense bone of very irregular surface and an intervening layer often of considerable thickness that contains a mixture of irregularly disposed bony elements separated by correspondingly irregular soft tissue mainly marrow and blood vessels. This is most commonly found in the skull vault.

The velocity of ultrasound in bone naturally varies with the type of bone but it is always much faster than in soft tissue probably as much as four times as fast. This ensures that a large part of the ultrasound is reflected at the bone surface thus increasing the power level in the immediately adjacent soft tissues.

As bone has such a high absorption rate compared with other tissues in practice it is found that the ultrasound is almost all converted into heat close to the surface of the first bone it strikes. Where there is no bone in its path it will seldom cause any significant rise in temperature in the tissues. Bone is very poorly supplied with nerves but the layer of fibrous tissue on its surface, the periosteum, is well supplied with nerves and this immediately responds to the temperature rise in the adjacent bone.

The heating of the periosteum is in practice the danger signal in ultrasonic therapy and the dose level is always intended to be low enough not to elicit pain. There are however some diseases in which the sensory nerves that record pain, are no longer able to give the warning signal. These are cases of neuropathy and such patients are usually without normal skin sensation also. The classic symptom is the discovery through the smell of burning instead of through the sensation of pain that a cigarette has burnt the finger.

It must be admitted that the use of ultrasound as a treatment in physical medicine has a very equivocal reputation. Many consultants in this field have abandoned its use after extensive clinical trial. Others are enthusiastic in its praise. The condition in which its value is accepted most widely is in the removal of scar tissue such as is needed in Dupuytren's Contracture. This is a slow formation of fibrous tissue just below the skin of the palm of the hand. In the course of time the fibrous tissue contracts and causes the fingers to be drawn down towards the palm giving a serious disability. Surgical attempts to relieve the condition are seldom very satisfactory and ultrasound has produced better results.

There are some other conditions where fibrous tissue forms in excess in the tissues such as keloid change in a scar. Here for no known reason instead of a wound healing with a normal amount of fibrous tissue, a great overgrowth occurs making the scar project above the normal skin surface and often causing further injury to occur at the site.

Recently it has been shown that ultrasound has sufficient value in the treatment of acute trauma in professional footballers to enable them to return to active play much more quickly than is possible with any other form of treatment.[1] The opinions of a club manager and a trainer are more objective evidence than most of that available. However for this it is necessary to employ small fields restricted to a haematoma, to give long periods of treatments at high power and several times per day, to omit the pulsing procedure and to select the frequency that will enable as much of the power as possible to be turned to heat at the site of the injury and as little as possible reach bone and cause pain.

This treatment is of quite a different order from that normally employed

161

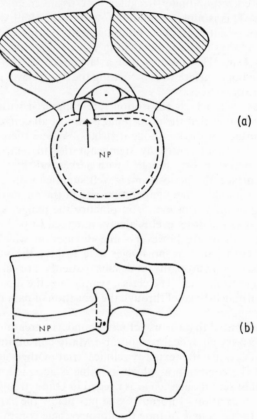

Fig. 8.1. Diagram of vertebrae and discs. (a) Horizontal cross section showing how a defect in the annular ligament (dotted lines) permits the soft nucleus pulposus (N.P.) to exude and press on nerve roots. (b) Lateral view showing how the lamina prevents access to the nucleus from behind. The large muscles (shaded) prevent close application of the transducer to the small gaps between the bones

in physical medicine and the joules delivered are clearly capable of causing a considerable temperature rise in the blood-clot.

When however the numerous conditions that are grouped under the title of Rheumatism are considered, the big argument begins. Undoubtedly fibrous tissue formation occurs in many of these conditions but while some clinicians find that ultrasound is of great value, others find it useless.

The way in which ultrasound produces its biological effect is discussed elsewhere but the way in which it could produce therapeutic effects in rheumatism is very hard to determine. Claims that ultrasound penetrates the soft tissues of the back far enough and precisely enough to generate heat in the nucleus pulposus, the gelatinous material that separates the bodies of the vertibrae, appear to be quite unjustified.

The discs vary in width from 3 or 4 mm in the cervical region to as much as 2 cm in the lumbar but the distance from the skin surface increases as the width increases. Further there is behind the body of the vertebra the neutral arch, a bony structure composed of a flattened part the lamina and three projections, a spinous process directed backwards and two transverse processes that project laterally.

The lamina in nearly all cases lies at a lower level than the body to which it is attached so that it must prevent ultrasound from passing between the vertebral bodies (Fig. 8.1). The neural arch surrounds the spinal canal which contains the spinal cord floating in a weak saline fluid the cerebrospinal fluid. A pair of nerves leaves the cord corresponding to the gap between each pair of vertebrae and emerges between the laminae by the inter-vertebral foramina. These nerves are both sensory and motor, they convey sensation from the periphery to the brain and they convey stimuli from the brain to cause the muscles to contract.

Nerve tissue has a peculiar characteristic which is probably more easily understood by physicists and engineers than by others. The classic unit of nerve tissue is the nerve cell with its long single nerve fibre and its multiple short fibrils or dendrites. In simplified terms, stimuli reaching the dendrites produce no effect on the nerve cell until a fixed threshold is reached. The cell then reacts like a univibrator giving a signal of fixed form that travels along the long nerve fibre at a readily measured but somewhat variable rate. No matter how large the stimulus the 'action potential' is always of constant amplitude. After the discharge there is a refractory period during which the cell will not respond to any further stimulus. Once the refractory period is over the nerve cell will react to further stimuli with its standard response, the action potential.

The general arrangement is the same in both sensory and motor nerves though the nerve fibre of a motor nerve ends in muscle while in a sensory nerve the nerve fibre terminates in one or more fine fibrils or in a special sense organ and the nerve fibre carries the action potential towards the brain or spinal cord.

The majority of nerve fibres are 'myelinated,' that is they are surrounded by a sheath of fatty material, myelin, that appears to have no active function and is probably protective and insulating in its function. The active element is the 'axis cylinder' that is surrounded by the myelin sheath. Nerve cells are grouped together and supported by a special connective tissue, the neuroglia, to compose what is called the grey matter. Many myelinated nerve fibres grouped together constitute the white matter of the brain and spinal cord. Outside the brain and spinal cord the nerve cells are grouped to form ganglia which appear as swellings on the course of the 'peripheral nerves' which elsewhere are composed of nerve fibres and a small amount of connective tissue.

This oversimplified description can readily be amplified by consulting any standard textbook on the physiology of the nervous system. It does however permit one to explain the possible ways in which ultrasound could function in medicine.

There can be no doubt that the most susceptible structure from the point of view of ultrasonic irradiation is the myelin sheath when the result is measured by what can be seen in the conventional microscope. It is far from certain that this would be true if electron microscopy were used. Probably the axis cylinder in the most suceptible through its proximity to the myelin but this subject is discussed elsewhere.[2]

In the intensive treatment of football injuries referred to earlier there can be little doubt that the intensity and duration of irradiation are sufficient to cause at least a temporary suspension of the function of the nerves in the direct beam if comparison is made with the action on the facial nerve during the irradiation of the inner ear.

If such effects should cause irreversible effects in that part of the nerve fibre this need cause no alarm as in these circumstances the nerve-fibre can regenerate quite quickly the short damaged termination.

It is a matter for speculation whether the prevention of muscle spasm by stopping pain plays a greater or smaller part in such cases than does the heating up of the blood-clot and the acceleration of its absorption.

In the other applications in physical medicine where the dose received by any particular mass of tissue is very much smaller, it is very difficult to believe that even a temporary suspension of nerve function occurs and the temperature rise must be a matter of only two or three degrees at most.

On general principles one would expect that if an intensity sufficient to have a reversible effect on deep structures were used it would inevitably cause an irreversible effect on superficial nerves which often supply skin at quite a distance. Though regeneration would occur this might take many weeks and one would expect areas of anaesthesia to be noticed and reported. This does not seem to have happened. All the references to overdose are concerned with heating of the bone or occasionally the skin from heating of the transducer.

Another difficulty arises from the fact that though the evidence of reversible effects from ultrasound is strong the possibility of achieving this with heat is much less. It is common knowledge that cold will cause numbness but that contact with a hot soldering iron has no anaesthetic effect at all.

The probable explanation is that direct action on the nerves plays little or no part in the ultrasonic treatment of rheumatism and that the effect is a dilation of the deep blood vessels in response to a rise in temperature produced by absorption of the ultrasound in the tissues, especially when bone or fibrous tissue is irradiated. Further more accurate research work is much needed in this field.

8.3 THE DISRUPTION OF BACTERIA

The use of ultrasound to disrupt the capsules of bacteria is now a routine procedure but it is of value mainly in specialized laboratories where bacterial toxins are needed for the manufacture of antitoxins and for research purposes.

For this work cavitation is essential and therefore low ultrasonic frequencies are used. There is no rupture of cell membranes even at power levels of tne order of 1 kW/cm^2 when this is obtained by focusing at 1 Mc/s and upwards.

The great value of the ultrasonic method is that it is possible to obtain the cell contents without the use of heat which always tends to alter the chemical composition. Some bacteria have a tough waxy capsule that can be ruptured in no other way at room temperature.

A bacterium, whose cell membrane has been ruptured, is of course dead and harmless so there has been a temptation to talk of ultrasonic sterilization. This is not attainable in practice though it is in theory. The reason for this is that sterility demands not merely the killing of 99 per cent of the bacteria present nor the killing of 99·9 per cent but the killing of exactly 100 per cent. If only the toxin is needed the unruptured bacteria can be removed by filtration but the survival of a single live bacterium invalidates the sterilization procedure entirely even though many millions have been killed.

In practice there are always some null points in any ultrasonic situation where a reflected wave cancels out the incident wave. A null point need only be the size of a bacterium to prevent sterilization. To employ sufficient power and sufficient agitation to attain 100 per cent killing of bacteria is impracticable.

The very high power attained momentarily with cavitation and the need to employ low frequencies that cannot easily be focused, make it very unlikely that it will ever be found useful to employ the technique *in vivo*. There would almost certainly be much more damage done to the tissues than to the bacteria within them. It is also unlikely that cancer cells would show more susceptibility to cavitation than would the normal cells.

8.4 ULTRASONIC SURGERY

Every tissue in the body has been irradiated with ultrasound and the results reported but the value of ultrasound as a destructive agent has been almost confined to the nervous system. This is because nerve tissue, particularly the myelinated fibres of the brain, spinal cord and peripheral nerves, shows exceptional susceptibility to ultrasound.

The value of this is enhanced by the relative immunity of the blood vessels. This is of particular value in the brain where the blood supply within the brain is mainly composed of 'end arteries.' Round the base of the brain the arteries of the Circle of Willis receive blood from four main sources, the two internal carotid arteries and the two vertebral arteries so that interruption of any artery is compensated for by increased flow in one or more of the others. Cases have been known where all save one of the major arteries have been blocked but still the blood supply to the brain has remained at a level compatible with life and full consciousness. The arteries that leave the Circle of Willis to supply the brain are however in very different circumstances. There is no communication between one artery and another inside the brain so that if an artery is blocked all the cells in the brain that are normally nourished by that artery must die. Recovery or regrowth of nerve cells does not occur so clinical recovery is only possible through the function of the dead cells being taken over by other nerve cells elsewhere. This can only happen to a limited extent and over a long period.

All the methods of destroying nerve tissue that have been developed suffer from the objection that they affect vessels more than the nerve tissue It is impossible to destroy nerve tissue therefore without risking damaging an artery that supplies tissue outside the actual target area. Numerous methods of destruction have been used. One of the earliest is electrolysis in which the passage of direct current from the exposed area of a needle deep in tissue to an indifferent remote electrode so disorganizes the polarization of the cell membranes round the needle that the cells die.

A large number of chemicals have been injected to produce a local effect. Local anaesthetics are often injected first to permit a reversible effect and check the functional change. Then a permanent destruction is obtained by injecting at the same site some more destructive chemical. The one that is most commonly used is ethyl alcohol in a buffering solution. Another commonly used destructive agent is phenol.

Electro-coagulation, though produced by radio-frequency current, is in practice merely a form of localized heat production and attempts have been made to monitor it by a thermocouple.

Recently 'cryolytic' lesions have been produced. In these a miniature refrigeration unit is constructed in the tip of a thick needle. A reduction of temperature causes a reversible lesion if of minor degree but an irreversible lesion if of major degree.

All these techniques are open to criticism not merely because of the unwanted damage to blood-vessels that they may involve but also because the size of the lesion cannot be predicted with any accuracy. Ultrasound gives promise of overcoming the latter objection as well as the former.

8.5 MÉNIÈRE'S DISEASE

The first form of ultrasonic surgery to achieve a wide degree of acceptance was the ultrasonic destruction of the vestibular apparatus in cases of Ménière's Disease, introduced by Professor M. Arslan of Padua, Italy in 1952.[3]

Ménière's Disease is a comparatively rare disease of unexplained cause which produces a progressive deterioration in the function of the Eighth or Acoustic Nerve. The acoustic nerve is composed of two divisions running together to two sense organs that are closely related physically but of quite different function. The auditory division runs from the cochlea, the organ of hearing to the brain. The vestibular division runs from the vestibular apparatus to the brain. The cochlea and the vestibular apparatus lie in a complex of cavities in the temporal bone which are almost entirely filled with a liquid, the endolymph and perilymph.

The cochlea is a snail-shaped structure with the spiral cavity divided into three by two membranous partitions, one of which carries the organ of Corti, the specialized nerve cells that respond to sound vibrations. The myelinated nerve fibres pass from ganglion cells in the centre of the spiral and transmit the sensation of hearing to the brain.

The vestibular apparatus is harder to comprehend. It consists of the crista and the otoliths, specialized sense organs in the semi-circular canals. They are much less important than the cochlea as there are other sensory mechanisms that supplement them and can in large measure replace them. The ability to tell which way the body is moving is shared between the vestibular apparatus, the eyes, the skin and the muscles.

In practice the eyes usually predominate. They are easily misled however as can be shown by the way that one thinks one's own train is moving if the train at the next platform starts to move and one's eye cannot see anything but the two trains. Once some stationary object like the platform beyond is seen, the correct situation is obvious.

On the other hand even if one's eyes are shut, emergency braking of a car is immediately obvious by the pressure on the soles of the feet and the tendency to slide forward in the seat. It has been said that an air pilot flies with the seat of his pants because the skin taking his body weight responds to all the complex forces produced by altering the course of his plane. Perhaps one should add as an additional sense organ the nerves of the abdominal viscera which are so sensitive to the rapid acceleration or deceleration of a lift.

If however anyone stands with their feet together and their eyes shut, they maintain their balance because of the stretching or slackening of the leg muscles if the body begins to lean in any direction. A normal person has no difficulty in remaining reasonably still simply through the use of the muscle sensation.

With so many indications of body movement it is not surprising that the vestibular apparatus is apt to be forgotten. The sense organs can best be described as strain gauges to measure acceleration. The otoliths are small calcified bodies supported by nerve cells which naturally are stimulated by acceleration of the body which causes relative movement of the heavy otolith and the nerve cells. The crista is a collection of nerve cells projecting into the lymph cavity which responds to the induced movement of the endolymph.

Complete loss of vestibular function on both sides causes virtually no disability because of the alternative sources of comparable information. In Ménière's Disease however one vestibular apparatus usually functions normally while the other functions abnormally giving incorrect information to the brain. The conflict between the correct and incorrect information manifests itself as very marked giddiness or vertigo. This occurs in bouts that may be as incapacitating as epilepsy.

The disease however affects both divisions of the Eighth Nerve and the patient suffers from a progressive loss of hearing and continuous buzzing in the ears, tinnitus. There is one further symptom that the patients suffer from but often fail to mention. This is a sense of tension within the ear.

167

It is only after successful ultrasonic operation that the disappearance of this symptom draws the patient's attention to it! This tension is very real. The liquid endolymph is under raised pressure and this probably in part accounts for the loss of hearing. Another feature of Ménière's Disease is its slow course with many spontaneous remissions in the symptoms but the long term trend is always towards deafness. Medical treatment is at best a palliation of symptoms. Theories that the disease was due to disordered salt metabolism have not been confirmed.

It was the accepted course in handling a case to wait until the hearing is so poor on the affected side that there is nothing to be lost by losing it altogether and then to operate and destroy the inner ear completely. As there is free communication of endolymph between cochlea and semi-circular canals, destruction of one involves destruction of the others if this is done by conventional surgery.

In this unsatisfactory situation, Arslan's technique has represented an enormous advance. Arslan realized that ultrasound could destroy the vestibular apparatus without destroying the cochlea if it was applied with care. An earlier attempt was made in Vienna to do this by filling the outer ear with water and directing ultrasound through the water. The weakness of this technique was the presence of air in the middle ear so that on reaching the ear-drum the energy was reflected back. Such energy as passed across the middle ear via the ossicles following the route of sound waves, would have reached the cochlea rather than the vestibular apparatus.

Arslan's technique was to operate on the mastoid process and to expose the lateral semicircular canal where it projects slightly into the middle ear. The bone over the canal was ground away until only half a millimetre of bone remained and the cavity of the canal could be seen showing through as a grey line (Fig. 8.2).

Arslan's original apparatus was composed of a metal velocity trans-former which became very heated by the ultrasound so that part of his effects were those of transmitted heat. Unfortunately the facial nerve travels through a canal in the temporal bone that is very close to the lateral semi-circular canal. Even more unfortunately its course is very variable so from time to time cases of facial paralysis have been produced particularly when a transducer that generated heat was used.

The measurement of the dose level inside the bone is clearly impossible but unfortunately a biological method of estimating the effect was available. Irritation of the vestibular apparatus causes a persistent twitching of the eyes to one side. This has long been the basis of the caloric testing of the vestibular apparatus. Hot or cold water injected into the outer ear causes sufficient temperature change in the endolymph to produce convection currents and hence nystagmus. In passing it should be mentioned that viewed purely as a thermal conduction phenomenon it is astonishing that enough cooling or warming action is possible via such small structures as the ossicles, the minute bones that transmit sound across the middle ear.

The production of convection currents in the endolymph, the weak salt solution that fills the cavity of the semi-circular canals, by whatever means stimulates the sense organs and by reflex action the eye starts to

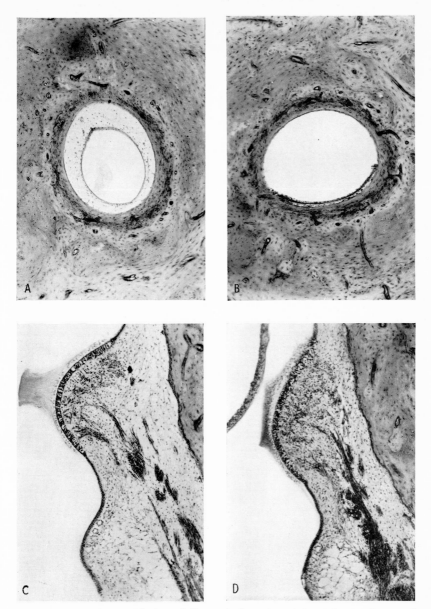

Plate 8.1. Ultrasonic irradiation of Cow: A. Posterior semi-circular canal, control; B. Posterior semi-circular canal, irradiated; C. Crista, control; D. Cirsta, irradiated

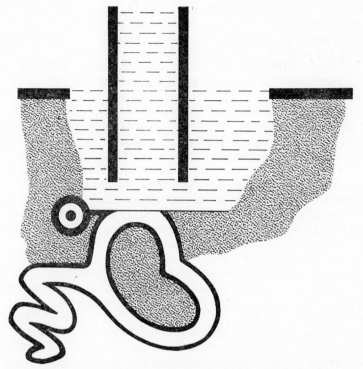

Fig. 8. . The Arslan technique for the ultrasonic surgery of Ménière's Disease. The closed loop on the right is composed of the semicircular canals. The bony wall has been thinned where the transducer is applied. Note that the cochlea, the spiral to the left of the canals, is unlikely to receive much energy while the facial nerve (above) is liable to be damaged by a divergent beam from the large transducer shown but not by one that covers only the thinned bone

rotate to one side. As soon as the effect on vision becomes significant the brain corrects the deviation which however is repeated so long as the stimulation continues. The rhythmic twitching movement of the eye is called 'nystagmus.'

Ultrasonic irradiation through the endolymph at first stimulates the sense organs giving what is called irritative nystagmus. When however the sense organs have ceased to function the twitches reverse their direction and this is called paralytic nystagmus. The usual practice is to select a dose that does not stimulate the sense organs too much at first as this would cause severe giddiness and perhaps vomiting. On the other hand the dose should be sufficient to initiate the destructive process. The power level can be increased later if need be.

After a variable time measured in minutes the change from irritative to paralytic nystagmus occurs. It is necessary to continue for some time after this as the damage may still be of a temporary nature. Total irradiation time of the order of 10 to 20 minutes is aimed at.

After irradiation the operation cavity is closed and the patient returns to bed. The nystagmus continues for a variable period but the interesting feature is that if caloric testing is applied next day there is almost always a normal response. On average it takes two weeks for the caloric response to disappear completely and the interval has been known to take as long as eight weeks. This delayed action is evidence either that the action of ultrasound cannot be a simple thermal action or that the action is an indirect one.

The major problem in research of this type is the practical impossibility of making observations on what is actually happening inside the temporal bone in a human being. Even when an individual donates his body for medical research it is inevitably some considerable time from the actual moment of death to the removal of the specimen and even if this period is short it is not possible to introduce preservative into the cavity of the inner ear without damaging it. In such circumstances the tissues tend to soften and disintegrate through the natural process called 'autolysis' so that when the tissues finally reach the microscope in the form of a thin wafer of decalcified tissue the results are of little value.

The development of the Royal Ear Hospital Tranducer presented the ethical problem of how to test a new instrument satisfactorily before using it on a patient. Other instruments had been tested on cats and dogs but in these animals the separation of cochlea from semicircular canals is so small that both were destroyed.

For a proper test it was necessary to find an animal which had a temporal bone approximately the same size as the human and with sufficiently similar anatomy. After studying domestic animals the writer decided that the cow was the closest match to the human available. Later workers have suggested that a better approximation is obtainable by using the giraffe or the lion but these are clearly unsuitable in other ways!

The use of a cow is fully described elsewhere.[4,5] The experiment confirmed that the major damage was to the epithelium and the nerve cells that project into the lymph while the nerves lying in the bony wall had escaped so far as could be seen (Plate 8.1).

From the physicist's point of view it is difficult to assess the exact method of transmission. Considering the high absorption by bone it must be assumed that only the ultrasound that passes through the place where the bone is very thin plays any effective part (Fig. 8.2). The Bristol workers have stressed the advantage of using a non-divergent beam and for this reason use 3 Mc/s rather than 1 Mc/s. While divergence is obviously á serious matter with a large 5 mm applicator as it endangers the facial nerve, it would seem reasonable to assume that with the smaller applicator a divergent beam would send a larger amount of energy round the wave-guide formed by the bony canal and a smaller amount would be converted into heat in the further side of the canal opposite the point of entry.

There can be assumed to be a wave-guide action because of the very small dose that has a demonstrable effect when compared with brain experiments. How such a complicated geometry affects the propagation of ultrasound is very uncertain and experiments to elucidate the point are

170

planned by the writer. However it is reasonable to assume that with a closed loop containing a liquid of low attenuation considerable interference occurs as the energy travels round and round in both directions until completely converted into heat. In such circumstances there must be many nodes and antinodes and how these occur relative to the sense organs is a matter of chance. It is therefore recommended that the transducer should be rocked through a small angle during irradiation to cause the sites of nodes and antinodes to shift.

No surgeon has done a large enough series under standardized conditions with only the frequency changed to permit a true assessment to be made of the effect of frequency. The writer has an open mind on the subject but regards the lower frequency as likely to prove rather better.

The risk of damage to the facial nerve undoubtedly was predominantly a matter of the conduction of heat from the solid metal rod in the earlier series of cases. With the reduction of size to 2 or $2\frac{1}{2}$ mm at the point of application and the use of water as the conducting material, the risk to the facial nerve was lessened but it still remains possible for a direct ultrasonic action to paralyse the nerve and of course some heating of bone must occur through the conversion of ultrasound. The skill of the surgeon in identifying the bony canal that carries the nerve is the only real protection.

In recent years Arslan[6] has applied a very small transducer directly on the round and oval windows obtaining good results with much less radiation.

8.6 PITUITARY IRRADIATION

Very recently Arslan has published the second application of ultrasonic transducers of this 'type, the irradiation of the pituitary gland.[7] This arises in three ways in medicine. The pituitary is one of the most important of the endocrine glands and appears to have a controlling effect on the growth of many organs. It has been found that the removal of the gland or the abolition of its secretion of hormones has a very significant effect on many of the forms of carcinoma that occur in the organs that it normally controls, particularly the breast, ovary and uterus.

More recently it has been found that reduction in pituitary function also benefits patients with diabetic retinitis. This is a rare complication of diabetes that often goes on to complete blindness once it has begun to affect a patient.

Thirdly there are the tumours that arise in the pituitary itself which differ in their effects according to the particular group of cells in which they arise. Here of course the treatment is directly applied to the abnormal cells.

The treatment of tumours of the pituitary is now almost always a surgical removal. This can be performed in two ways the more usual route being by opening the skull quite extensively, gently raising the brain from

171

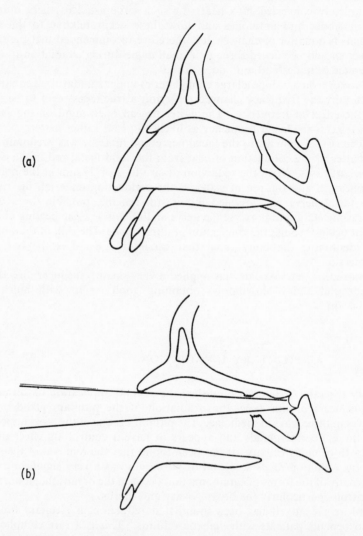

(a)

(b)

Fig. 8.3. The Arslan technique for the ultrasonic surgery of the pituitary. (a) Normal anatomy showing the relationship of the sphenoidal sinus to the pituitary fossa. (b) The removal of two small pieces of bone permits the applicator to reach the dura mater covering the pituitary

the floor of the skull and then scooping the gland out from above (Fig. 8.3). The more recently introduced technique is to operate through the nose, removing the front wall of the sphenoidal air sinus first, then the bony anterior wall of the pituitary fossa.

The cranial cavity is lined throughout with dura mater, a strong fibrous membrane that is usually closely applied to the skull bone just as is the periosteum in long bones. The dura mater however continues as an unbroken protecting layer down the canal that passes almost to the lower end of the spine and contains the spinal cord. The dura mater also has various additional folds that to some extent divide the cranial cavity into compartments.

To remove the pituitary through the nose it is inevitable that the dura mater should be opened. When removing it from above, the dura below the gland is left intact. To repair the damage when the operation is performed by the nasal route, it is usual to plug the opening with a piece of muscle. This is not always satisfactory and undoubtedly the risk of infection entering the cranial cavity from the nose and the risk that the cerebro-fluid from above will leak into the nose, have both militated against this type of operation.

Furthermore there are on either side of the fossa large venous blood reservoirs known as the cavernous sinuses. It is not uncommon for one or other of these to extend far enough round the front of the pituitary for the surgeon to open it during the operation.

When the palliative treatment of carcinoma was introduced it was not always necessary to remove the whole gland physically. Active glandular tissue like the pituitary is susceptible to ionizing radiation. It was therefore possible as an alternative to abolish function without physical removal. Neutron bombardment has been used but in general it has become a common technique to implant small seeds of radioactive matter usually Yttrium.

This can be done also in two ways. Either a small hole is made in the top of the skull and a hollow tube passed right down through the brain to reach the fossa and then the seeds are pushed through it and the tube withdrawn or a similar procedure is performed through the nose.

All these procedures are serious hazards for a patient in most cases expected to die of carcinoma in the fairly near future. The nasal route involves less serious surgery but even with isotope seeds the risk of infection tells against it.

With the technique introduced by Arslan one can combine the best of both techniques for it is not necessary to open the dura mater. Once the bone is removed, the ultrasound can be applied directly to the dura and even if the cavernous sinus is interposed this has virtually no attenuating effect and there is of course no risk of bleeding.

Arslan's technique was to use his 5 mm transducer tip and move it over the anterior surface of the gland to distribute the dose. The Royal Ear Hospital Transducer can be used with any geometry of applicator and as is described elsewhere[5] this has been tried out on cat brain.

Behind the pituitary fossa there is one of the most important parts of the brain which contains those centres that control functions essential to life such as breathing, circulation etc. Arslan relied on the bony posterior wall of the fossa to protect the brain stem but it is suggested when the technique is used on patients one should reinforce this protection by introducing air by a needle in the lumbar spine. Air injected in this way is routinely used to fill the ventricles of the brain in X ray investigations of the brain. If however the chin is raised the air always passes to the back of the pituitary fossa. Air of course acts as a complete protection as total reflection of ultrasound occurs at any fluid-gas interface.

It should be stressed that this technique has only as yet been used on a limited number of patients and some animals. It will probably take some years to win acceptance but on first principles it would appear to be the method of choice.

8.7 ULTRASONIC NEURO-SURGERY

The ability to focus ultrasound to a sharp point has been known for many years and Fry and his co-workers have been applying this to neuro-surgery for over a decade. Naturally the early work was all on animals but more recently a series of operations on patients has been published.

Neuro-surgery is of course the surgery of the nervous system and it may at first seem surprising that anyone needs to have part of his or her brain destroyed. As already mentioned there are parts of the brain that are vital and no surgeon dare operate on them. There are however quite large parts of the brain that can be dispensed with without loss of ability. In the early days brain surgery was virtually restricted to the removal of tumours that were pressing on the brain from outside, the control of bleeding arteries and the removal of blood clots.

The next stage was to diagnose and then remove tumours that occurred within the brain. This was only possible in the upper part of the brain at first but later the cerebellum, the small projecting portion behind the brain stem concerned with balance, was able to be operated upon.

In an earlier chapter the all-or-none response of the nerve cell has been mentioned. This compares quite well with the function of a univibrator or a thyratron. In the brain where there are a vast multitude of nerve cells all coupled to other nerve cells by numerous nerve fibres and all with the same all-or-none response pattern, it is not surprising that it is quite easy for feedback to produce a multivibrator phenomenon. Some degree of feedback is always taking place so that the tension in the muscles in the front of the legs is adjusted to balance the tension in the muscles in the back of the legs keeping the legs straight and the person standing erect.

It will come as no surprise that occasionally this smooth balancing act gives way to a fierce 'motorboating' at a low frequency if the standing bias drifts to a critical level. In medicine this shows up as a muscular tremor or twitch.

The disease known as Parkinsonism is the one that has received by far the largest amount of interest. In this for reasons often quite unexplained, the nerve cells become much more easily triggered than usual, as if they had lost most of their negative bias and pass easily from being monovibrators to being multivibrators. The result is that there is a much greater permanent stiffness of the muscles and any attempt to perform some muscular action results in a coarse tremor that often makes such necessary actions as drinking from a cup impossible, as the contents are shaken out long before they can be swallowed.

Cooper of New York noticed that this tremor was stopped if certain parts of the brain were put out of action. From this original observation the whole subject of 'stereotaxic surgery' became of clinical importance.

Stereotaxic surgery was first put on a sound basis as long ago as 1908 when Horsley and Clark established how any desired point in the cat's brain could be reached with an electrode by dead reckoning in three dimensions. The cat's skull was fixed rigidly by conical rods inserted in the outer ears and hooks pressing on the lower margins of the orbits. From these fixed points on the skull, standard reference planes and points were laid down and the various structures in the cat's brain were given three dimensional code references in millimetres. In spite of the early date of this work it is still accepted as the standard throughout the world though naturally some structures have had to be given fresh coordinates.

One of the reasons for the success of this technique is undoubtedly the fact that cats once fully grown show a uniformity in their brain size that is quite remarkable when one considers the extent to which their heads appear to differ. Furthermore the variation in brain anatomy from cat to cat is slight.

Unfortunately other animals and in particular man show much less consistency. Dogs vary vastly in size from the St. Bernard to the Pekinese for example. No comparable standard atlas is therefore possible. Human anatomy is even more variable not merely in the shape of the skull and hence of the brain but much more seriously because of the inconstancy of the internal anatomy of the brain.

Fortunately the feedback path which is affected in Parkinsonism passes through the Globus Pallidus and some parts of the Thalamus and if the appropriate cells in these structures are destroyed it is possible to abolish the stiffness and the tremor without interfering with the normal voluntary movements of the part of the body concerned. Equally fortunately it is possible to establish the site of these structures with good accuracy by their relationship to the ventricles.

The other place in the brain where it was found to be of value to destroy what appeared to be normal nerve cells and fibres was in the very front of the brain. It was found that the cutting of certain nerve tracts broke a vicious circle in patients suffering from abnormal anxiety states. Regrettably this procedure became excessively popular in psychiatric circles and indiscriminate tract cutting resulted in more widespread effects than were desired. There has been an inevitable reaction and many have abandoned the procedure altogether. There can however be no doubt that with careful selection of cases and experienced surgeons it is possible to benefit patients without unwanted character changes.

The operation of 'leucotomy' or 'lobotomy' has always been performed with a knife. The 'pallidectomy' for Parkinsonism has been performed in several ways. Three of these are in common use, the injection of alcohol, electro-coagulation and 'cryogenic' lesions. The last is the introduction of a needle with a minute refrigerator in its tip. This can be cooled down to a temperature where it abolishes function temporarily or alternatively to a much lower temperature which kills the adjacent cells as frostbite does.

The knife is the most certain of methods but of course if too many fibres are cut nothing can be done to make them good. The deep situation of the Globus Pallidus rules out the conventional knife. The cryogenic technique gives a trial stage. Alcohol injection can be preceded by injection of novocain to give a similar trial stage. Electro-coagulation lacks this and makes it more like a knife. However stimulation and recording from the electrodes help to verify their correct position so there is little to choose between the methods.

Unfortunately none of these techniques gives a lesion of exactly predictable size even though its site may be known to be correct. Further any of them may involve the destruction of a small artery and cause the death of other cells that should be preserved.

Ultrasound gives promise of being able to meet these objections. Lindstrom in the U.S.A.[8] has used a plane wave transducer to irradiate the frontal region and has now performed the procedure so often and over such a long period that he has obtained post-mortem specimens on several occasions. It seems probable that with a large target of this nature he has been able to obtain reversible lesions and yet cure the patient. It will be interesting to see how this work is explained in purely physical terms as Lindstrom has produced areas of necrosis deep in the brain without focusing.

The classic work of Fry and Meyers[9] employed four focused transducers with their foci accurately superimposed. Though this produced a very spherical focus, it required a very large total solid angle though the total solid angle of the four crystals and their polystyrene lenses was not large. It was thus necessary to remove a very large amount of the vault of the skull if lesions were to be made at any depth. These cases were mainly those of Parkinsonism with a minority of pituitary gland irradiations for palliation of carcinoma elsewhere. The removal of such a large amount of bone deprived the brain of its normal support and allowed it to move much more than a normal brain could. It is not surprising that the results compared unfavourably with the established methods and the series was discontinued. Similarly with the irradiation of the pituitary fossa from above the rays had to pass through important cranial nerves just before reaching the fossa. There were in consequence complications from damage to these nerves. It is very unlikely that the interlocking beam array will become accepted practice.

The use of a single source makes it possible to utilize virtually the whole solid angle of skull opening available. Fry has always used this for animal experiments[9] and Ballantine,[10] and his co-workers have used it for animals and a limited number of patients.

176

There can be no doubt that this makes an admirable tool for animal experiments in neuro-physiology. The absence of a track and the ability to spare the blood-vessels makes it preferable to any other method.

For man however it is necessary to establish first that a new technique has a significant advantage over any existing technique before one can expect a clinician to agree to its use. The existing techniques for Parkinsonism are so good that one cannot reasonably advocate their replacement by ultrasound. There are however neuro-surgical problems that seem suitable for ultrasound where surgery at present is not even attempted.

The only condition where good results have been obtained already is in 'stump neuromas.' When a limb is amputated its nerves have to be cut through. In the course of time these nerves attempt to regrow along their original paths. This is naturally impossible and there forms a mass of nerve fibres in the stump that is very tender and make the fitting of an artificial limb difficult. Ultrasound has proved more satisfactory than surgery in dealing with these stump neuromas.

The spinal cord travels down the canal in the centre of the vertebral column giving off nerves both sensory and motor to the trunk and limbs. Sometimes when there is incurable disease it is necessary to prevent the pain sensation from reaching the brain. This can be done by cutting some nerve fibres in the spinal cord. This is usually done by a knife but it is now beginning to be done by ultrasound. The ability to cause destruction within the cord without cutting the surface fibres, is a new tool for the surgeon and has considerable possible value.

Sometimes tumours occur deep in the brain in places where they are covered by structures needed for an important function such as speech. In these cases surgeons normally do not operate as the loss of speech or some such function is considered too mutilating particularly as brain tumours are usually very slow growing. The ability to cause necrosis in the deep tumour tissue while leaving the important superficial structure undamaged, represents a welcome addition to the surgeon's tools.

Furthermore there are places like the brain stem where no surgeon dare operate at all. Here the possibility of being able to shrink down a tumour arises, though of course it will be long before ultrasonic surgery can be expected to be applied with the confidence such a technique would require.

Very recently a further possibility has been shown by the writer to be possible. This makes the attack on dangerous sites more promising. It has been shown that the highly focused transducer of ceramic developed for lesion-making can be operated as a diagnostic instrument. This has been described elsewhere at length[11,12]. It permits the demonstration of the internal anatomy of the brain in three dimensions automatically by writing out on teledeltos paper those echoes that occur at the time corresponding to the focus and ignoring all others by suitable gates. By a parallelogram pantograph the write-out of a small structure like the spinal cord could be two or three times larger than the structure.

Once the cross-sectional anatomy has been demonstrated the part composed of tumour tissue can be assessed from knowledge of what the normal anatomy would look like. The focus is then set for places in tumour tissue and high power delivered by the same transducer can destroy any desired volume of tissue.

The inherent technical problem of this technique is that for diagnosis the transducer needs to be of low Q with heavy damping to obtain short pulses while for power generation a high Q undamped transducer is needed for efficiency. These conflicting requirements at first seemed to demand that two transducers would be needed with their foci adjusted to have the same relationships to the mount so that after using the damped transducer to demonstrate the anatomy, one could replace by the undamped transducer for surgery and yet have the same accuracy of positioning for the focus.

Recently however it has been discovered that even though a ceramic bowl has a natural frequency of 1 Mc/s and is undamped it is possible to obtain pulses of the higher harmonics sufficiently short to be acceptable. Operation at 1 Mc/s with the same transducer gives a pulse length equivalent to two or three centimetres of water.

8.8 OPHTHALMIC SURGERY

As mentioned in Chapter 5 there are tumours that occur at the back of the eye which can be diagnosed by ultrasound. Naturally enough the combined diagnostic and surgical transducer technique may have applications in this field. At present much research is being devoted to develop lasers to produce small focal lesions at the back of the eye but coherent light is still light and though it will attain very high intensities it still cannot penetrate opaque matter. On general principles it seems likely that ultrasound has inherent advantages for the treatment of tumours but as yet no clinical work has been attempted so far as is known.

There is less expectation that ultrasound will compete favourably with the laser in the surgery of detachments of the retina. The laser has also already been used to destroy small areas of the retina with some success. Here the important thing is that the healing reaction should cause scarring that unites the retina to the outer wall of the eye. Laser lesions are open to the objection that each lesion is very small indeed. On the other hand ultrasound's great advantage of sparing the blood vessels makes it less likely to produce the sort of healing reaction that is needed.

8.9 OTHER SURGICAL POSSIBILITIES

Ultrasound has been used in biological experiments by Bell[13] to separate layers of embryonic tissues from one another but it is doubtful if this has applications in clinical medicine. Lesions have been produced in liver in animals and Janes[14] has treated bone sarcoma in dogs. Neither seems likely to become the basis of clinical procedures. Liver tissue seldom needs removal and if it did would be removed much more easily in other ways.

178

An unfocused beam would be too indiscriminate while the sharply focal lesion a millimetre or two in size would be very tedious in use for destroying large masses of tissue.

One cannot exclude further developments but in all frankness it seems unlikely that there will be any large field of use apart from the nervous system.

REFERENCES

1. BASS, A. L., Personal communication (1966).
2. GORDON, D., *Ultrasound as a Diagnostic and Surgical Tool*, 33, Livingstone, Edinburgh (1964).
3. ARSLAN, M., *Ultrasound as a Diagnostic and Surgical Tool*, 288, Livingstone, Edinburgh (1964).
4. FORMBY, M. L., 'Ultrasonic destruction of the labyrinth,' *Acta oto-laryngol. Suppl.*, **56**, 139 (1963).
5. GORDON, D., 'Studies in the measurement of ultrasonic energy and its effects on nerve tissue,' *Acta oto-Laryngol. Suppl.*, **192**, 175 (1964).
6. ARSLAN, M., 'The Ultrasonic Selective Irradiation either of the Oval or of the Round Window,' *Bull. Soc. Ital. Fon. E. Audiologia*, **15**, 1–21, (1966).
7. ARSLAN, M. 'Ultrasonic Hypophysectomy,' *J. Laryng.* **80**, 73, (1964).
8. LINDSTROM, P. A., 'Prefrontal ultrasonic irradiation—substitution for lobotomy,' *Arch. Neurol. Psychiat. (Chic)*, **72**, 399 (1954).
9. FRY, W. J., MEYERS, R., FRY, F. J., SCHULTZ, D. F., DREYER, L. L. and NOYAS, R. F., 'Topical differentia of pathogentic mechanisms underlying Parkinsonian tremor and rigidity as indicated by ultrasonic irradiation of the human brain,' *Trans. Amer. Neurol. Ass.*, 16 (1958).
10. BALLANTINE, H. T., JR., BELL, E. and MANLAPAZ, J., 'Progress and problems in the neurological applications of focused ultrasound,' *J. Neurosurg.*, **17**, 858 (1960).
11. GORDON, D., *Ultrasound as a Diagnostic and Surgical Tool*, 233, Livingstone, Edinburgh (1964).
12. GORDON, D., 'The limitations and uses of ultrasound in localizing cerebral lesions,' *Proc. Roy. Soc. Med.*, **58**, 1058 (1965).
13. BELL, E., 'Removal of embryonic layers with ultrasound,' *Anat. Record*, **125**, 622 (1956).
14. JANES, J. M., DAHLIN, D. C., HERRICK, J. F. and HIGGINS, J. M., 'The effect of ultrasonic energy on osteogenic sarcoma: An experimental study,' *Arch. Phys. Med.*, **38c** 148 (1957).

9

EQUIPMENT AND TECHNIQUES IN ULTRASOUND SURGERY

A. E. Crawford, C.Eng., M.I.E.R.E., Sen. M.I.E.E.E.

9.1 INTRODUCTION

The development of ultrasonic equipment for therapeutic and surgical applications has closely followed the progress of ultrasonic applications in industry. In both categories it has been necessary to produce controllable ultrasonic energy with intensities varying from a few watts to many hundreds of watts per square centimetre. Similarly, both applications use basic equipment comprising a transducer in which electrical energy is converted to acoustic energy, and an electronic generator for producing electrical energy at the correct frequency to energize the transducer.

As in all branches of electronics advantage has been taken of the development of new devices, materials and techniques. Transistorized generators have tended to replace valve circuits and piezoelectric ceramics are used instead of quartz crystals. The rapid growth of applications in the immediate post war period has now settled down to a more ordered advancement in both applications and equipment and this is reflected in the careful design of modern ultrasonic therapeutic apparatus. However, unlike most industrial applications the time-energy factor is highly critical when ultrasonic energy is used for surgery. There are many difficulties in the precise measurement of high power acoustic energy at any frequency and this is generally complicated in medical applications. The propagation of ultrasonic energy at intensities below the cavitation threshold in liquids usually follows a linear relationship, but when this threshold is reached the characteristics become non-linear. It has been shown that plane wave propagation over an infinite path length follows established laws of divergence and attenuation. The human body possesses no such path length and represents a conglomerate of varying acoustic impedances, wave guides and tortuous acoustic channels.

180

In all applications of acoustic energy the important factor is the amount of energy experienced at a particular point in the propagation path and not necessarily the total amount of energy being dissipated at the face of the transducer. Almost all biological effects depend on the acoustic energy intensity per unit area and this value may vary widely over a complex propagation path. As an example, consider the simple case of a tapered liquid filled tube in which the tube walls totally reflect all acoustic energy back into the liquid. If a standing wave formation is neglected and with a transducer propagating a wave from a large diameter to a smaller diameter the unit area energy will progressively increase as a ratio of the areas. This means that intensities below cavitation level may be increased to values well above this limit. In certain medical applications this can be dangerous as the high energy concentrations can produce rapid local heating due to acoustic absorption. In other cases this can be advantageously used to obtain cellular destruction at a point remote from the transducer without appreciable physical effect on the intervening medium.

It has been shown that the acoustic impedance of a medium is the factor determining the efficiency of transfer of acoustic energy from one medium to another. When this factor differs widely the boundary layer between the two media represents a barrier to efficient propagation and the inefficiency is manifested in the form of localized heating.

Both principles are used in ultrasonic surgery and equipment has been specifically designed to take advantage of them.

9.2 BASIC EQUIPMENT DESIGN

The generation of ultrasonic energy is usually based on the conversion of electrical power to acoustic energy and invariably consists of an electrical frequency converter and a transducer. The transducer is usually operated at its fundamental resonant frequency and this is determined by specific physical dimensions of the element. Deviations from the frequency will largely affect the acoustic output power and also materially alter the propagation pattern. Thus, the initial criterion for the electrical supply is frequency stability if it is a tunable system, or the use of a feedback circuit designed to maintain a matching frequency under any external influences on the transducer.

As with any form of energy used in medicine or surgery it is essential to be able to monitor and control the magnitude of the output. In many cases, there is a cumulative effect and the degree of magnitude will have a relationship to dosage time. There are many inherent difficulties in accurately measuring ultrasonic energy in terms of absolute units, particularly under non-linear conditions of operation. However, absolute measurements are not essential for general usage and arbitary units can be used, when there is an assurance of stability in the relationship between the acoustic output and the parameter being measured.

All ultrasonic surgical equipment operates in the frequency band of 0·5 Mc/s to 5 Mc/s. This frequency range requires the use of electronic oscillators for generation and both valve and semiconductor circuits are employed in modern equipment. It should be emphasized that the use of valves instead of transistors is not necessarily a retrograde step as the transistor still has certain limitations, particularly where high output powers are required. A valve circuit is inherently simple as the components can be subjected to considerable overloads without permanent damage. A transistor is designed to operate efficiently at levels near the maximum rating and overloading often destroys the device. Thus, the semiconductor generator must contain a complexity of circuits solely incorporated to protect stategic components. The cost is increased and there is a greater possibility of unreliability on the basis of the larger number of circuit elements.

The characteristics of a transducer under electrical drive vary considerably with the type of transducer material and the physical dimensions. To obtain efficient acoustic outputs the generator output circuit must be matched to the transducer. Although it is possible to provide a wide range of output conditions from a particular oscillator, it has become standard practice to provide a generator that produces power for a specific transducer. Since the transducer may well be individually designed for only one purpose it is generally found that the two units are designated as a complete equipment for performing only one function. With the present state of knowledge on ultrasonic surgical techniques this is highly desirable as factors such as power levels and dosage rates do not necessarily apply when generators or transducers are interchanged. Further work on measurements in absolute units will probably enable this stage to be reached.

9.3 EQUIPMENT

During the past decade a great many specialized ultrasonic generators and transducers have been described covering specific uses in surgery. They were usually experimental in nature and have been used for various investigations in techniques. Early efforts to develop a universal equipment were not fully acceptable to the surgeon and a study of the required surgical techniques revealed the necessity for a more positive design approach based on operational experience. Several units were specifically engineered for specific operations, but of these, only one has been generally accepted. This is the operation for selective destruction of the vestibular end organ in the treatment of Ménière's disease. A number of equipments are now commercially available and have the same fundamental principles, but differ in the design and complexity.

The second field of ultrasonic neurosurgery must still be considered as experimental, although several equipments have been designed for this purpose and successfully demonstrated.

Both applications have a similar goal in the destruction of nervous tissue but differ widely in the equipment design. The applicator for Ménière's disease treatment takes advantage of the natural wave guide properties of the semicircular canals, as a means for accurately locating the build-up of ultrasonic energy. With brain surgery the energy is often required to pass through intervening tissue without producing damage and the positioning becomes critical.

It is not proposed to discuss the many proposed experimental designs but to restrict descriptions of equipment to well established apparatus that has been successfully operated. Both the above fields of use embody the basic principles found in all ultrasonic surgical equipments.

9.4 MÉNIÈRE'S DISEASE EQUIPMENT

The Bristol Hospital generator is essentially a high frequency oscillator in which frequency stability and constancy of output has been achieved by the use of several unique circuit features.[1,2,3] The complete equipment is shown in Plate 9.1. A thermistor thermometer circuit is included in the equipment and dosage time is indicated by a clock with resetting facilities.

Referring to the circuit diagram in Fig. 9.1,[4] the mains supply is fed to the input transformer via a switch and fuse, a pilot lamp indicating the switch position. D.C. power is produced by a well smoothed rectifier circuit, the resistor R_9 being incorporated to prevent overvoltage on C_3 when r.f. power is switched off.

Output power from the oscillator is varied by control of the D.C. voltage and this is carried out using a series valve V_1. The bias on this valve is separately supplied by an additional winding on the mains transformer and rectifier D_3. Potentiometer VR_1 varies the bias voltage. Full transient suppression is formed by the network R_1 and C_1.

A safety circuit consisting of R_{19} and the relay RLY_1 controls the supply voltage to the oscillator. Should the bias circuit fail allowing full H.T. to be applied the relay de-energizes and opens the cathode circuit of V_1, completely cutting off the H.T. supply.

S_2 also isolates the oscillator supply and is in series with links on the probe equalizer plugs. This prevents operation of the equipment if the probe equalizers are not inserted.

The oscillator consists of a tuned anode circuit using two valves V_2 and V_3 in parallel. The tank coil L_1 is parallel tuned by VC_1 with feedback applied by coil L_2. A trimmer capacitor C_Y enables the mid scale frequency of 3·5 Mc/s to be set up. The output is series capacitor coupled to the transducer and a potentiometer tap across it is rectified to form a D.C. voltage measured by a meter. This is calibrated in terms of power per unit area (W/cm²) and has been established by a direct measurement of the radiated power. Since the probe frequency and efficiency varies with different transducer elements, it is necessary to match the characteristics to that of the generator. Equalizer plugs are provided with each probe and these contain a selected capacitor and resistor. The capacitance adjusts the generator frequency to provide approximately the mid range of the tuning control. The resistance sets the output meter to give a correct reading for the particular probe used.

183

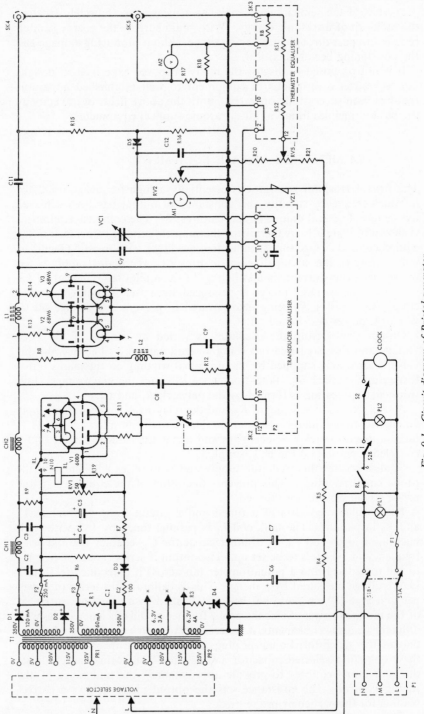

Fig. 9.1. Circuit diagram of Bristol generator

Plate 9.1. Ultrasonic therapy equipment for treatment of Ménières Disease. (Courtesy Elliott Bros. (London) Ltd.)

Plate 9.2. Friston ultrasonic generator for general surgical use

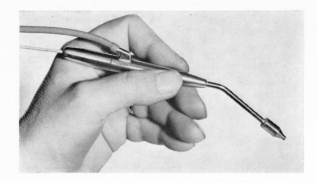

Plate 9.3. Bristol transducer

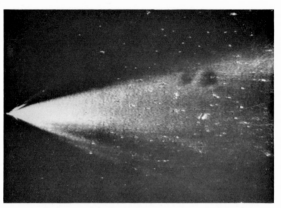

Plate 9.4. Schlieren photograph of radiation from Bristol transducer

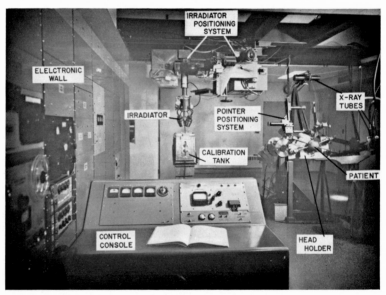

Plate 9.5. Irradiation room at the Biophysical Research Laboratory, University of Illinois

The thermometer circuit consists of a simple bridge in which the thermistor forms one arm. D.C. power for the bridge circuit is stabilized with a zener diode. Each thermistor probe is preset with an equalizer plug to match the meter calibration.

The CAL generator is basically similar but is somewhat less complicated and is based on transistors instead of valves.[5] The first two stages are conventional consisting of a variable amplitude and frequency oscillator followed by a buffer push-pull stage. The design of the Class B output stage is determined by the electrical parameters of the transducer and a π network is used to match these characteristics. The particular output transistor used and the value of the resistive component of the transducer equivalent circuit necessitates a large value of shunt capacity to match the load. This capacity reduces the effect of variations in the capacitive transducer component. A regulated power supply holds the output constant under normal operating conditions and the output intensity is varied by a potentiometer. Output power is indicated by measurement of the D.C. collector current in the output stage and a calibration curve is supplied for each probe. A separate electric clock shows dosage time. The circuit diagram is given in Fig. 9.2.

Two further generators are currently available, both using valves in the main circuit functions. The Friston generator has been designed as a versatile supply of high frequency electrical power and can be used in conjunction with a wide range of transducers.[6] This unit is shown in Plate 9.2. It consists of two circuit modules, each of which can be changed to suit different transducers. A conventional power supply provides smoothed D.C. to a Class C oscillator comprising two small transmitting valves and a tapped tank coil. The tapping position can be varied to suit the impedance of different transducers. The tank coil and its associated tuning capacitor constitutes one module and is replaced when the transducer is changed.

The Class C power stage is driven at varying frequencies by a tetrode oscillator valve. The output is adjustable in amplitude by controlling the screen grid voltage.

Due to changes in valve characteristics it is necessary to provide a tuning indicator. While a diode voltmeter could be employed to read the output obtained from a separate electrode on the transducer crystal, this is not found to give a reliable indication of acoustic output. A more satisfactory indication is given by controlling the phase angle, where the resistance component equals the reactance at resonance. A cathode ray tube is used for this purpose and the Lissajous figure becomes a straight line when peak tuning is reached. To achieve this it is necessary to introduce a phase-shift network between the transducer cable and the tube deflector plates. The capacitance and resistance used for this purpose can be pre-set for different transducers and cables. When the phase angle is constant the diode voltmeter gives an accurate indication of power in spite of variations of crystal temperature. The second interchangeable module consists of the oscillator tuned circuit, and the tuning indicator phase-shift circuits.

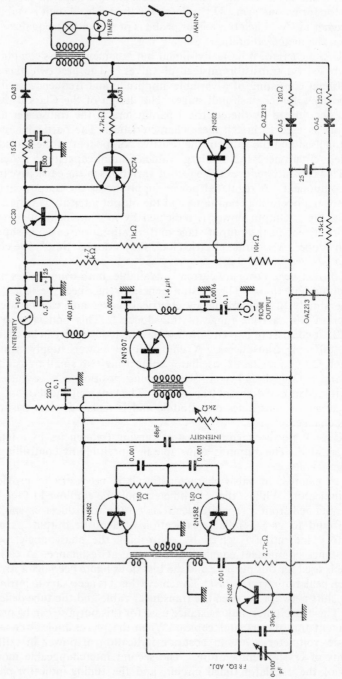

Fig. 9.2. *Circuit diagram of CAL generator*

Self-tuning is possible with this generator by using the generated signal obtained from a second electrode on the transducer. The main oscillator frequency and the feed-back frequency are phase-shifted to compensate for the cable capacity and then compared in a phase discriminator circuit. A D.C. potential can be produced that is proportional to the phase difference. This is used to modify the value of a variable capacitance transistor in the oscillator circuit and thus alter the output frequency to maintain resonant conditions.

The feed-back voltage may also be used to control the oscillator screen voltage whenever the former exceeds a predetermined level.

The Federici Generator was the first ultrasonic equipment specifically produced for work on tissue destruction.[7] Basically a simple Hartley oscillator using a large transmitter valve, the output was designed to operate with a quartz crystal requiring high voltage. The tank coil was used as a Tesla coil to obtain 3,500 V peak at the 1 Mc/s frequency normally required. A meter on the control panel is scaled to read watts per square centimetre but in fact this is a measurement of D.C. current in the oscillator valve. There are few circuit refinements such as overload safeguards for the transducer, but it should be remembered that the design originated in 1953.

9.5 TRANSDUCERS

As described, the electronic generators employ conventional circuits with some modifications to enable stability to be improved or feedback to be incorporated. The designs are largely dictated by available components and thus little modification is possible. It is in the design of transducers where individuality is shown by the physicist and surgeon and a number of transducers are available that differ widely in construction. In terms of ultrasonic surgery the transducer must be as small as possible to avoid masking the operating area, but at the same time the acoustic beam produced should be completely identifiable without stray radiation or variable power densities. The assembly must be robust, capable of complete sterilization, light in weight and electrically safe. For convenience in use it is desirable to incorporate saline irrigation and also some form of temperature measurement at the operating head.

The early Federici transducer used a quartz crystal element of circular form with a diameter of 4·1 cm. This is acoustically coupled to a conical concentrating velocity transformer ending in a cylindrical sleeved rod 5 mm in diameter. The sleeve provides an air gap in an attempt to reduce side radiation from the rod. The assembly is mounted in a pistol-grip applicator and circulating water cools the rear of the crystal chamber. The complete transducer is bulky and inefficient in operation, but despite these limitations many successful operations have been performed using the Federici equipment. Modifications to the applicator head have been reported but there are inherent disadvantages in the use of quartz crystals in combination with a solid velocity transformer. The use of a solid metal cone introduces inefficiencies due to transmission losses and this produces

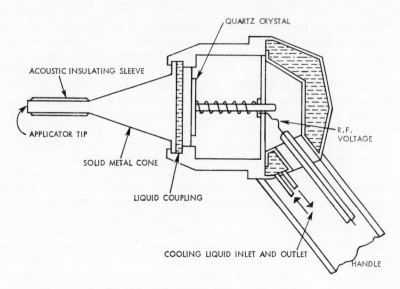

Fig. 9.3. *Federici transducer construction*

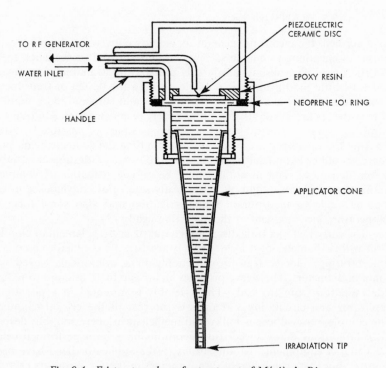

Fig. 9.4. *Friston transducer for treatment of Ménière's Disease*

heating within the structure. Apart from the possible effects on tissue in contact with the hot metal, the temperature rise alters acoustic characteristics in the cone by length variations due to expansion. The general construction is shown in Fig. 9.3.

The transducer developed by the Royal Ear Hospital and used in conjunction with the Friston generator is a considerable improvement on the Federici as it uses lead zirconate-titanate piezoelectric ceramic instead of quartz.[8] This permits lower operating voltages to be used with greater safety for the operator and patient. Instead of a solid metal velocity transformer, the cone and extended tip are hollow. Saline solution circulates continuously through the cone, passing out of the tip into the operating cavity. The construction is shown in Fig. 9.4. The overall size is still comparable with the Federici, but the greatly extended tip allows the surgeon a full view of the operating zone. It is claimed that the large dimensions enable an operator to change applicator cones or even the transducer element while wearing rubber gloves. No attempt is made to reduce side radiation by sleeving the probe tube, but the technique in use is not to flood the operating cavity. A sucker tube is placed in the cavity to restrict the amount of saline and thus there is no direct transmission of energy at points remote from the tip.

The transducer can operate at either 1 or 3 Mc/s without changing the crystal. It is only necessary to change the coil modules in the generator. It can also operate with large fields for pituitary surgery.

Both the Bristol Hospital and the CAL transducers are of a compact pencil sized design, using very small ceramic transducer elements.

The CAL applicator has a piezoelectric ceramic element shaped as a focusing bowl, the diameter of the bowl being 5 mm. A conical chamber is positioned over the bowl with an open tip of 1·87 mm. Saline solution is held in the chamber of capilliary action. No attempt is made to incorporate continuous irrigation or temperature measurement.[5]

The Bristol Hospital design, shown in Plate 9.3 is perhaps the most sophisticated of the present applicators and incorporates a number of features not found in other probes.[2] The transducer element is a plane faced disc of lead zirconate-titanate ceramic 5 mm in diameter and resonating at a frequency of 3 Mc/s. A hollow cone with a short straight tip is fitted to act as a concentrator and the cone is double skinned to provide an air gap. This design permits complete immersion in saline with elimination of side radiation. Saline solution is fed into the body of the applicator and issues through a concentric channel round the transducer element into the cone. This cools the element and also provides irrigation in the operation cavity. The cone and transducer is secured to an angled tube with the main body constituting a handle. The complete instrument is manufactured from stainless steel and since the transducer element can withstand high temperatures it is possible to sterilize by autoclave. A very small thermistor is mounted on a flexible lead and positioned at the side of the tip to sense the temperature of saline within the operating cavity. This is normally held to one side during the operation to allow the surgeon a full view of the irradiated area. The component parts are shown in Fig. 9.5.

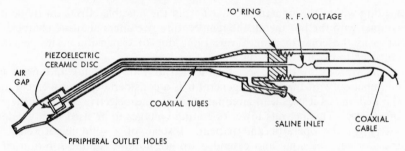

Fig. 9.5. General assembly of Bristol transducer

Schlieren photography shows that the double walled cone completely suppresses any side radiation and the beam divergence is 50°. Since the tip diameter is only 2 mm this divergence is acceptable for normal operating conditions, Plate 9.4. It has been found that 25 W/cm² is a satisfactory acoustic dissipation for most operating techniques and the transducer can adequately handle this power level.

For irradiating the round and oval windows special miniature transducers have been developed by Kossoff and Arslan. As very low power is needed the crystal is applied directly to the tissues without saline cooling.

9.6 ULTRASONIC NEUROSURGICAL EQUIPMENT

Many applications of high power ultrasonic energy for neurosurgery require the destruction of deep tissue without damage to intervening tissue. This necessitates the use of focusing transducers in which individual beam path energies are low enough to pass through tissue layers without producing local damage, but the combined energy at the focus point has an amplitude sufficient to produce lesions. Before the advent of piezoelectric ceramics it was extremely difficult to manufacture focusing bowls but a certain amount of work was carried out using quartz crystal mosaics mounted in bowl form. The ability of piezoelectric ceramic to be preferentially polarized means that a preformed bowl will produce ultrasonic energy normal to any point on the surface. Thus, a bowl will act as a focusing radiator and optical principles can be applied to the design.

An alternative is to use a plane propagating source and concentrate the acoustic energy by means of a lens. A number of plastics can be used for this purpose and several focusing systems have been described in which simple transducers and lenses are employed. A third method uses multiple transducer heads arranged to converge their energy paths at a common point.

In all cases the major problem is not the method of energy generation, but the precise location of the energy combined with adequate intensity control. Since the location involves three dimensional control of the axes of irradiation, the location methods are often complicated. The skull and the position of the brain within it varies widely in size and shape.

It is therefore necessary to employ accurate ventriculography before irradiation to determine dimensional factors and then to map the skull to enable repeatability of positioning relative to the ultrasonic transducer.

9.7 GENERATORS

Ultrasonic energy is required at high intensity over a small area and this means that the power requirements of the generator are relatively low. Most of the experimental work has been carried out with generators providing between 50 W and 250 W of r.f. power.

A typical generator has been described consisting of a tuned anode oscillator designed specifically for good calibration stability, and operates over the range 900 kc/s to 4·5 Mc/s.[9] The use of a triode oscillator value gives a direct relationship between the anode voltage and the r.f. voltage output with a predetermined transducer load and tuning position. By accurately measuring the applied anode voltage before irradiation commences it is possible to set the acoustic output to the required value.

Facilities are available for continuous irradiation over a preset time interval, or intermittent irradiation in short duration pulses. The latter can be adjusted for pulse duration of between 0·005 to 2·0 sec and pulse intervals of 0·1 to 10·0 sec. Radiation can be remotely controlled or automatically triggered by a present pulse counter. Synchronizing pulses are available to operate oscilloscope sweeps or a stimulator.

The coaxial cable coupling the generator to the transducer together with the transducer element forms part of the tank capacitor. The tuning control allows micrometer adjustment of the output frequency for accurate matching and resonance is indicated on a meter. The cathode current in the oscillator valve is monitored with a d.c. milliameter and also traced with a pen recorder. This provides a permanent record of the radiation dosage in terms of the r.f. power output and also records pulse duration and pulse spacing. An audible signal is operated during irradiation.

9.8 TRANSDUCER DESIGN

Transducers for neurosurgery fall into two categories dependent on the focusing means. A plane face piezoelectric element is used in conjunction with acoustic lenses or concentrators. Alternatively, the element is formed into a bowl with a pre-determined focus point. The former are simpler in construction and permit the focal length or the degree of concentration to be changed. The lens material and coupling inefficiencies will limit the power handling capability. A focusing bowl is difficult to manufacture, particularly for frequencies above 1 Mc/s but the absence of coupling surfaces with direct transmission of power enables very high acoustic powers to be produced at the focus. Liquid coupling is always used between the transducer and the skull or exposed brain.

An example of the lens transducer, shown in Fig. 9.6, consists of a

191

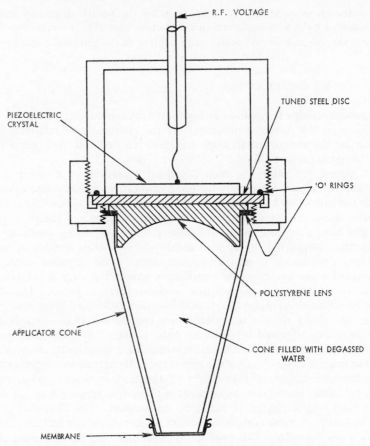

Fig. 9.6. Irradiation head for neurosurgery using an acoustic lens

ceramic or quartz plate clamped or cemented rigidly to the plane surface of a plano-concave plastic lens. A tuned metal plate can be interposed between the crystal face and the lens but is not essential. An applicator cone is mounted over the lens and has a shape following the converging energy path. The end is closed with a thin membrane of rubber or gold-beaters skin and the cone is filled with degassed water.[10]

An elaborate system using lens focusing has been described in which four small applicators, each with its own lens, are mounted in a frame to combine the beam paths at a common point. In use, the skull cap is removed and an open bottomed pan is secured to the head, the exposed dura mater forming the bottom. The pan is filled with saline solution and the applicators are submerged in this solution.[11]

Plate 9.5 shows a general view of the irradiation room used by Fry for sononeurological work. The awake patient can be seen with the head supported in a holder by four stainless steel rods, the tips of which engage hemispherical indentations in the outer skull table. These tips can be

192

accurately reset for sequential irradiations by micrometer adjustments provided on the supporting posts. Three X-ray tubes and the cross-hair positioning system used to determine land marks are shown mounted on the head holder. The four beam ultrasonic irradiator is in position over a calibrating tank. This is moved into position over the patient after the coupling liquid container has been secured to the patients scalp. Since the skull is intact during irradiation there is no need for sterile procedures once the small scalp incisions are sealed. These incisions are made for the supporting rods used to position the skull. Electronic instrumentation and the generator are mounted on the left wall with the control console in the foreground.

Focusing bowl transducers are being used experimentally, although some difficulty is experienced in obtaining piezoelectric ceramic blanks large enough to produce the necessary large diameter bowls. The manufacture follows optical techniques and the shape is critical if accurate focusing is to be obtained. As with other focusing arrays, it is necessary to determine the focus point in order to position the bowl for lesion production. Various methods are described using absorber pads and thermocouples. One procedure employs a flaw detector and an additional electrode on the bowl, the main electrode and this signal electrode being used as the transmitter and receiver. If a small sphere is moved into the focus point maximum echo strength will indicate the position.[12]

With the focus accurately defined, the bowl can now be used in a similar fashion to a lens type transducer. The transmission medium is contained in a pan fixed to the skull and the focusing bowl positioned at the correct distance and on the required axis.

Bowl transducers producing sharp focusing can also be used for nondestructive examination of the internal anatomy of the brain. Echo techniques are employed with relatively low pulse powers energizing the transducer. This is covered in Sect. 8.6.

REFERENCES

1. ANGELL JAMES, J., DALTON, G. A., BULLEN, M. A., FREUNDLICH, H. F. and HOPKINS, J. C., *J. Laryngol. Otol.*, **74**, 10 (1960).
2. BULLEN, M. A., WELLS, P. N. T., FREUNDLICH, H. A. and ANGELL JAMES, G., *Ultrasonics*, **1**, 1 (1963).
3. ANGELL JAMES, J., *Ann. Roy. Coll. Surg.*, **33**, (1963).
4. *Instruction Manual, Ultrasonic Therapy Equipment*, Elliott Bros. (London) Ltd.
5. KOSSOFF, G., *I.E.E.E. Trans. Sonics Ultrasonics*, **SV-II**, 2 (1964).
6. GORDON, D., *Ultrasound as a Diagnostic and Surgical Tool*, Chapter 10, Livingstone, Edinburgh (1964).
7. ARSLAN, M., *Proc. 5th. Cong. Int. Oto-rhino-laryng.*, 429 (1953).
8. GORDON, D., *Ultrasound as a Diagnostic and Surgical Tool*, Chapter 25, Livingstone, Edinburgh (1964).
9. COSMAN, B. J. and HUETER, T. F., *Electronics*, **32**, 20 (1959).
10. BALLANTINE, H. T., JR., HUETER, T. F., NAUTA, W. J. H. and SOSA, D. M., *J. Exp. Med.*, **104**, 3 (1956).
11. FRY, W. J. and MEYERS, R., *Confinia Neurol.*, **22**, 3–5 (1962).
12. GORDON, D., *Ultrasound as a Diagnostic and Surgical Tool*, Chapter 20, Livingstone, Edinburgh (1964).

10

THE APPLICATION OF ULTRASONIC ENERGY IN THE DENTAL FIELD

L. Balamuth, Ph.D.

10.1 INTRODUCTION

Ultrasonic energy is present in any medium which is vibrating mechanically at a frequency above about 16,000 c/s. Thus we deal here with mechanical vibration energy whose frequency is above that of normal human hearing. This high frequency mechanical vibration spectrum covers a range from 16,000 c/s up to Giga c/s. So far, dentistry has been interested essentially in only two ranges out of this large relatively unexplored spectrum.

These ranges include a low one which is just above the level of human hearing and another one which is as much as forty to fifty times the lower range. Quantitatively, these ranges correspond to 20–30 kc/s and 800–1000 kc/s. The low range has come into relatively wide use in professional dental prophylaxis and in the treatment of periodontal disease. On a more limited scale low range ultrasonic dental drills are in use. Thus, the low range corresponds to dental operations which are ordinarily associated with the simple mechanical procedures.

The higher range of frequency is used in quite a different way and is currently more experimental and less widely used than the lower frequency range. The low range and the high range differ in one aspect, the understanding of which is essential in order to see the basic difference which arises in practice. This difference is in the ability of the human tissues to transmit or absorb these vibrations. At the low frequencies, the absorption coefficient is so low that the tissue may be regarded as transparent for most practical purposes. At the higher frequencies the absorption increases linearly for soft tissues and quadratically for hard or bonelike structures. Therefore, at 10^6 c/s anywhere from 50 to 2500 more energy absorption may occur than at 20,000 c/s!

194

As a result of this elementary physical difference the low energy range is used in dentistry chiefly in mechanical operations such as drilling teeth, gum surgery, root canal therapy, periodontal prophylaxis, amalgam packing and other procedures, all of which are otherwise also carried out with mechanical instruments. The high frequency band cannot be used in this simple mechanical way and so is exploited mainly for its energy absorption effects similarly to the way in which diathermy is used. This latter area has involved such studies as staining tissues,[1] treatment of pulpitis, referred pain, post extraction oedema, neuralgia,[2] and many other clinical conditions.[3,4]

10.2 THE LOW RANGE (20-30 Kc/s) APPLICATIONS

10.2.1 PAST

In November, 1952, a popular article on ultrasonics appeared in the American magazine *Life*. The front page showed a corkscrew penetrating a block of glass. This picture apparently fired the imagination of numerous dentists who sent in letters suggesting the use of the ultrasonic principle shown as a dental drill. The block of glass was hard like a tooth, and the corkscrew was certainly an odd-shaped metal drill making an unusual excavation in the tooth-like glass block.

Actually, the picture and the *Life* article were about an industrial ultrasonic machining process which had been discovered by Balamuth in 1942 and had been patented.[5,6] The process being illustrated was the use of a vibrating tool (20–30 kc/s range) to penetrate hard, brittle materials with the aid of an abrasive slurry.

In any event, this was the beginning of a substantial development in the U.S.A. which resulted in a commercially available ultrasonic dental unit. A typical example of such a unit is shown in Plate 10.1. As an offshoot of the original work which was carried out at the Cavitron Ultrasonics Company's laboratory, the United States Navy became interested and developed a laboratory dental cutting device using the slurry principle.[7] Their work was performed on very small guinea pig's teeth with unpromising results.

One of the earliest reports by a dentist on the possibilities of the new method was published in 1953 less than one year after the *Life* article.[8] The first actual dental preparations on human patients were performed by Dr. Carl R. Oman, head of the Operative Division of the Columbia University Dental College.[9] His effort was joint with Dr. Edmund Applebaum of the same College.

The significant fact about ultrasonic tooth drilling is its relative comfort as a procedure compared with conventional techniques. Since the tooth structure is removed by very light taps of minute abrasive particles at incredible repetition rates of twenty to thirty thousand taps per second, the total force need to cut a tooth is only a few ounces compared with pounds of force used with an ordinary drill. But, although a relatively painless technique was at hand, and the histopathological findings[10] established biological safety, several factors mitigated against widespread adoption of the ultrasonic method.

In the first place, the dentist had to learn a completely new technique requiring going against many years of habitual work with the rotary drill.

Also, the reliance on tactile sensitivity had to be increased, because of the poor vision in the operative field due to the presence of an abrasive slurry of white powder (aluminium oxide). At the same time, a new development came along in the form of the high speed rotary instrument, capable of cutting at rotary speeds of more than 100,000 r.p.m. The new high speed drill cut tooth structure faster than the ultrasonic drill and required only very light pressure just like the ultrasonic device. Being a rotary procedure requiring far less accommodation by the dentist, the high speed rotary drill has all but replaced the ultrasonic drill at the present time.

Nevertheless, some fifteen hundred ultrasonic dental drills of the type shown in Plate 10.1, did get into actual clinical or dental office use. A number of dentists state that there is always a small percentage of patients (approximately 15 per cent) who will not have any drill but the ultrasonic type. This is related not only to the less traumatic procedure, but is also dependent on the fact that the ultrasonic drill is silent and gives no impression of motion. Out of this small core of practising dentists, using ultrasonic drills, there gradually grew up applications to periodontal and prophylaxis problems. These are the procedures which are normally carried out with hand scaling instruments. Hand held chisels and points are used to break off hard calcified tartar deposits on teeth, and the hand scrapers are used to finish the periodontal prophylactic cleaning of side wall and root surfaces of teeth. It did not take long to discover that the ultrasonic drill could be used just as a hand instrument is used, except that much less force is required and rapid cleaning of hard deposits occurs. The interest aroused by this development stimulated periodontal specialists to explore the possibilities.[11,12,13]

Cavitron Ultrasonics, Inc. then developed a small ultrasonic prophylaxis unit consisting of an electronic generator (25 kc/s) a handpiece and a series of special inserts for use with the handpiece. Each insert bore at its output end a special tip necessary to the dentist for some type of periodontal or prophylactic operation. Plate 10.2 shows this unit, and Plate 10.3 shows a variety of tips which may be used with this type of unit. The handpiece is water-cooled and the motor and electric current are conveyed to the vibrator by means of a single multichannel cable. The magnetostrictive nickel vibrator portion of the insert supplies heat losses during operation, which serve to warm the cooling water so that as it emerges near the tip of the instrument it will not be too cold on the exposed tooth surface.

10.2.2 PRESENT

At this writing there is a compact ultrasonic dental prophylaxis unit which is finding a rapidly growing use in America, Europe and in Japan. The model most widely used in the U.S.A. is shown in Plate 10.4. The number of different types of inserts has proliferated with the years and at the present time energized dental tools of the following types are in general use:

1. Standard hand instrument type tips for prophylaxis, including calculus removal and general cleaning;
2. Surgical knives for gingivectomy;
3. Amalgam packing tools (also usable for gold foil);
4. Special vibratory chuck for holding standard root canal files and reamers;
5. Diamond files for orthodontic work.

A survey of present techniques of ultrasonic dentistry as practiced in the United States may be obtained from a perusal of the attached references.[14] In a general way, it may be stated that ultrasound has endowed many conventional hand instruments with a new power combined with a gentleness of operation, which permits to the dentist the full skill of his present manipulative techniques without the hand fatigue which accompanies uses requiring higher force levels.

Ultrasonic prophylaxis is accomplished by applying the vibrating tip directly to the tooth in the presence of a water spray. No external abrasive slurry is used. However, the disintegrated calculus particles form their own slurry which assists in rapidly removing the deposits. Another factor present in this operation is the low fatigue strength of the calculus deposits compared with tooth structure. The thousands of vibrations per second rapidly fatigue the calculus thereby providing an additional aid in forming the calculus slurry. Accompanying both of these effects is the effect of cavitation, which always accompanies the vibrations in the water spray.

This cavitation effect has been fully described in earlier chapters and does not require further elaboration here. The effect of the shock waves associated with cavitation in producing atomization of the water spray striking a vibrating dental tip may be seen in Plate 10.5. These shock waves are the same as those currently used in ultrasonic industrial cleaning equipment, such as is used in rapidly cleaning the works of fine watches. The same cleaning power goes to work on the gums and teeth and their many interproximal crevices. Additionally, ultrasonic massage of gingival tissue assists penetration of antiseptics and other medicaments.

A further item of importance is the fact that the sharpness of the vibratory tools used is not as crucial as it is in conventional hand instrument use. Since the vibration does the work, a dull tool will often work quite satisfactorily. This factor is also expressed in the gentle pressure required to remove calculus. Actually, pressure employed is minimal, and if extra pressure is applied there is a tendency to damp out the vibrations and hamper operation efficiency. Dentists today are learning this light fingered technique and find that it fits in very well with the similarly gentle techniques needed when using high speed dental drills for cavity preparation.

One property of ultrasonic vibrations not usually brought to light is that they are essentially low speed. They have a very high repetition rate and are capable of producing extraordinary accelerations, but they do not reach very high peak speeds. If this seems difficult to comprehend, let us take a simple example by way of illustration. Since the vibrations are simple harmonic, it is possible to write down formulae for the displacement, speed and acceleration of a point on a vibrating tip. They are:

$$\text{Displacement} = \text{Maximum displacement} \times \sin (2\pi) \text{ ft}$$

where $f = $ frequency and $t = $ time

$$\text{Speed} = \text{Maximum speed} \times \cos (2\pi) \text{ ft}$$

$$\text{Acceleration} = \text{Maximum acceleration} \times \sin (2\pi) \text{ ft}$$

But, since the speed is the time derivative of the displacement and the acceleration is the time derivation of the speed, we may write:

$$\text{Maximum speed} = 2\pi f \times \text{Maximum displacement}$$

$$\text{Maximum acceleration} = 2\pi f \times \text{Maximum speed}$$

Now, suppose we have a dental tip which is vibrating at 25,000 c/s and with a maximum displacement of 0·001 in. Then the above formulae permit a ready computation of both the maximum speed and acceleration respectively from the frequency given and the assumed maximum displacement. In part, we get:

$$\text{Maximum speed} = 13 \text{ ft/sec} = 9 \text{ mph}$$

$$\text{Maximum acceleration} = 60{,}000 \text{ g}$$

where g is the acceleration of gravity (approx. 32·2 ft/sec^2). Thus, we see that such a vibrating tip reaches only about 9 mph, but achieves the astonishing acceleration of 60,000 times that of gravity. This is a very important difference from high speed rotary instruments, when we consider the possibility of accidentally cutting soft tissues such as gum, lips, cheek or tongue. The low speed of the ultrasonic tip makes accidental soft tissue laceration practically impossible. Therefore, the dentist has a much greater control over bleeding during his work. In fact, one very unusual case has been reported of a periodontist in the United States who undertook the prophlyaxis of the mouth of a boy who was a hemophiliac. No dentist would undertake the job with ordinary instruments because of the bleeding hazard. However, with due care the dentist was able to clean the deposits on the teeth of this patient without drawing a single drop of blood.

Let us carry the inquiry into the technical properties of the low range ultrasonic vibrations a little further. This will serve not only to illuminate further the technical background of current ultrasonic dental practices, it will also aid in understanding the prognosis for the future. As already hinted, most of the unique properties of ultrasonic instruments arise from the extraordinarily high accelerations at the working tip. It has already been seen how this high acceleration combined with a high repetition rate permits rapid periodontal prophlaxis with minimum hand pressure. Now we will turn to another important consequence of such accelerations.

198

Fig. 10.1 shows an enlarged tool end vibrating at 25,000 c/s and with an excursion of 0·002 in. The data accompanying Fig. 10.1 shows the peak speed and acceleration produced in such a tip. The excursion is shown as $S = AB$, the centre of the motion is the position of the tip when it has its peak speed of 13 ft/sec. At this point, C, the acceleration is zero and reaches peak values at the end points of the motion at A and B. This peak is 63,000 times the acceleration of gravity.

Now, the interesting thing about the region ACB, swept out continuously by the tool tip 25,000 times every second, is that it defines what we may call a zone of motion. This zone of motion is essentially impenetrable precisely because of the high acceleration. For example, if the tip is lightly pressed against a tooth when it is in position B, the tip will be just reversing

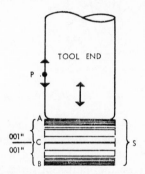

Fig. 10.1. Vibrating tool end showing zone of motion: frequency 25,000 c/s; excursion 0·002 in; peak speed 13 ft/sec; peak acceleration 63,000 g

its forward vibratory motion and will pull back toward A. While this is occurring the tip will be out of contact with the tooth and the tool end will start moving toward the tooth. But, the acceleration of the tool end due to the gentle hand pressure will be a fraction of g. Meanwhile the tool end will go to A and back to B in one twenty five thousandth of a second, and what's more will do this traversal with an average acceleration of thousands of g. Therefore, the distance which the hand pressure causes the tool end to move will be the distance an object will move in 1/25,000 sec at an acceleration of a fraction of g. If we assumed a full g acceleration the distance in question would be $1/2\ gt^2$ where g is 32·2 ft/sec^2 and t is 1/25,000 sec. This distance calculates out to be about a third of a microinch. Thus, the point is made that for all practical purposes the tool end will be out of contact with the tooth during most of one cycle of vibration, that is, the zone of motion is practically impenetrable.

This has very important implications for dentistry because it means that the tooth is 'resting' most of the time during an ultrasonic treatment. All the work is done during only a minute fraction of each cycle of vibration. This is what makes the ultrasonic technique one of very low friction, light force requirement, and relatively comfortable as a procedure.

Now perhaps a perceptive reader will note at this juncture that the point, P, in Fig. 10.1 is also moving back and forth just as the tool end is moving. But, the side surface of the tool, if it is in contact with tissue, will be in a rubbing relation with it. Also, since there is no separation of tool and

199

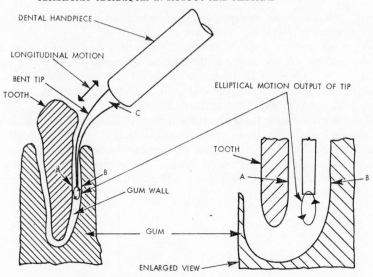

Fig. 10.2. Periodontal tip between gum and tooth

tissue in this case, there should be considerable friction, hence heat, and therefore patient discomfort. Fig. 10.2 shows a schematic portraying the relations of a vibratory tool when used between a tooth wall and gum tissue in periodontal root surface cleaning.

We are here concerned with relieving the possible rubbing action at such points as A (tooth wall) and B (gingiva) while treating the root surfaces of the tooth. Now, at C the tool is vibrating as shown along the long axis of the handpiece. But as we proceed down the tool towards its end, a bending vibration is induced and for a properly designed tip this new vibration will combine with the initial axial vibration so as to produce a resultant elliptical motion. Plate 10.6 shows such an elliptical motion obtained by microphotographing a dental tip of this type while vibrating. A little reflection will now reveal that this elliptical vibration will cause the tool to oscillate at high frequency and high acceleration between such points as A and B in Fig. 10.2. So, once again, the tool surfaces will be most of the time out of contact with the treated parts with resultant friction reduction and more comfortable operation.

These elliptical vibrations perform another very important function in periodontal treatment. The water spray which constantly flows on to the tool while it is in operation in the mouth, will be propelled by the elliptical motion of the tool towards the operating end. Thus, this vibration acts as a pump which guarantees coolant fluid where it is needed at the end of the tool.

Summarizing, one may state that the currently most widely used ultrasonic dental instrument is a transducer in the 20–30 kc/s range of frequency carrying a tool whose end is bent and designed so as to produce elliptical vibrations whose major and minor axes do not exceed a few thousandths

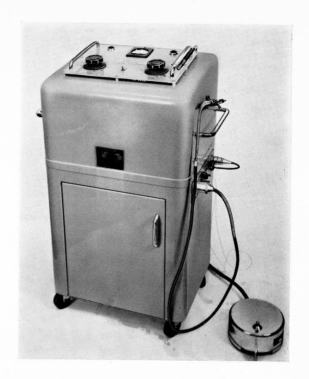

Plate 10.1. Ultrasonic
dental unit, early type

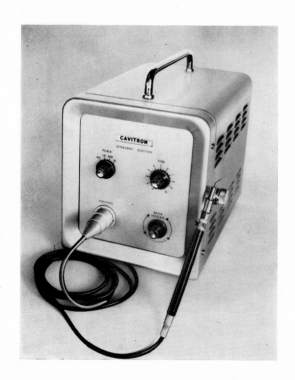

Plate 10.2. Dental
prophylaxis unit,
early type

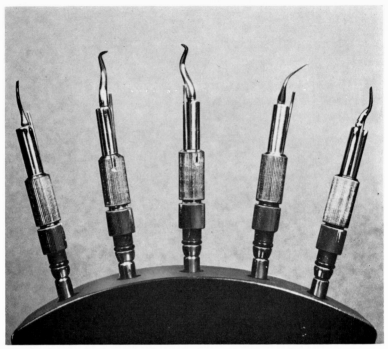

Plate 10.3. Typical dental tips for ultrasonic periodontology

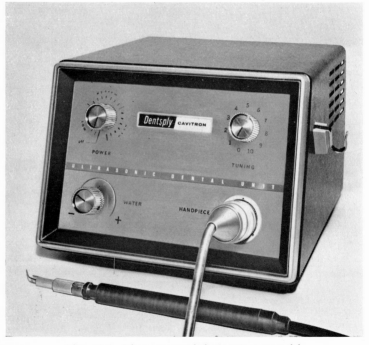

Plate 10.4. Ultrasonic prophylaxis unit, new model

Plate 10.5. Effect of shock waves on vibrating dental tip

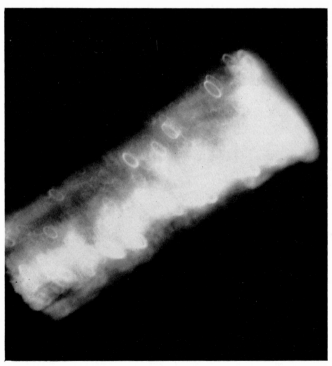

Plate 10.6. Microphotograph of ultrasonic tool tip undergoing elliptical vibrations

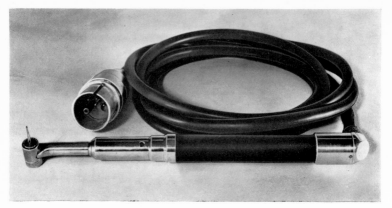

Plate 10.7. Ultrasonic high speed rotary drill prototype

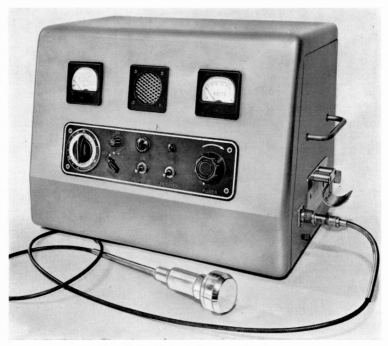

Plate 10.8. Medical ultrasonic therapy unit

of an inch. These vibrations cause the tool to be a powerful but gentle and relatively frictionless agent for the treatment of numerous dental problems.

Those who wish to look more thoroughly into the details of the dental devices and methods described will find them in the references[17] provided at the end of this chapter.

10.2.3 FUTURE

The most remarkable fact which has emerged from over ten years of use of the low range ultrasonic frequencies in dentistry is: that every distinctive and unique effect of ultrasonically vibrating elements appears to have a useful application, potential or actual, in the dental office. Let us briefly review these effects, they are:

1. Cavitation.
2. High repetition rate.
3. Low peak speed.
4. High acceleration.
5. Minute amplitude of vibration.
6. Elliptical vibrations.

Various combinations of these basic physical characteristics of ultrasonic vibrations, are responsible for such diverse phenomena as:

1. Cleaning.
2. Sterilization.
3. Mixing, dispersion, emulsification.
4. Calculus and stain removal.
5. Low friction, low force tool operation.
6. Pumping without moving parts.
7. Chemical activation of oral agents.
8. Welding of metals to teeth.
9. Increased diffusion and penetration of chemicals into tooth structure.
10. Micromassage and blood circulation stimulation (includes debridement of soft tissue).
11. Surgery (gingivectomy, removal of impacted teeth).
12. Root canal therapy.
13. Amalgam packing (gold foil also).
14. Orthodontic assists.
15. Drilling and forming non-round holes in teeth.

This list is not exhaustive, yet it certainly is impressive and reveals the potential that low range ultrasonic instruments have in the future of dentistry. There is no doubt that the foundation has already been laid paving the way to a dental office which employs ultrasound in many phases of the dental procedure.

Since the drilling of teeth is so commonplace a dental procedure, consider this from the point of view of current dental practice and the potential held out by ultrasonic technology. The history of ordinary rotary drills is one wherein the speed of rotation has been increased gradually over the years from less than 1000 rpm up to rotary speeds greater than 300,000 rpm. At the same time ordinary burrs have gone from steel to tungsten carbide to diamonds. Now as a drill rotates and is placed against a tooth each cutting edge will successively strike tooth structure and remove some of it. The total number of these edge impacts made per second will determine whether the drilling is gentle or not. Clearly the more edge or point impacts per second the smaller the piece of tooth broken off by each impact in order to drill at some desired rate. This point of view enables the trend in rotary drilling to be assessed. It has been to more point impacts per second so as to allow light pressure operation with faster and gentler removal of tooth structure. For example, a six edged steel burr turning at 1000 rpm would produce 6000 impacts per minute or 100 impacts per second. But, a diamond impregnated modern drill containing, say, two hundred diamond chips and turning at 300,000 rpm (or 5000 rps) will produce one million point impacts per second. So, it is easy to see why the newer high speed drill is gentler. There is no question but that the large number of point impacts per second method of tooth drilling has entered to dominate the field for some time to come.

How does the ultrasonic drill compare with the above? Suppose we consider drilling a one millimeter diameter hole in a tooth using a vibratory drill executing 25,000 vibrations per second and operating with an abrasive slurry of water and aluminium oxide grains whose average diameter is about two thousandths of an inch. The abrasive grains will be distributed over an area 1 mm or 0·04 in on a side. If we assume that only twenty per cent of the grains in the cross section are active on each vibration we would have about eighty impacts per vibration. For 25,000 vibrations per second this means two million point impacts per second which is in the same arena as the very high rotary drill with a diamond burr. The number of point impacts per second may be easily increased in the ultrasonic case by increasing the frequency of operation or by decreasing the grain size of the abrasive grains. In any case, it becomes clear that the ultrasonic drill in effect reached in one stride the goal toward which the rotary drill had been striving for years. But, in addition, the high speed drill can reach its high goals and higher only by going to faster speed. This introduces other hazards associated with very high speed tools in the mouth. On the other hand, the ultrasonic approach is a low speed high repetition rate and so does not have this defect. In order for the ultrasonic impact cutting drill to be more widely used in the future it would be necessary for the dentists to work out the necessary new techniques required and these would have to be introduced at the dental school level where students can be trained before having crystallized habitual patterns in other methods.

But, since we are looking toward the future, it is appropriate at this juncture to show that a high speed rotary drill may be actuated by an ultrasonic rather than by the air or water turbines now in general use.

To understand how this is possible we must refer to the use of elliptical vibrations for this purpose. Imagine an elliptically vibrating tool tip being brought into tangential contact with a drill which is mounted in low friction miniature ball bearings. Then the tool will, during each vibration, be out of contact with the drill shaft for part of the time and for the other part of the time will be in a wiping relation with the shaft. In other words, we will have a situation similar to that found in a log-rolling contest. The contestant causes a log in water to spin by constantly wiping the surface of the log with his feet. A complete description of this type of ultrasonic rotary drive may be found in the following references.[15,16]

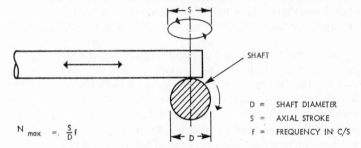

$$N_{max} = \frac{S}{D} f$$

D = SHAFT DIAMETER
S = AXIAL STROKE
f = FREQUENCY IN C/S

Fig. 10.3. Computation of the rotational speed, N (in rps), of the shaft in terms of the ultrasonic vibration parameter

Fig. 10.3 illustrates how to compute the rotational speed arising from an elliptical vibration. For a shaft diameter of 0·5 mm and an elliptical vibration of 0·002 in axial stroke at 30,000 c/s, we would reach a speed of 180,000 rpm. An actual working model of such a drill is shown in Plate 10.7.

Other areas of future promise for the low range ultrasonic vibrations in dentistry are in the fields of orthodontia, where the currently used instrument is already being used in removing braces and plaster which adheres to the teeth. An interesting technique, being studied in this field, is the ultrasonic grinding of very thin layers of enamel from the sides of teeth in order to shape them and to permit relocation of the teeth in the mouth. This is important both for cosmetic and bite-correcting reasons.

10.3 THE HIGH RANGE - (800-1000 Kc/s)

As was pointed out earlier in this chapter the chief value of the high range of ultrasonic energy is in its ability to produce energy which may be readily absorbed in the soft and hard tissues of the oral cavity. A survey of experimental and clinical work in this area has already been referred to.[1,2,3,4]

This type of energy has been used as a therapeutic agent in the medical field, for many years in Europe and for the past ten years or more in the U.S.A. A typical medical unit is of the type shown in Plate 10.8. The active head in this unit is a quartz crystal, resonant at about 800 kc/s.

In order to allow the ultrasound radiation from the head to penetrate the desired site, it is necessary to coat the tissue and the head with a sound coupling means such as a mild petroleum jelly or mineral oil. Usually, the active head is moved about in the neighbourhood of the treatment in order to avoid overdosing a particular spot. However, there is a kind of built-in safety feature in such instruments which is unpleasant and is never relied on in actual practice. As soon as the level of absorbed energy in bony tissue reaches a certain high but still safe level biologically, there is induced a specific periosteal pain which is quite difficult to bear.

In the medical area the high range energy has been used for reducing pain levels, especially dramatically in the case of that experienced in amputated members. This pain relieving action of high frequency ultrasonic energy is perhaps one of the more promising possibilities in the dental field.

But, there is no lengthy past or present history of routine usage of such energy in dentistry today. This particular area is just about entirely reserved for the future. What is needed is a sufficiently small radiator which may be safely applied to all parts of the oral cavity. It is important that such an instrument be fitted either with a timer or some dosage level indicator so as to be able to monitor the energy accurately in clinical studies. Considering the widespread use of this type of therapy in medicine, it is really surprising that there has not been a greater tempo of study for its use in dentistry. It will surely find its place in due course in the dental field.

REFERENCES

1. CORONINI, C. V. and LASSMAN, G., 'Intenswierung der Silberimprägnation des Nervengewebes nach Gratzl durch Ultraschallung,' *Kongressbericht der Erlanger Ultraschall-Tagung*, 72 (1949).
2. DENOO, C. J., 'L'ultrasonotherapie en art dentaire,' *Rev. Belge Stomatol*, 49, 189 (1952).
3. LEONE, V. and VISENDAZ, A., 'Gli ultrasuoni nella terapie stomatoloica,' *Gaz Med. Ital.*, 112, 29 (1953).
4. STÖGER, H., 'Zur Frage der Anwendung des Ultraschalls in der Zahn-Mund-und Kieferheilkunde,' *Österr. Ztschr. fur Stommatol*, 50, 3565 (1953).
5. British Patent No. 602, 801 (Filed April 14, 1945, Granted June 3 1948).
6. U.S. Patent No. 2,580,716: January 1 (1952).
7. NIELARDS, A. G., RICHARDS, J. R. and WALCOTT, R. B., 'Ultrasonic dental cutting instruments,' *J. Am. Dental Assoc.*, 50, 399 (1955).
8. CATUNA, M. C., 'Sonic Energy: a possible dental application,' *Ann. Den.*, 12, 100 (1953).
9. OMAN, C. R. and APPLEBAUM, E., 'Ultrasonic cavity preparation. Preliminary report,' *N.Y.J. Dentistry*, 20, 256 (1954), 'Ultrasonic Cavity preparation. II Progress Report,' *J. Am. Dental Assoc.*, 50, 414 (1955).
10. ZACH, L. and BROWN, R. N., 'Pulpal Effect of Ultrasonic Cavity Preparation. Preliminary report,' *N.Y.J. Dentistry*, 22, 9 (1956).
    ZACH, L., MORRISON, A. and COHEN, G., 'Ultrasonic cavity preparation: histopathologic survey of effects on mature and developing dental tissues,' *J. Am. Dental Assoc.*, 59, 45 (1959).
11. WILSON, J. R., 'The use of ultrasonics in periodontal treatment,' *J. Prosthetic Dentistry*, 8, 161 (1958).
12. RICHMAN, M. J., 'The use of ultrasonics in root canal therapy and root resection,' *J. Dent. Med.*, 12, 12 (1957).

13. GOLDMAN, H. M., 'Histological assay of healing following ultrasonic curettage versus hand-instrument curettage,' *Oral Surg., Oral Med. Oral Pathol.*, **14**, 925 (1961).

14. EWEN, S. J. and TASCHER, P. J., 'Clinical uses of ultrasonic root sealers,' *J. Periodontol*, **29**, 45 (1958).

    EWEN, S. J. and TASCHER, P. J., 'Clinical applications of ultrasonic scaling,' *N.Y.J. Dentistry*, **28**, 97 (1958).

    EWEN, S. J. and TASCHER, P. J., 'Instrumentation in ultrasonic periodontal therapy,' *J. Periodontol*, **30**, 67 (1959).

    TASCHER, P. J., 'The present status of ultrasonic dentistry,' *N.Y.J. Dentistry*, **25**, 183 (1959).

    EWEN, S. J., 'Ultrasonics in periodontal therapy (a pictorial review),' *N.Y.J. Dentistry*, **26**, 409 (1960).

    EWEN, S. J., 'Ultrasound and the treatment of acute and chronic gingivitis,' *J. Periodontal*, **31**, 399 (1960).

    EWEN, S. J., 'Ultrasound and periodontics,' *J. Periodontal*, **31**, 101 (1960).

    MCCALL, C. M. JR. and SZMYD, L., 'Clinical evaluation of ultrasonic scaling,' *J. Am. Dental Assoc.*, **61**, 559 (1960).

    EWEN, S. J., 'Composite periodonal therapy,' *N.Y.J. Dentistry*, **27**, 169 (1961).

    EWEN, S. J., 'General ultrasonic theory and periodontal therapy,' *N.Y.J. Dentistry*, **32**, 278 (1962).

15. U.S. Patent No. 3,058,218; Oct. 16, 1962; 'Methods and Means for driving small diameter shafts at high rotational speeds.'

16. BALAMUTH, L., 'A new ultrasonic rotary drive,' *I.E.E.E. Trans. P.T.G.U.E. UE-10*, **2**, 96 (1963).

17. U.S. Patent No. 2,580,716—British Patent No. 602,801.
    U.S. Patent No. Re 25,033—British Patent No. 810,457.
    U.S. Patent No. 2,990,616—British Patent No. 830,142.
    U.S. Patent No. 3,076,904—British Patent No. 936,296.
    U.S. Patent No. 3,058,218—British Patent No. 960,453.
    U.S. Patent No. 3,075,288.
    U.S. Patent No. 3,086,288.

11

SOME BIOLOGICAL APPLICATIONS OF ULTRASOUND

E. A. Davidson, Ph.D.
T. Rosett, Ph.D.

11.1 INTRODUCTION AND TECHNIQUES

The primary biological usage of ultrasound stems from the need to study metabolic pathways that are utilized by different cells for converting materials presented to them by their environments into sources of energy and essential cellular constituents. In a very real sense, the biologists consider that the basic unit of life is the cell. Even in grossly dissimilar organisms, ranging from unicellular bacteria to highly complex metazoans, one finds certain features in common as regards the utilization of material by the cell. This unifying theme in biology supports the evolutionary concept wherein by selection processes, whether a result of time or environmental effects, efficient methods have been developed within cells for the conversion of chemical potential energy into useful functional roles. Once such a mechanism is developed, or if it be at some primitive organizational level as far as the whole organism is concerned, it is not likely to be drastically altered as one progresses up the evolutionary ladder. Thus, there are very many metabolic sequences and pathways which are common to all forms of life. Primarily for this reason, the practising biologist feels that information gained from a study of simple cellular organisms will be in large measure applicable to the same processes in higher animals. However, there are many advantages in using single cell or simple organisms as experimental tools. These include the virtual elimination of animal to animal variation, since one generally deals with extremely large populations. The second advantage is the ability to control completely the external environment and thereby to insure a certain measure of reproducibility from experiment to experiment. As a result of this, there is a very broad interest in extracting as much information as possible from single celled organisms so that it may be possible at some future time to reconstruct the processes which are under study and to apply the information gained thereby to higher forms of life.

The ability to carry out so-called cell-free studies of various enzyme systems is extremely dependent upon one's efficiency in disrupting the cell and releasing cellular contents without at the same time destroying them. This is much more difficult than it appears on the surface. The problem may be stated as follows: Most simple one-cell organisms have an exceedingly tough cell wall which is only a few microns in diameter, and similar in density to the medium that surrounds it. The protein and nucleic acid components contained within the cell are large macromolecules, easily denatured by extreme conditions of temperature or oxidation and sufficiently large in size so as not to be able to penetrate through this outer cell covering. One of the methods of choice currently used to disrupt the outer cell covering is ultrasonic treatment which at the same time avoids extensive destruction of the cellular components.

Since the breakage of the outer cell wall by ultrasound takes place by a machine-gun-like phenomenon whereby extremely small cavitation bubbles driven at very high speed from the probe tip of the sonic device actually penetrate through the cell wall and disrupt its integrity[1] it is obvious that the efficiency of such a process is going to be very dependent on the power delivery of the instrument and the ability to keep a given cell within the effective area of the probe for a sufficient length of time so that disruption

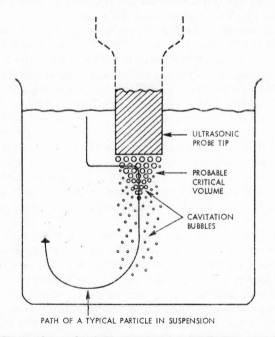

PATH OF A TYPICAL PARTICLE IN SUSPENSION

Fig. 11.1. Cavitation due to ultrasonic energy. A very small volume, just below the probe tip contains cavitation of sufficiently high energy to disrupt micro-organisms

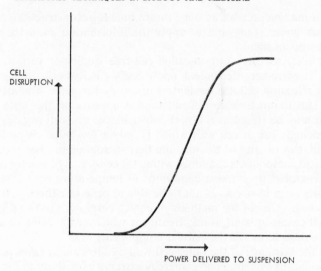

Fig. 11.2. Cell disruption as a function of ultrasonic energy. The initial plateau shows that a minimum energy is required

takes place. This is a probability function since the bubbles generated do not have an infinite life time in the solution and indeed, their critical size and velocity for cell disruption are confined to a very small space near the probe tip. This is graphically illustrated in Fig. 11.1. If one considers that the number of bubbles formed and that their velocity is going to be a function of the power output of the instrument, then the disruption rate for a given organism will also relate to this power output. This function is not very well described since quantitative measure of number and velocity of bubbles is an extremely difficult task requiring ultra-high-speed photographic devices. Nevertheless, if cellular disruption or release of contents is taken as an index, then the correlation between power delivered and disruption efficiency is very good. This type of relationship is illustrated in Fig. 11.2. It can be seen that there is a threshold phenomenon for a typical organism wherein at power levels below this, no disruption will take place because the cavitation bubbles or fluid streams are not driven with sufficient speed to disrupt or penetrate the cellular envelope. Beyond this point there is a direct relationship between power output and disruption.

One might conclude from a rough correlation of the type mentioned above, that if an instrument delivering let us say, a 100 W of power at the probe tip is good, then one delivering 200 W would be twice as good and so on. However, this is obviously not the case and brings up the second major problem in cellular disruption which is control of both local heating and total solution heating during the insonation process. The power delivered to the solution is dissipated almost entirely in the form of heat, and a typical heat rise curve is illustrated in Fig. 11.3. Even with instruments of moderate power delivery, in volumes as large as 50–100 ml,

208

the heat generated in the solution will be sufficient so as to destroy sensitive cellular components long before complete cellular breakage has taken place. Whereas the disruption of any given cell will be a probability statement which will reflect the length of time it spends in the critical area for disruption, the denaturation of released subcellular components will depend upon the properties of the whole solution and not so directly on the time that the material will spend in any given area of the container. Accordingly, any disruption experiments must take particular account of local heating problems and ensure adequate heat transfer or cooling by some device. A container has been developed in our laboratory which utilizes the

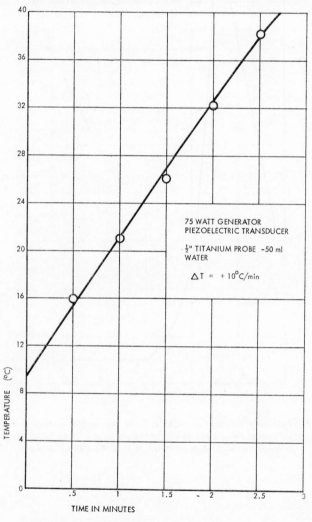

75 WATT GENERATOR
PIEZOELECTRIC TRANSDUCER

$\frac{1}{2}$" TITANIUM PROBE –50 ml WATER

$\Delta T = +10^\circ C/min$

Fig. 11.3. Temperature rise due to heat released by insonation. Under the conditions shown this rise is about $10^\circ C/min$

209

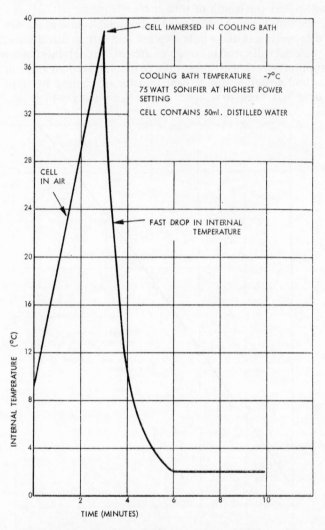

Fig. 11.4. Internal temperature of a cooling cell. As the sonic treatment proceeds, it rises at the rate of 10°C/min. When the cell is immersed in a cooling bath, the temperature generally drops to approximately 9°C above that of the bath

following principle. The downward force generated by the probe tip is used to drive the solution through the sidearms of the vessel thus ensuring adequate circulation of material.[2] This is illustrated in Plate 11.1. Since the sidearms have a large surface to volume ratio, when the entire container is immersed in a suitable cooling bath, the excellent mixing plus the large opportunity to exchange heat with the surroundings results in very efficient temperature control as illustrated in Fig. 11.4.

Experimentally, it is very clear that the efficiency of mixing is going to be a function not only of the size and shape of the container but also of factors such as the viscosity of the cellular suspension. Thus in very dilute solutions where power transfer is very efficient, disruption may still be rather slow due to the lowered probabilities for individual cellular breakage, whereas in very concentrated suspensions, disruption may be equally low due to the high viscosity, inadequate mixing and greatly extended periods of time required to get 99 per cent cellular breakage. 100 per cent disruption is never achieved and total sterilization is not feasible by this technique.

It is also clear that the disruption susceptibility varies greatly from organism to organism. This will be a function largely of the composition and properties of the cell wall of the organisms under study and accordingly, the ideal conditions for such destruction must be empirically determined.

Although the control of temperature is probably a most critical feature with regard to prevention of denaturation of released subcellular components, there are other problems which are more of a chemical than a physical nature. When the sonic probe tip is operated in aqueous solution for a limited period of time, the force generated is sufficient to promote reaction between the oxygen and nitrogen present in the entrapped air with the concomitant formation of nitrogen oxides which may be extremely deleterious in their action on both protein and nucleic acids.[3,4] Although it has been repeatedly demonstrated that the presence of a gas is necessary in order for cavitation and cellular disruption to take place,[3] it is not obligatory that this be air or oxygen since nitrogen or helium will serve the purpose equally well. For reasons that are not entirely clear, carbon dioxide appears to be non-functional in this respect. Accordingly, when particularly sensitive materials are being examined it is customary to employ either a sealed atmosphere chamber which can be purged with nitrogen or helium or to have the appropriate gas rapidly bubbling through the solution to reduce oxidative destruction. It is also customary as in extraction of cells by a variety of other techniques, to add an appropriate reducing agent to protect sensitive sulfhydryl enzymes against oxidation reactions.

There is a clear relationship between the shape of the container employed and the efficiency of cellular disruption. Intuitively, it seems obvious that a conical shape would be efficient, since the area below the probe tip would be relatively restricted and cells will come into the critical range more frequently as they circulate. This is confirmed experimentally and inverted designs such as a pyramidal container, large beaker, and so on are appreciably less efficient.

The size of samples that one may wish to disrupt may range from 1 ml or less to volumes in the range of 5 l or more. For volumes up to 200–300 ml which would contain as much as 20 g to 100 g of cells, batchwise treatment in containers of the general design described above is usually satisfactory. However, when processing extremely large quantities of material, the increased time necessary for exposure so as to get adequate disruption presents denaturation problems which are not readily overcome. Accordingly, several continuous flow devices have been developed, one of which is illustrated in Plate 11.2.

It is necessary in such experimentation to use an appropriate buffer so as to control pH and to promote solubilization of released protein. pH ranges between 5 and 9 are frequently satisfactory for biological materials, but the actual pH employed and the choice of buffer will be variable depending upon the organism under consideration, and accordingly, must be determined by experimentation.

When dealing with pathogens, there is a very real problem as regards aerosol prevention and sterility control. This is akin to the types of problems encountered when harvesting large quantities of micro-organisms by continuous flow centrifugation. A sealed attachment is necessary before this kind of extraction should be considered. One such is illustrated in Plate 11.3.

With the above general principles outlined, it may be worthwhile to survey briefly the types of enzymes and the types of organisms that have been studied by ultrasonic devices and also to indicate where effects on specific macromolecules have been recorded so that adequate precautions may be taken by workers interested in studying them.

Listed in Table 11.1 are various micro-organisms and the activity or extract under study. Generally, the kinds of preliminary studies which are requisite to establish optimal conditions have not been detailed in the publications referred to. Notice that a broad range of organisms ranging from common ones such as *E. coli* and yeast to pathogens have all been satisfactorily disrupted. This table is certainly not complete but fairly representative.

In Table 11.2 are summarized various other effects of ultrasonic treatment of biological materials.

Specific effects on macromolecules have been reported primarily for proteins and nucleic acids. In the former class, the most common disruption effects are those which involve oxidation of sensitive sulfhydryl groups either directly by oxygen or by free radical chains generated as a result of cavitation. Secondarily, some disruption of the three-dimensional protein structure takes place in a manner apparently analogous to heat denaturation. Finally, there is some evidence that actual peptide bond cleavage can occur.[5,6] Whether this is subsequent to some other unfolding or denaturation phenomenon has not been satisfactorily defined.

The effects of ultrasound on nucleic acids apparently do not involve denaturation of the two-stranded helix in the case of DNA but rather cleavage of phosphodiester bonds to give material of much lower molecular weight. Biological activity such as transforming ability is also lost.

212

Table 11.1

Reference	Activity or Extract	Organism
8	Respiratory particles	Streptomyces griseus
		Streptomyces rimosus
		Streptomyces lavendulae
		Streptomyces coelicolor
9	Ergothionine degrading enzyme	Alcaligenes faecalis
10	Ethanol dehydrogenase	Aerobacter aerogenes
11	Cytochrome c	Vibrio succinogenes
	Cytochrome b	
12	Catalase	S. faecalis
13	Krebs cycle enzymes	Thiobacillus thioparus
14	Poly-β-hydroxy butyric acid	Bacillus megatherium
15	Electron transport enzyme	Mycoplasma hominis
16	Cell free extract	Escherichia coli
17	Amino acid synthesizing enzyme	Acetobacter suboxydans
18	Botulism toxin	Clostridium botulinum
19	β-galactosidase	Escherichia coli
20	Adaptive enzymes	Pseudomonas aeruginosa
21	Krebs cycle enzyme	M. sodonensis
22	Nucleotidases	Haemophilus influenzae
		Haemophilus aegyptus
23	Hemolysin	Group A streptococcus
24	Aureomycin sensitive electron transport enzyme	Escherichia coli
25	Glycerol degrading enzyme	S. faecalis
26	Succinoxidase	Pasteurella tularensis
27	Glycolytic enzymes	Claviceps purpurea
28	Glycolytic enzymes	Erwinia amylovera
29	Krebs cycle and electron transport enzyme	Proteus vulgaris
30	Aspartase and Glutamic dehydrogenase	Escherichia coli
31	β-glactosidase	Paracolobacterium erogenoides
32	Asparaginase	Mycobacterium tuberculosis
		Mycobacterium smegmatis
33	Pyridine ribosidase	Xanthomonas prunii
34	Cells walls	Listeria monocytogens
35	Electron Transport enzyme	Bacillus cereus cells and spores
36	Glycolytic enzymes	Cytophaga succinicans
37	Hexose monophosphate shunt and glycolytic enzymes	Myobacterium lacticum
38	Oleic acid dehydrogenase	Chlorella vulgaris
39	Phosphopyruvate carboxylase	Escherichia coli
40	Aconitate hydrolase	Micrococcus sp.
41	Catalase	Pedicoccus cerevisiae
42	Benzene oxidizing enzymes	Mycobacterium rhodocrous
		Pseudomonas aeroginosa
43	Glycolic acic carboligase	Escherichia coli

Table 11.2

Effect of Ultrasound	*Reference*
Degradation of DNA	45
Production of lesions in brain tissue	46
Alteration in Angiotensin	47
Alteration of Enzyme Tryptophanase	48
Decalcification of Bone	49
Accelerate Hatching of Mosquito Eggs	50
Change in Renal Circulation in Frogs	51
Mutation in goldfish	52
Increase yeast susceptibility to photodynamic effects of eosin	53
Destruction of brain tissue	54
Cause Mutation in Actinomyces aureofaciens	55
Treatment of seeds increases crop yields	56
Change structure and activity of insulin	57
Produce Mutation in Hamsters	58
Change Antigenic structure of Shigella and Salmonella	59
Extraction of Alkaloids from plants	60
Release of Calcium from F-actin	61
Review of Chemical and Biological Effects	62

Biologically active RNA is also susceptible to this type of denaturation. Effects on small molecules and carbohydrates have not been extensively investigated.

More recently, other effects of ultrasound on biological materials have been studied. The first of these is a non-destructive change in the permeability of cell membranes. When low intensity ultrasound is used to treat cells of various types, their cell membranes become freely permeable to most of the constituents of the medium in which they are suspended. Braungart[7] has shown that such treatment of tumor cells allows anti-tumor drugs to gain access to their interiors. Hughes[7] has shown that red blood cells will release their hemoglobin into the medium under these circumstances, then after some time actively concentrate this protein back inside the cell wall. If one regards the surface of cell membranes as well oriented structures containing lipid, protein, and enzymes capable of concentrating various types of materials, then any slight disarray of this structure might allow free entrance and egress until such time as repair might take place.

Dyer[7] has shown that low intensity ultrasound can give rise to heritable mutation in mosses. With the known effects of ultrasound on DNA, this is hardly surprising, although only very low intensity was required.

11.2 EXTRACTION OF SOME ENZYMATIC ACTIVITY FROM A SUSPENSION OF MICRO-ORGANISMS

Let us consider an example of the extraction of some enzymatic activity or other material from a micro-organism. The first requirement is a

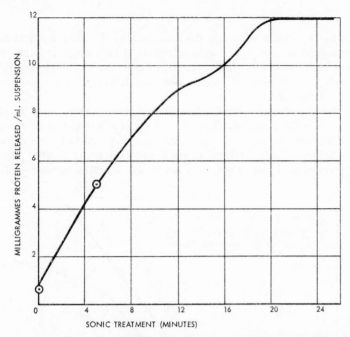

Fig. 11.5. Release of protein from a suspension of micro-organisms. The initial rise reflects rupture of cell wall, and the second rise probably indicates its disintegration

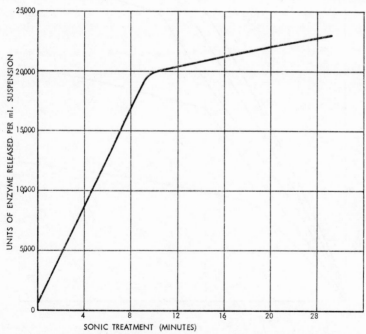

Fig. 11.6. The release of enzymatic activity from a suspension of micro-organisms. The initial rapid rise reflects rupture of the cell envelope, while the second slower rise reflects disruption of smaller particles which were binding activity

reliable assay. In the following discussion all of the sonic extracts are to be centrifuged at high speed in a refrigerated centrifuge and the supernatant solution assayed for the material or activity. As previously stated, containers are available to ensure adequate temperature control during ultrasonic treatment.[2]

For the preliminary survey an internal temperature of 5°C (Bath temperature −4°C) will be adequate. 10 per cent suspensions wet weight per unit volume of the micro-organisms are prepared in different buffers and in distilled water. 100 ml of each suspension are poured into the cooling vessel and the suspension insonated for approximately 20 min

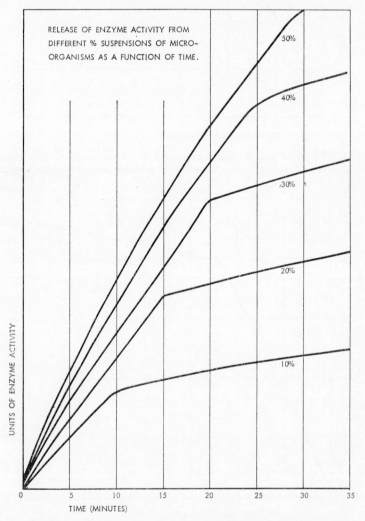

RELEASE OF ENZYME ACTIVITY FROM DIFFERENT % SUSPENSIONS OF MICRO-ORGANISMS AS A FUNCTION OF TIME.

Fig. 11.7. As the concentration of the micro-organism suspension increases, more activity is extractable, but the insonation time required is correspondingly longer

Plate 11.1. Cooling cell in position for use in disrupting micro-organisms. When jack is raised ice bath comes into contact with cell

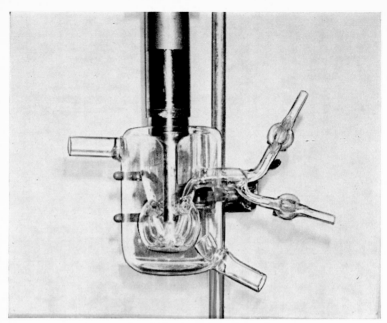

Plate 11.2. Continuous flow cell

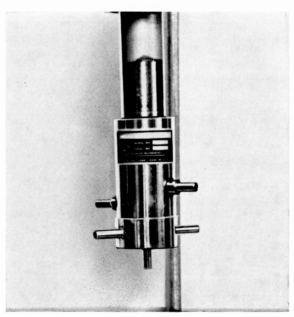

Plate 11.3. Sealed atmosphere cell

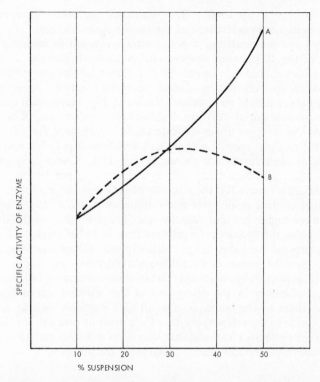

Fig. 11.8. Release of enzymatic activity from various percentage concentrations of a micro-organism. Increasing concentration can give better release of activity (A) or loss of activity (B)

removing 1 ml aliquots every 2 or 3 min.* Each aliquot is centrifuged and following centrifugation the supernatant is assayed for protein content and enzymatic activity. The results are graphically evaluated as indicated in Figs. 11.5 and 11.6. Figs. 11.5 and 11.6 show that the rupture of the cell envelope is complete where the curve first breaks, because at this point the soluble contents of the cytoplasm are thoroughly mixed with the medium. The next break in the protein release curve is probably due to fragmentation of the cell wall with further release of soluble protein. The slow rise in the curve of Fig. 11.6 is probably due to further release of enzymatic activity from sedimentable particles to which it may be bound. Selection of buffers and anti-oxidants or other additives is generally made on the basis of literature survey or previous experience. When the results of this preliminary survey are plotted, the particular combination of buffer and other additives which gives superior results is selected for further study.

The next problem is to determine the best temperature. Various mixtures of salt, ice and water can be prepared for the cooling bath,

* This may be scaled down by a factor of 10 using an appropriately smaller container.

ranging from $-8°$ up to $0°$. The ultrasonic treatment is repeated at various internal temperatures, and the results again plotted.

In very large preparations, it is not always efficient to insonate 100 ml portions of the 10 per cent suspension. A survey of cellular suspension concentrations should also be carried out. Since heavier suspensions take longer to disrupt, insonation should be carried out for 30–40 min. A family of curves should be obtained, similar to Fig. 11.7. Each one shows the characteristic initial steep rise followed by the slow rise. The specific activity of the enzyme under consideration is measured for each curve, and plotted to show specific activity as a function of per cent suspension. Examples of such curves are shown in Fig. 11.8. Curve A is the ideal situation where specific activity rises as a function of per cent suspension. One might obtain curve B if the viscosity of very high suspensions rendered temperature control inadequate and internal heat tended to denature the activity in the higher per cent suspensions. The economics of the situation may well guide the decision. Organisms such as baker's yeast can be obtained in pressed wet cakes at very little expense. Other micro-organisms, however, must be grown in carefully specified media and the expense of growing these micro-organisms may dictate the conditions of cell disruption.

Further efficiency in the disruption of the resistant micro-organisms can be obtained by the addition of small hard particles such as fine glass beads or Celite to the cell suspension. Care must be taken to see that such additions are perfectly clean and that they do not possess properties which tend to adsorb or denature the activity being extracted.

REFERENCES

1. HUGHES, D. E. and NYBORG, W. L., *Science*, **138**, 108 (1962).
2. ROSETT, T., *Appl. Microbiol.* **13**, 254 (1965).
3. GRABAR, P., *Advan. Biol. Med. Phys.*, **3**, 191 (1958).
4. KANIG, K. and KUNKEL, H., *Z. Physiol. Chem.*, **309**, 171 (1957).
5. WU, H. and LIU, S. E., *Proc. Soc. Exptl. Biol. Med.*, **28**, 782 (1935).
6. KANIG, K. and KUNKEL, H., *Z. Physiol. Chem.*, **309**, 166 (1957).
7. Abstracts of the 69th Meeting of the Acoustical Society of America, Washington, D.C., June (1965).
8. NIEDERPREUM, D. J. and HACKETT, D. P., *J. Bacteriol.*, **81**, 557 (1961).
9. KELLY, B. and APPLEMAN, M. D., *J. Bacteriol.*, **81**, 715 (1961).
10. MCPHEDRAN, P. M., SOMMER, B. and LIN, E. C. C., *J. Bacteriol.*, **81**, 852 (1961).
11. WOLIN, M. J., WOLIN, E. A. and JACOBS, N. J., *J. Bacteriol.*, **81**, 911 (1961).
12. JONES, D., DEIBEL, R. H. and NIVEN, C. F. JR., *J. Bacteriol.*, **88**, 602 (1964).
13. COPPER, R. C., *J. Bacteriol.*, **88**, 624 (1964).
14. MERRICK, J. M. and DOUDOROFF, M., *J. Bacteriol.*, **88**, 60 (1964).
15. VANDEMARK, P. J. and SMITH, P. F., *J. Bacteriol.*, **88**, 122 (1964).
16. LEAVITT, R. I., *J. Bacteriol.*, **88**, 172 (1964).
17. KERWAR, S. S., CHELDELIN, V. H. and PARKS, I. W., *J. Bacteriol.*, **88**, 179 (1964).
18. BONVENTRE, P. F. and KEMPE, L. C., *J. Bacteriol.*, **79**, 18, 24 (1960).
19. KUNKEE, R. E., *J. Bacteriol.*, **79**, 43, 51 (1960).
20. EAGON, R. G. and WILLIAMS, A. K., *J. Bacteriol.*, **79**, 90 (1960).
21. PERRY, J. J. and EVANS, J. B., *J. Bacteriol.*, **79**, 113 (1960).
22. WHEAT, R. W. and PITTMAN, M., *J. Bacteriol.*, **79**, 137 (1960).
23. SCHWAB, J. H., *J. Bacteriol.*, **79**, 488, 496 (1960).
24. SAZ, A. K. and MARTINEZ, M., *J. Bacteriol.*, **79**, 527 (1960).
25. JACOBS, W. J. and VANDEMARK, P. J., *J. Bacteriol.*, **79**, 532 (1960).

26. FELLMAN, J. H. and MILLS, R. C., *J. Bacteriol.*, **79**, (1960).
27. MCDONALD, J. K., CHELDELIN, V. H. and KING, T. E., *J. Bacteriol.*, **80**, 61 (1964).
28. SUTTON, D. D. and STARR, M. P., *J. Bacteriol.*, **80**, 104 (1964).
29. FELDMAN, W. and O'KANE, D. J., *J. Bacteriol.*, **80**, 218 (1960).
30. HALPRIN, Y. S. and UMBARGER, H. E., *J. Bacteriol.*, **80**, 285 (1961).
31. ANDERSON, J. M. and RICKENBERG, H. V., *J. Bacteriol.*, **80**, 297 (1964).
32. OTT, J. L., *J. Bacteriol.*, **80**, 355 (1964).
33. VAN EYS, J., *J. Bacteriol.*, **80**, 386 (1964).
34. KEELER, R. F. and GRAY, M. L., *J. Bacteriol.*, **80**, 683 (1900).
35. DOI R. H. and HALVORSEN, H., *J. Bacteriol.*, **81**, 51 (1961).
36. ANDERSON, R. L. and ORDAL, E. J., *J. Bacteriol.*, **81**, 139 (1961).
37. KRICHEVSKY, M. L. and WOOD, W. A., *J. Bacteriol.*, **81**, 2116 (1961).
38. HARRIS, R. V. and JAMES, A. T., *Biochem. J.*, **94**, 15C (1965).
39. ASHWORTH, J. M., KORNBERG, H. L. and WOOD, R. L., *Biochem. J.*, **94**, 28P (1965).
40. COOPER, R. A., ITIBA, N. and KORNBERG, H. L., *Biochem. J.*, **94**, 25 (1965).
41. DELWICHE, E. A., *J. Bacteriol.*, **81**, 425 (1961).
42. MARR, E. K. and STONE, R. W., *J. Bacteriol.*, **81**, 425 (1961).
43. KRAKOW, G., BARKULIS, S. S. and HAYASHI, J. A., *J. Bacteriol.*, **81**, 509 (1961).
44. SAGERS, R. D. and GUNSALUS, I. C., *J. Bacteriol.*, **81**, 541 (1961).
45. HAWLEY, S. A., MACLEOD, R. M. and DUNN, F., *J. Acoust. Soc. Am.*, **38** (8), 1285 (1963).
46. COWDEN, J. W. and ABELL, M. R., *Exptl. and Molecular Path.*, **2** (4), 367 (1963).
47. LEVITON, A. and MARSH, W. H., *Federation Proc.*, **22**, 485 (1963).
48. GEYER, A., *Arch. Mikrobiol.*, **46** (1), 9 (1963).
49. THORPE, E. J., BELLOMY, B. B. and SELLERS, R. F., *J. Bone Joint Surg.*, **45A** (6), 1257 (1963).
50. QURAISHI, M. S., OSMANI, M. H. and AHMED, S. A., *J. Ean. Entomol.*, **56** (5), 668 (1963).
51. TVERDYNSKII, M. A., *Akad. Nauk., S.S.S.R.*, **3**, 71 (1958).
52. AN-CHI, W. and CHEN-YIN, W., *Acta Biol. Expu. Sinica.*, **8** (2), 131 (1963).
53. EL'PINER, I. E. and SHEBALDINA, A. D., *Radiobiol.*, **3** (5), 646 (1963).
54. NAKASHIMA, N., *Nagoya J. Med. Sci.*, **25**, (1), 11 (1962).
55. GOL'DAT, S. Y. and SOKOLOVA, R. V., *Antibiotiki*, **9** (2), 126 (1964).
56. LUTSENKO, A. M., RUTTER, E. G., FRINSHTEIN, Z. B., PEVZNER, M. L. and SOBOLEV, A. I., *Vestn. Sel'Shokhoz Nauki*, **9** (1), 128 (1964).
57. EL'PINER, I. E. and STEKOL'NIKOV, L. L., *Biokhimiya*, **28** (3), 801 (1963).
58. WEINLAND, L. S., *Proc. Penn. Acad. Sci.*, **37**, 48 (1963).
59. PERS, I. F. and ZHDANOVA, L. G., *Zh. Mikrobiol, Epidemiol. Immunobiol.*, **41** (3), 27 (1964).
60. LOTT, J. A. and DeMAGGIO, A. E., *Science*, **139**, 825 (1963).
61. BARANY, M. and FINKELMAN, F., *Biochim. Biophys. Acta*, **63**, 98 (1962).
62. EL'PINER, I. E., *Ultrasound, Physical Chemical and Biological Effects*, Consultants Bureau, New York, (1964).

12

MUTATIONS AND ULTRASOUND

A. G. Gordon, B.Sc.

12.1 INTRODUCTION

It is now over a century since Gregor Mendel, the Austrian monk, first discovered that there was a predictable mathematical relationship between certain characteristics of peas. His findings were not made known to the world until the beginning of this century however, by which time other workers had investigated the relationship of heritable characteristics and the cell. Thus, it was Weissmann in 1892 and Roux in 1905 who first became aware of the fact that hereditary material is found in the nucleus. When Mendel's results were re-investigated in the light of this knowledge, it became clear that the grouping of two similar parts of the nucleus at a particular stage in the cycle of the sex cell, corresponded to the two factors which Mendel had predicted in his explanation of the observed mathematical relationships of a pair of characteristics such as red and white flower colour of peas.

These findings stimulated a very intense research into the cell and its hereditary characteristics. It was soon discovered that the process of growth takes place by repeated cell divisions. In plants this takes place mainly in definite regions, known as meristems, but in animals growth is more general. A cell division in which the same number of chromosomes are produced in both daughter cells is known as mitosis. A chromosome is the name given to the parts of the nucleus of the cell which become plainly visible as deeply stainable rods at the divisions of the cell. All cells of an organism except those which are formed as gametes or sex cells are therefore produced by mitosis and contain the so-called diploid number $(2n)$ of chromosomes. It soon became obvious that a reduction division of the nucleus, meiosis, forming a haploid number of chromosomes (*n*) must take place in the life cycle of an organism to ensure there is no build up in the number of chromosomes in the nuclei of subsequent generations, as it was early found that a particular species had a constant number of chromosomes in its nucleus. During meiosis it was observed that chromosomes became differentiated and that they came to lie close to each other in pairs as though they were identical. It was thus assumed that one half of these similar (homologous) chromosomes came from the female parent and half from the male parent. This was definitely proved in 1927, when Morgan, working on Drosophila discovered that male and female flies had a pair of chromosomes which were not always homologous, the male having one chromosome which was shorter than the other of the pair, which itself resembled both chromosomes of the female. It was later found that any organism which demonstrates sex has this or the exact opposite disparity in this pair of chromosomes, the so-called sex chromosomes.

It soon became obvious by overwhelming circumstantial evidence that the pairs of hereditary factors were situated on pairs of homologous chromosomes, which appeared as easily stained sausage-shaped rods during divisions of the nucleus. Microscopic examination of the large chromosomes of some species revealed that the chromosomes had bands in them which seemed to correspond to particular characteristics. These are known as genes, and it has been shown that they are arranged on the chromosomes in a definite order which can be determined by experiments with identifiable factors situated on the same chromosomes. Thus chromosome maps can be produced for organisms, detailing the positions of most known genes in the organism. The exact composition of a gene is not known but it appears that they are nucleic acids, which seem to govern the production of enzymes which are responsible for the regulation of all biochemical processes within the cell. Some genes seem to have a simple effect, e.g. presence or absence of colour, while others have a complicated effect, governing many seemingly unrelated chracteristics. In divisions therefore the genes on the chromosomes somehow reproduce themselves identically, to form two daughter chromatids, one of which passes to either daughter cell. But before continuing with a discussion of mutations we must look at the cell and its division a little more closely.

12.2 THE CELL

A typical plant cell in its active state is represented in the diagram Fig. 12.1. It comprises three main parts. (1) The cell wall, which may be thin (and primary), that is all increase in thickness has taken place before extensive growth has finished, or thickened (secondary walls). (2) The protoplasm which comprises the cytoplasm and the nucleus. The cytoplasm is of a very complex colloidal nature, and is the seat of action of the vital processes of the cell. The nucleus is composed of a nuclear membrane, nuclear sap, chromonemata (= colour threads) and a nucleolus. The chromonemata are so called due to their possession of chromatin, a substance strongly

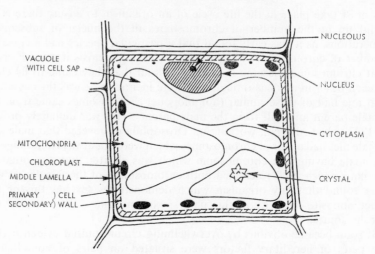

Fig. 12.1. Diagrammatic representation of a typical plant cell

stainable with certain dyes, enabling the chromonemata to stand out clearly in the unstained cell sap. They appear in the active nucleus as a network or reticulum and in fact represent the chromosomes seen in mitosis and meiosis. The nucleolus is a small easily differentiated object usually associated with particular chromosomes. (3) The vacuole, which contains cell sap (water and compounds in solution or colloidal dispersion) and crystals.

12.3 MITOSIS

This is the nuclear division of the somatic (body) cells of an organism—it is a process in which each of the chromosomes of the nucleus undergoes a longitudinal doubling, half of each chromosome separating into two similar groups, which become the daughter nuclei. In the metabolic stage the nucleus is more or less adpressed to the cell wall; during the prophase of mitosis it assumes a more central position and the chromonemata become combined with a matrix substance from the nuclear sap which enable them to be easily stained, becoming the compact separate structures we easily recognize as chromosomes. In the early stages of prophase close examination of the chromonemata reveal that they consist of pairs of very fine threads. Gradually the mass of chromonemata becomes less uniform and the threads stand out separately. They become more compact and with deposition of matrix become easily stainable. At the end of prophase the chromosomes are thus thick double bodies with two chromatids, each composed of chromonema and matrix. The nucleolus may or may not disappear.

Next the nucleus passes into the metaphase in which, by a complicated series of chemical changes within the nuclear sap, a spindle is laid down.

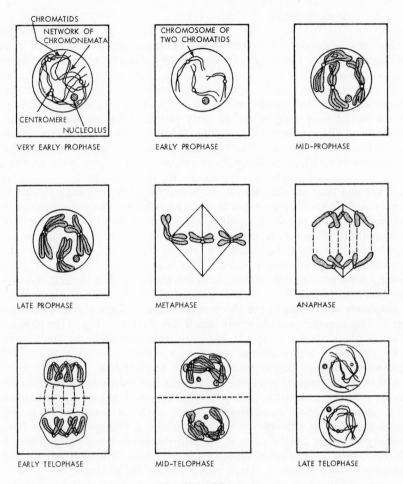

Fig. 12.2. Mitosis

(This change is probably a re-arrangement of colloidal proteins in the sap.) At this stage the nuclear membrane disappears leaving the chromosomes in the midst of the spindle. In each of the chromatids there is a specialized region called the centromere which is the region of spindle attachment. In the next stage, anaphase, the two chromatids of each chromosome separate and pass to opposite poles; as soon as the breakage occurs the two chromatids are known as chromosomes. When the chromosomes have reached their respective poles they enter telophase in which the nuclear membranes reappear, the matrix is dispersed and the chromonemata once more become reticulate. A cell wall is formed between the daughter nuclei, and the cells enter the active stage of their life. The process is illustrated in Fig. 12.2.

12.4 MEIOSIS

This, as has already been mentioned, is a reduction division of sex cells of the organism. The stages of this division correspond to mitosis except in prophase which is a very complex stage. The nucleus of an ordinary cell consists of two haploid sets of chromosomes which were brought together at the last gametic union. It is thus necessary that this haploid state be obtained once more. In early prophase the chromonemata are present as distinct, very long, slender threads, each of which represents a chromosome. These come together to lie in pairs of homologous chromosomes, all pairs being more or less parallel one with another. The next stage of prophase is typified by the threads becoming noticeably thicker and they are then said to be bivalents, since they each consist of two homologous chromosomes in close association. Soon each chromosome is seen to consist of a pair of chromatids, the whole forming four chromatids, known as tetrads. In a later stage of prophase the tetrads try to separate only to be hindered by one or more points where two of the chromatids have changed position. This is known as a chiasma or cross over. A tetrad with one chiasma thus has the form of an X, and one with two chiasmata at either end the form of an O. If crossing-overs occur completely at random in the chromosomes the frequency with which two genes stay together will obviously bear a direct relationship to the physical distance between the genes. It is experiments measuring the frequencies of combination and recombination of pairs of factors, which have enabled chromosome maps, already mentioned, to be compiled.

In the final stage of prophase the tetrads sort themselves out into four even shorter chromatids, the processes involved being as in mitosis. The spindle is next formed and half (two) of the chromatids pass to one pole and half to the other. The chromosomes, though they may have undergone some genetic change, are still present in the diploid state. A further division thus takes place to produce four cells with the haploid number of chromosomes. These cells represent the gametes. It should be emphasized that in both mitosis and meiosis it is the identical self-reproduction of the genes which is responsible for the formation of chromatids. The process is illustrated in Fig. 12.3.

12.5 MUTATION

With this brief description of the cell we are now able to consider mutations and their importance to breeders. The broad definition of a mutation is therefore, any unexpected change in the configuration of the chromosomes. They can arise either as chromosome mutations or gene mutations. A gene mutation can arise if in the reproduction process something happens to hinder the gene from reproducing itself identically. (See scheme of break down of nucleic acids, Fig. 12.4.) A change, however small, in the chemical composition of the base might cause a gene mutation. Chromosomes are made up of a very large number of these nucleic acids, which

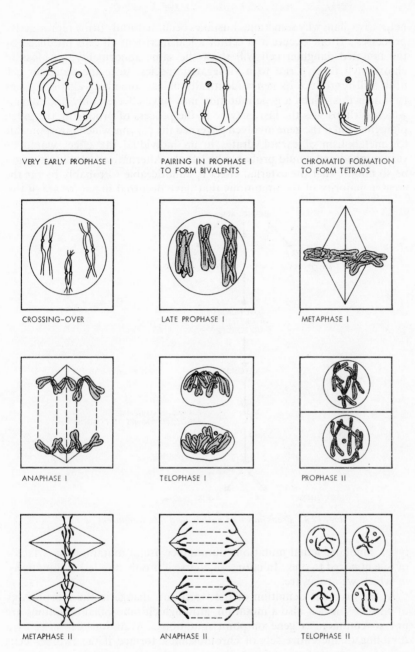

VERY EARLY PROPHASE I

PAIRING IN PROPHASE I
TO FORM BIVALENTS

CHROMATID FORMATION
TO FORM TETRADS

CROSSING-OVER

LATE PROPHASE I

METAPHASE I

ANAPHASE I

TELOPHASE I

PROPHASE II

METAPHASE II

ANAPHASE II

TELOPHASE II

Fig. 12.3. Meiosis

helps to explain why sometimes mistakes occur naturally in the reproductive processes. If one occurs in a cell of a leaf meristem all cells produced by the mutated daughter cell will show the same abnormality, e.g. loss of chlorophyll to give rise to a variegated species, since the daughter cell itself will reproduce its genes identically unless something again happens to hinder this. Such a gene mutation may have affected only one enzyme which perhaps was the last enzyme in the process of producing the green pigment. But if the gene involved governed the enzyme which is responsible for metabolism of carbohydrates in an individual the effect would be very marked and would probably be lethal. Alternatively the effect might be so minute that the external effect is unnoticeable. Probably by far the greater majority of the mutations that have occurred in nature are of this

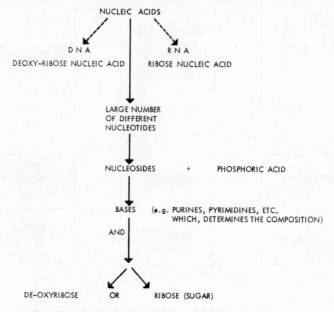

Fig. 12.4. Break-down of nucleic acid into component parts

type. Similarly lethal mutations outnumber useful mutations by a factor of one hundred to one. In nature of course it is only non-lethal mutations, of which we are aware.

In the broadest definition of the word any change in the morphology of chromosomes is also a mutation, although chromosomal mutations are not so common as gene or point mutations. Mutations can arise by a doubling of the entire sets of chromosomes, formed if the two sex cells fail to divide to form a haploid gamete, the fusion product having $4n$ chromosomes. This is called a tetraploid. Similarly a tetraploid can give rise to an octaploid, and fusion of gametes from a diploid and a tetraploid, to a hexaploid. Such mutations are perhaps in the plant world of most benefit to commerce as there is usually a striking increase in the vegetative growth of the plants. If a whole chromosome is lost during cell division, which can happen if for some reason the chromosomes are divided unequally, the zygote, i.e. product of male and female sex cells will contain $2n - 1$ chromosomes, the other gamete being normal. This is called a monosomic. If the zygote is formed by the fusion of one gamete with one chromosome in excess with one normal, it would have $2n + 1$ chromosomes. This is called a trisomic. In both these cases because there is an uneven number of chromosomes present the subsequent meiotic division would be abnormal and the sex cells thus produced would probably be sterile.

The chromosomal mutations mentioned so far have been changes in the basic number of chromosomes. However mutations can occur due to a change in the number and arrangement of the genes within the chromosome. We have mentioned that one stage in the reduction division of a nucleus is the pairing of homologous chromosomes. If by some chance there is an inversion, i.e. part of one chromosome turns upside down, it will be impossible for the chromosomes to come to lie beside each other in a normal fashion. The same will happen if part of one chromosome breaks off and joins itself to another chromosome—such a happening being called a translocation. In all cases along the length of the chromosome there is an area called the centromere which governs the attraction of the dividing chromosomes to the opposite poles of the dividing cell. Any part of a chromosome which has a centromere will be represented in the daughter nuclei, but any part without will remain unattracted to either end and so in turn will become lost. Breaks occurring in a chromosome in the absence of translocation or inversion will therefore give rise to deficiency of at least part of the chromosome in the end. These deficiencies are very often lethal in their effect.

12.6 HISTORY OF MUTATION BREEDING

Long before the significance of the nucleus and the chromosomes became known, sudden unexpected changes in the external appearance of various organisms had been observed. Darwin called these changes sports, but more recently they have become known as mutations. Until 1927 every effort to produce mutations artificially had failed but then X-rays were discovered to produce mutations at a maximum rate of about 25 per ten thousand gametes. Since that date ultraviolet light, alpha particles, neutrons, gamma rays and various chemicals have also been found to produce mutations. All these mutagenic processes have some disadvantage or other. About 1950 ultrasound became added to this list of mutagens. Soon after the original discovery of artificial mutagens the Swedish Plant Breeding Station became very interested in barley mutation breeding. However in all the years during which their search has gone on, only one new variety has been released to commerce. One variety of mustard, and one of rape have also been released from Sweden. In the United States one variety of bean has recently been released. Mutation breeding has a place in the research of most recognized agricultural breeding stations, but at the moment the part played by it is relatively small, except in Sweden. In that country a relatively large proportion of barley breeding is carried out by searching for useful mutations. It should be mentioned that although much mutations research is being and has been carried out using the vinegar fly, *Drosophilia melanogaster*, as treated material, there is no demand for mutations in animals to the same extent as in plants. Useful animal mutations have been found however, e.g. hornless state in cattle, but it is not the general custom to treat animals to obtain these mutations.

The usefulness of mutation breeding is very definitely related to the efficiency of detecting these mutations. In some simple mutation studies for new strains of fungi and bacteria, the 'screening process' is very easily carried out, but in higher plants there are rarely such efficient methods. In barley for instance a mutation would be sought for in a variety with most other good characteristics, i.e. good yield, early ripening etc., the search being for a strong strawed mutation. In one thousand treated grains it would obviously not be an easy process to detect the useful mutated plant if it existed.

There are as yet several unsolved questions with regard to mutation breeding. For instance do artificially induced mutations differ in any way from those occurring naturally? In some cases, for example, chlorophyll deficiency, it is easy to see the similar effect from natural and artificial mutations, but it is still not clear whether the fundamental biochemical process involved was the same. Again do useful mutations occur often enough to make the search profitable? The Swedes obviously think so but as yet no mutagenic process has been discovered, whether physical or chemical which produces mutations at a sufficiently great rate. These facts should be viewed in the light of the fact that for X-rays, which have the highest mutagenic rate so far investigated, unfavourable mutations outnumber useful mutations by a factor of 800 to 1. However there is no doubt that mutation breeding does free the plant breeder from dependence on natural variability, but this fact is hardly enough to make him adopt mutation breeding as a major method of plant improvement.

12.7 HOW DO MUTATIONS OCCUR?

There are two recognized basic processes involved. First the target theory, which believes that a mutation occurs as a result of mechanical disruption at a particular point in the hereditary material and secondly the indirect activation theory, which believes that mutations are induced more or less indirectly by a chemical alteration of hereditary materials as a whole. In the former case we can think in terms of the mutagenic force acting on a particular bond in the nucleic acid, whereas in the latter the action is on the nucleic acid as a whole.

Both alpha particles and neutrons, which are densely ionizing materials, seem to act primarily mechanically as most of their action is the production of chromosomal alterations; some point mutations do however occur, which also seem to be either mechanical in nature, or a secondary reaction of chemicals produced by ionization of the protoplasm. The less densely ionizing radiations, X-rays and gamma rays have accordingly a lesser tendancy to produce chromosomal alterations but correspondingly more point mutations. Ultraviolet rays excite the electrons, but do not cause ionization of the chemicals forming the chromosomes, and hence show an even lesser tendancy to produce chromosomal aberrations; they produce a relatively high proportion of point mutations. In general, the more energy a physical mutagen gives off the higher the proportion of chromosomal aberration to point mutation. Where ultrasound fits into the scheme of things had best be left until we have discussed the mutagenic properties in some detail. To complete the list we should mention chemical mutagens which achieve their effect fairly obviously by a direct chemical reaction with the nucleic acids of the chromosomes.

As regards the uses of mutations in breeding, we should also mention that mutations are of particular use in changing a single simply inherited characteristic in a highly developed species—thus in the process of hybridization of such a highly developed variety the superior combination of genes may be disrupted, leading to the plant succumbing to a new disease. A simple screening test would soon discover a newly mutated resistant variety. Also mutations are of particular use in adding specific characteristics to fruit trees and other plants which are propagated vegetatively involving no sexual process, for example strawberry runners, suckers from trees and cuttings. By applying a mutagenic agent to a cutting of a high yielding variety of apple, resistance to a disease might be produced.

Against all this it should be emphasized again that all these processes involve the testing of a very large second generation population, and hence demonstrate the dependence of mutation breeders on efficient screening techniques.

12.8 ULTRASOUND AS A MUTAGEN

The literature on the mutagenic effect of ultrasound falls very clearly into two halves, depending upon whether the workers have studied the phenotypic (external observable expression of the genes on the chromosomes) or whether they have studied the cytological evidence for the occurrence of mutations. As soon as some positive mutagenic effects were produced by ultrasound, the questions which had to be answered were naturally if ultrasound gave as high a mutation rate as the other recognized mutagens and also did ultrasonic mutations resemble other mutations. In all the literature it must be admitted that ultrasound does not give mutations at the rates which the best mutagens do, but if once the optimum dose and frequency can be discovered this does not necessarily rule out the use of ultrasound, as it does have certain advantages. It is a great pity that more workers did not devote their time to obtaining positive phenotypic evidence. Instead the majority of evidence was gained by studying the cytology of the action of ultrasound. Their investigations were thus rather more subjective than objective, their approach being to prove that nothing should happen with ultrasound before showing that something in fact does.

The phenotypic evidence can best be treated chronologically. It was Hersch et al.[1] in 1930 who first attempted to obtain mutations using ultrasound. That they were unsuccessful has since been attributed to their technique, which was rather crude. Their material, Drosophila melanogaster, the vinegar fly, was treated unanaesthetized in glass vials immersed in an oil bath over a crystal oscillating at 285 kc/s. Few details are given of their doses but it is justifiable to suppose that only a third of the acoustic energy produced could have reached the flies in the vials. They mated treated males with untreated females and discovered that in the 26,135 offspring which were raised from the 20 per cent which survived, there were only 52 abnormals, and only one characteristic of these, mottled eye colour, was continuously heritable. Such a rate is hardly more than a natural rate. Their search for mutations however was restricted to sex linked mutations (that is mutations that occur on the pair of sex chromosomes) and did not account for any mutations on the autosomes or ordinary chromosomes.

No further direct evidence of ultrasound as a mutagen was published until 1948, when Wallace and Bushnell,[2] Bushnell and Wallace,[3] and Wallace, Bushnell and Newcomer[4] reported on more or less the same evidence in three different periodicals. Technical details are only given in that of Wallace, Bushnell and Newcomer and one must assume that similar apparatus was employed in the others. This was a crystal capable of generating 150 acoustical watts (measured calorimetrically) in the zone where the material was treated. Dealing first with mutations produced in Drosophila, Bushnell and Wallace found, using glass vials and unanaesthetized males, that the rate was only twice normal. When young males were treated etherized in plastic or thin metal containers a much higher mutation rate was produced. Employing a special test to spot sex linked mutations 7·2 per cent proved to be lethal and 15·9 per cent to be semi-lethal. (c.f. controls with one lethal and one semi-lethal out of 184.) Visible mutations affecting the wings were observed which proved to be caused by chromosome inversions, when a cross-over test was performed. Such mutations were still observable in the second generation (F_2) when the progeny of the treated flies were interbred. Once again only sex linked mutations were investigated, since an efficient screening test existed for such mutations. The material is so small that non sex-linked mutations can only be observed on careful study by trained personnel.

These references also provide the first evidence of mutations produced by ultrasound in plant material. Wallace, Bushnell and Newcomer observed changes in the phenotype of Helianthus (Sunflower) shoots, which were highly suggestive of genetical change, and which were substantiated by cytological study of root tips. Further experiments by Wallace and Bushnell on seedlings of eight species including Helianthus, Pisum, Phaseolus and Ipomea, using ultrasound for 5 to 60 sec at an intensity of 8–10 W and at 400 kc/s, endorsed these findings. In general, flowering was advanced and the seedlings developed rosettes and other abnormalities.

The first generation seedlings of the treated plants produced some seed which in their turn produced some abnormal plants, indicating the variations were heritable, that is, they involved a definite change in the genetical make-up. In continuation experiments, mainly looking for cytological proof, Newcomer and Wallace[5] again found morphological abnormalities, but this time they were in roots. Loza,[6] in another cytological investigation observed similar abnormalities, while he experienced a stimulation of the roots.

It was about this time that Conger[7] investigated the effect of ultrasound in conjunction with X-rays in the production of mutations in *Drosophila*. He reported that ultrasound alone was unable to produce detectable mutations, but thought that the mechanical movement of chromosomes, by the ultrasound, having first been split by the X-rays, would possibly result in an improved mutation rate. He in fact did achieve a significant increase in the mutation rate of *Tradescantia* buds. He used ultrasound, produced by magnetostriction at a frequency of 9·1 kc/s but gives no details of the acoustic energy which he employed.

In the early 1950's Haskell and Selman[8] investigated the effects of ultrasonic energy on seeds of maize. They observed no phenotypic abnormalities in any plants grown from the seeds, imbibed and treated at 10–35 W/cm^2 with 1 Mc/s ultrasound. In a cytological study at a later date, Selman[9] found no morphological abnormality in onion roots, at doses up to 5 W/cm^2, using the same apparatus, but in an investigation of pollen of *Tradescantia* he did observe an abnormality in the pollen tube development. Together with Counce,[10] Selman examined the effect of ultrasound on the development of the embryos of *Drosophila*. Using ultrasound at 0·3–0·5 W/cm^2 for 30 sec they obtained abnormal developments of embryos, but did not investigate their heredity. They did conclude that ultrasound might be of great use in similar development studies, by producing abnormalities from completely outwith the embryo. Other mutation investigations on animals at this time were carried out by Bessler,[11] Brettschneider,[12] Lotmar,[13] and Fritz-Niggli.[14]

In 1952 Spencer[22] produced some very interesting evidence of phenotypic variations induced by ultrasound. Using a frequency of 500 kc/s for 20 sec at 20 W/cm^2 he treated pea root tips and found that 20 per cent of the treated material, when it had recovered from the dose, had an increased growth rate. In order to investigate the heritability of the improvement, Spencer endeavoured to produce a similar effect in shoot tips. Seeds imbibed for 6 hr and kept moist for a further 12 hr were treated for up to 30 sec at 20 W/cm^2. Germination percentages were as follows: Control 28 per cent, 10 sec 79 per cent, 15 sec 56 per cent, 20 sec 29 per cent and 30 sec 9 per cent. Of the 20 sec batch 22 per cent had a very noticeable increase in root growth, but only 2 per cent of the 15 sec batch. These results were highly repeatable; the improvement was also very significant in later growth. The difference between the elongated and control plants was greater at 20 days than would be expected between a dwarf and a tall variety of that time. Reciprocal crosses were made between these elongated plants, and controls, and plants resembling controls from the 78 per cent

231

remaining from the 15 sec batch. In all cases where the female parent was elongated, the characteristic was passed on to the offspring, but in no cases were the reciprocal crosses effective. In plants there is invariably some cytoplasm present with the female gamete while there is none with the male gamete. It thus became apparent that the abnormality which had occurred had taken place in the cytoplasm and was not nuclear at all. Such an abnormality, which usually lasts for seven or eight generations, but with diminishing strength, is known as a dauer-modification, and is not in fact a mutation in the accepted sense of the word. Spencer's findings were however of such interest to be worthy of mention here.

In 1954 Newcomer[15] published the results of his cytological investigations into the effects of ultrasound on Narcissus root tips. In this he mentions that the abnormalities which had been produced in *Helianthus* by Wallace and Bushnell, were still growing, and were exhibiting Mendelian ratios, undoubted evidence of mutations. This is corroborated by Obolensky,[16] who reported that seed sent to him in Canada by Wallace from first and second generation mutated plants, still produced these abnormalities in Mendelian ratios. The seed had been obtained by grafting the albinos on to green stalks to enable them to grow. He also achieved outstanding figures for growth of *Helianthus* plants from these seeds, and in further experiments larger than normal flowering heads. The latest available report is from Bulgaria where Geogieva *et al.*[17] (1962), using ultrasound of 9·9 W/cm² for up to 4 hr on germinating seeds obtained plants of lucerne, maize, cucumber and melon with obvious deformations and abnormalities. (No frequency is specified.) Foliar deformations were shed after a term of growth, and treated plants were usually smaller and gave a decreased yield, compared with controls. The seeds of melon and cucumber were also deformed. The course of these deformations in future generations was to be investigated. To complete the picture mention should be made of an investigation by Miszynsky[18] into mutations induced in potato Virus X by ultrasound. His evidence was inconclusive, but it did appear that some change in the effect of Virus X on Tobacco plants was produced by treatment with ultrasound. He used ultrasound of 600 and 1200 kc/s at 5 W/cm² for 4 hr.

Table 12.1 summarizes the mutation evidence.

It is not possible to draw many firm conclusions from the above with regard to the mutagenic action of ultrasound. Certainly it appears that frequency has little effect, within fairly broad limits, but it has been suggested that ultrasound with a wavelength nearer that of the chromosomes own dimensions would have a greater mutagenic effect.[9] No evidence to verify this is at hand yet however. In contrast to this it is possible to say that fairly high power is required to produce a mutagenic effect; fragile tissues such as root tips, are very easily destroyed by ultrasound at high energy levels as will be seen, and there are frequent reports of damage being done to tissues, before mutations were produced. No optimum dosage has been discovered. Much depends no doubt upon the method of treatment. Wallace and Bushnell were successful by immersing growing shoots directly in an ultrasonic column, while Hersch *et al.* were unsuccessful,

Table 12.1

Author	Country	Date	Material	Freq. kc/s	Power w/cm²	Duration	Effect
Hersch[1]	U.S.A.	1930	Drosophila	285	low	?	—
Wallace Bushnell[2]	U.S.A.	1948	Helianthus, Pisum, Phaseolus, Ipomaea	400	8–10	5–60 sec	+
Wallace Bushnell Newcomer[4]	U.S.A.	1948	Allium, Narcissus, Helianthus, Drosophila	400	8–10	?	+
Bushnell Wallace[3]	U.S.A.	1948	Drosophila	400	8–10	?	+
Dubow[25]	U.S.A.	1949	Drosophila	?	?	?	+
Conger[7]	U.S.A.	1949	Drosophila	9·1	250 v	?	+ —
Newcomer Wallace[5]	U.S.A.	1949	Root tips	400	8–10	up to 60 sec	+
Haskell Selman[8]	U.K.	1950	Maize seeds	1000	10 and 35	?	—
Fritz-Niggli[14]	Germany	1950	Drosophila	?	?	?	+
Loza[6]	France	1951	Rice, Soya, Pea, Radish, roots	960	14	?	+
Selman[9]	U.K.	1952	Allium, Chick, Tradescantia	1000	5	3 min	+ —
Bessler[11]	Germany	1952	Triton	800	1·5	5 sec	+
Brettschneider[12]	Germany	1952	Hens' eggs, Frog spawn	?	?	?	+
Lotmar[13]	Germany	1952	Drosophila	?	?	?	+
Koch	Germany	1952	Barley	350 430	4	5–30 sec	+
Spencer[22]	U.S.A.	1952	Pea	500	10–20	up to 30 sec	+ —
Selman Counce[10]	U.K.	1953	Drosophila	1000	0·3–0·5	up to 30 sec	+
Miszynsky[18]	Poland	1954	Virus X	600– 1200	5	4 hr	+
Newcomer[15]	U.S.A.	1954	Helianthus	400	8–10	?	+
Obolensky[16]	Canada	1958	Helianthus	400	8–10	?	+
Georgieva[17]	Bulgaria	1962	Lucerne, Maize, Cucumber, Melon	?	9·9	4 hr	+ —

presumably because their flies were treated unanaesthetized in glass vials, placed in an oil bath over an oscillating crystal. The coupling between the oil and the flies was so poor that it is surprising that they expected favourable results. Most other experiments were carried out by holding the material in either a focused or unfocused column of ultrasound, with water as the medium. In some the crystal of quartz or other piezo-electric crystal was in direct contact with the liquid coupling medium,[19,20,21] in others a thin diaphragm of metal separated the oil and coupling liquid.[5,9,15] It should at this point be mentioned that it is impossible to compare these power levels as they have been computed in different ways. Some have been measured calorimetrically,[2,15,22] and some by thermocouple[21] or radiation pressure balance[20] while some seem to have been arrived at more or less by guess work or computed from electrical data.[17,23] In many references there is very little data at all concerning the apparatus used. It would be fair to say that what is lacking is a controlled experiment using similar apparatus for every frequency and intensity. Only then would it be really possible to determine whether ultrasound is to be of any use as a mutagen.

12.9 THE CYTOLOGICAL EVIDENCE OF MUTATIONS

There is more cytological evidence concerning the effect of ultrasound as a mutagen, than there is phenotypic evidence. The results are however, no less confusing, since some are positive and some negative. The investigations are carried out using material which is undergoing some kind of division. For this reason root tips have been mainly investigated, but shoot tips also have received some attention. Flowering buds, with their meiotic divisions have also been used.

Most of these experiments were carried out with a view to comparing ultrasound with other mutagens. The theory behind the investigations was that mutations will only occur effectively, if the chromosomes which are broken by the ultrasound subsequently rejoin in a new configuration. In this way the normal chromosome pairings are upset and new characteristics result. In cases where a split chromosome does not rejoin, it will eventually be lost and the resultant plant though not actually killed, will be seriously affected in its vigour. Such mutations are some of the very high proportion of deleterious mutations which occur. Evidence of chromosomal rearrangements and rejoining are found by examining mitoses and meioses for obvious differences in the division figures on comparison with normal plants. It is at metaphase and anaphase that these differences will be most noticeable. In meiosis we have said that homologous chromosomes are attracted to each other. If a translocation or inversion takes place at metaphase, the attraction of one similar gene in a chromosome for its pair will not be upset, but will necessarily produce an abnormal metaphase figure. If chiasmata subsequently occur in the inverted segments the anaphase figures will also be abnormal, forming chromatid bridges (See Fig. 12.5). Their exact fate will of course depend upon the position of the centromere. The appearance of these unusual forms will eventually mean the loss of these chromosomes, and subsequent death of the cells, but these effects are taken as being circumstantial evidence that, chromosomal rearrangement having once taken place, it will also take place in other cells with a non lethal effect. The literature has mainly reported searches for these chromatid bridges, their absence being taken as indicative of the failure of ultrasound to produce mutations.

The great majority of authors have found that ultrasound is able to cause breakages in chromosomes,[4,5,9,11,15,21-8] and in single chromatids,[4,5,15,28] but the evidence on recombination of broken parts is not so extensive. Also by far the most work has been carried out on mitotic divisions. An increase in the rate of mitosis has been specifically mentioned by Olivier,[19] Bessler,[11] Loza,[6] and Newcomer,[15] though in one case no increase or decrease in the rate was noticed.[9] When treating root tips, however, it has been found on the whole that doses which are effective in producing nuclear disturbances have also been effective in causing death or at least a certain amount of necrosis of the tissues. The technique which has been generally applied has been to treat the root tips in a column of ultrasound for a given period and then to fix samples having allowed 0, 12, 24, etc. up to 120 hr to elapse since treatment. Smears or squashes are made on a slide and then stained with a suitable chromatin stain. Differences in mitotic and meiotic figures which occur when compared with control slides similarly prepared, are taken as being evidence of the effect of ultrasound. In such experiments it is impossible therefore to get

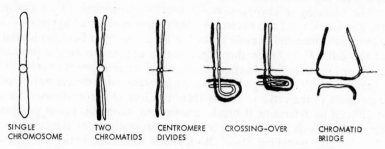

SINGLE
CHROMOSOME

TWO
CHROMATIDS

CENTROMERE
DIVIDES

CROSSING-OVER

CHROMATID
BRIDGE

SOMATIC CROSSING-OVER THE CHROMATIDS ARE DIFFERENTLY COLOURED FOR EASE IN
DISTINGUISHING. THEY ARE NOT OF COURSE A PAIR OF HOMOLOGOUS CHROMOSOMES.
THE PAIR OF CHROMATIDS BECOME COILED, A BREAK OCCURS AND DIFFERENT PARTS REJOIN.
A CHROMATID BRIDGE RESULTS. THIS IS ONLY ONE WAY IN WHICH THESE BRIDGES CAN
OCCUR.

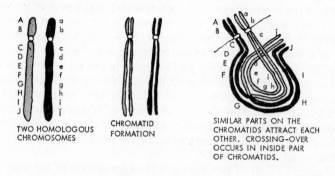

TWO HOMOLOGOUS
CHROMOSOMES

CHROMATID
FORMATION

SIMILAR PARTS ON THE
CHROMATIDS ATTRACT EACH
OTHER. CROSSING-OVER
OCCURS IN INSIDE PAIR
OF CHROMATIDS.

ANAPHASE WITH BRIDGE AND
FRAGMENT

TWO NORMAL NON-CROSS-OVER
CHROMOSOMES AND TWO INVIABLE

Fig. 12.5. Chromatid bridge formation in meiotic division

final proof that ultrasound has caused a particular mutation—the evidence is at best circumstantial.

The breaking of chromosomes is usually accompanied by a change in the chromaticity of the nucleus.[21] Thus there is often an agglutination of a chromatic material outside the cell rather as though a fluid has leaked out of the cell.[23,27,28] Often this agglutination appears to be the product of three or four cells.[22,23] In contrast the nuclei often appear to become more highly stained[21] as though there was an increase in the concentration of the chromatin in the cell. In others there is a loss of chromaticity[5,6] making it difficult to determine if breaks are present, though it is not possible to say whether this is caused by a loss of chromatin from the cell or some chemical change taking place. Both effects have been noticed in the same tissue.[20,22,28] In general the higher the intensity of ultrasound the greater will the effect be. At very high intensities the effects are more or less explosive,[7,17,28] fragments being scattered throughout the tissue. Such nuclear damage is often accompanied by necrosis of the cells, and subsequent death of the treated organ.[9] In others after a static period, growth takes place, with peculiar root formations and in some cases increases in rates of growth.[15] In other cells the mitotic cycle is completely stopped.[28] The degree of disturbance caused to the cell appears to be some function of the age of the cell, thus in newly divided cells, in the meristem region, where the vacuoles of these isodiametric cells are relatively small, the effects are small, while in the larger more mature cells the effects are more explosive and drastic. In most root tips a central core of relatively unaffected tissue, corresponding to the vascular cylinder is clearly visible.[5,6,22] In others the effect was seen to correspond to the presence or absence of nodes of ultrasound, in the tissue.[26]

Another frequent result of ultrasound is the aggregation of the nuclear fragments to form strangely shaped associations. It is not clear however if these fragments are just in close proximity or whether they are fused together.[5,15,28] Evidence has been produced that sometimes there is no synapsis, or close association, equivalent almost to fusion, of the homologous chromosomes in prophase of meiosis.[28] Such associations, even if produced in cells which have shown no cell wall ruptures, will of course be unable to divide again, as they will be unable to separate with ease into two equal groups. These divisions are so delicately controlled that even small abnormalities in the mitotic figure may prove fatal.

It will be best to follow the evidence for chromosomal reorganization in a chronological order. It was Yamaha and Ueda[26] who first examined the effect of ultrasound on root tips of *Vicia faba*. They found chromosome breaks which were healed by a fusion of rearranged chromosome parts. Similar structural evidence was obtained by Wallace, Bushnell and Newcomer,[4] Dubow,[25] and Carpio and Orellana.[27] In a later work on mitosis Carpio[28] was unable to find obvious chromosomal reorganizations though she was confident that they should have been observed. Doubts as to the efficiency of ultrasound as a mutagen began to be voiced as early as 1949, when Newcomer and Wallace were unable to find any evidence of chromosomal rearrangement. As a result Newcomer made a further study[15] and was able to state categorically that none occurred, though he thought it was possible that new undetectable rearrangements did. Before his evidence was produced, both Spencer[22] and Selman[9] had been unable to find positive evidence of chromosomal rearrangements. It was this negative cytological evidence which was largely responsible for the dampening of enthusiasm as regards ultrasound as a mutagen. Since that date some cytological study has gone on,[21,24] the latest being Georgieva et al.[17] in 1962. Although they have produced other positive evidence of mutations, they do not admit to having seen chromosomal rearrangement.

More positive evidence of rearrangement of chromosomes has been obtained as explained above, by examination for chromatid bridges. It was Newcomer and Wallace who first obtained evidence of bridges in mitotic figures. Since somatic chromosomes do not pair, the bridges can only be formed by crossing over of the two daughter chromatids. (See Fig. 12.5.) If cross-overs occur in such a way that both centromeres are found on the same chromatid, during their repulsion at anaphase a bridge between the poles will be formed. Such a bridge, though it will eventually be lost, has demonstrated that an abnormality has occurred. Further evidence of somatic crossing over was obtained by Carpio, who showed diagrams with as many as five obvious somatic cross-overs. Other investigators who have observed chromatid bridges are Asche, Selman, Baldes et al. and Georgieva et al. In Selman's case it is interesting to note that he was unable to obtain any such effect when he treated onion root tips in water, but in sugar, which removed by osmosis some of the hydrostatic pressure from the cell, he obtained a high percentage of bridges. In chick heart fibroblasts in water, he also obtained the effect. Carpio and Orellana achieved an increase in the rate of crossing over in meiotic cells also. (See Fig. 12.6.)

Yet another effect which has been widely reported is a doubling of the chromosomes to form polyploids. The most usual agent which is employed for this purpose is colchicine which acts in such a way as to hinder the development of the spindle. In the absence of the spindle the chromatids remain together and the tetraploid condition is formed. The failure of the chromatids to divide is referred to as stickiness. Wallace, Bushnell and Newcomer[4] first noticed in onion and narcissus root tips that the spindle figures were destroyed, but did not mention that polyploidy was a result. However they did mention that the phenotypic effect on leaves was reminiscent of the results of colchicine. Newcomer and Wallace[5] produced cytological evidence of this so-called C-mitosis, in narcissus root tips, Asche[23] on Vicia faba, and Carpio[28] on onion root tips also. Other authors who have observed the C-mitotic effect are Selman (onion root tips),[9] Newcomer (narcissus root tips),[15] Lehmann et al. (onion root tips)[20] and Georgieva et al.[17] (lucerne, maize, cucumber, melon). These last named investigators obtained abnormal diploid chromosome numbers in these plants as well. This was due to an unequal division of chromosomes at anaphase, perhaps some function of the centromere. Thus the diploid number for lucerne is $2n = 32$, and they obtained 16–18 chromosomes, for maize $2n = 20$ and they obtained 12 and 13 chromosomes, and

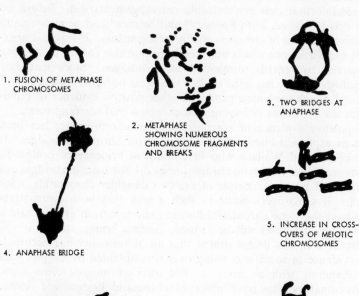

1. FUSION OF METAPHASE
CHROMOSOMES

2. METAPHASE
SHOWING NUMEROUS
CHROMOSOME FRAGMENTS
AND BREAKS

3. TWO BRIDGES AT
ANAPHASE

4. ANAPHASE BRIDGE

5. INCREASE IN CROSS-
OVERS OF MEIOTIC
CHROMOSOMES

6. CLEAR INDICATION OF BREAKAGE OF
THE LARGE 'M' CHROMOSOME TO FORM
EXTRA PAIR

7. C-MITOTIC EFFECT

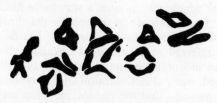

8. OBVIOUS ABNORMAL REPULSION OF CENTROMERES

9.. FRAGMENT OF CHROMOSOME
REMAINING AFTER BRIDGE
FORMATION

1,2,3,4 NARCISSUS
5,6,9   VICIA FABA
7,8   ALLIUM CEPA

Fig. 12.6. Examples of nuclear abnormalities caused by ultrasound

for melon $2n = 22$, they obtained 8–9 chromosomes. If the centromere is damaged in some way, and thus hinders division of the chromosomes, the entire chromosome will pass to one pole and the daughter cells will be unevenly distributed. Carpio and Orellana[27] obtained abnormal diploid numbers, but in their case they arose by a fracture of a large chromosome to form seven pairs instead of six. Of course this seventh 'chromosome' would not survive in the subsequent divisions, having no centromere. Carpio achieved a true tetraploid with ultrasound, an effect which until then had only been obtained with chemicals.

Finally mention must be made of another cytological effect which has been observed; this is a marked action on the centromere with subsequent abnormalities in divisions, which has been reported by Carpio and Orellana,[27] Carpio,[28] and Newcomer.[15] In the former case an opening of the pairs of homologous chromosomes took place, after synapsis and before the division into chromatids. In the large chromosome of *Vicia*, the tension thus set up was taken as being responsible for the rupture of the chromosomes to form the seventh pair. This premature separation at metaphase was clearly noted also in some mitotic divisions of onion by Carpio. The chromosomes, clearly in the metaphase stage, were held together only by their extremities. This is illustrated in Fig. 12.6.

The apparatus used by these workers was basically the same as that used by those who produced phenotypic evidence of mutations, although as Selman points out there is often a lacking of such information. Again very little conclusive information can be gained regarding frequency and doses as can be seen from Table 12.2.

12.10 CONCLUSIONS FROM THE TABLE

There is usually a certain threshold value below which no breakage of chromosomes takes place, for example all intensities above $1 \ W/cm^2$,[15] but in others no chromosome fragments or abnormalities of any kind are observed in material which is capable of further growth after treatment.[9] In general however there is a more or less linear relationship between increased dosage (intensity × time) and effect,[6,15] but degrees of damage or abnormality are not easy to determine. Not all investigators mention the effect of ultrasound upon the subsequent growth of the plant. Whether no experiments were performed or whether the results were unfortunately negative is of course open to conjecture. Both Newcomer[15] and Selman[9] mention however that any dose which produced chromosome fragments proved lethal to the tissues, though the former does mention that chromosome and chromatid breaks did occur at intensities well below those which produce gross nuclear abnormalities. Of course, as Newcomer points out chromosome fragmentation is not necessary for genetical change to take place, a fact which their early work suggests.

From all this evidence it would seem that ultrasound can produce mutations, as is shown by the continued growth of mutant *Helianthus* plants. That the rate of production of these mutants does not compare

Table 12.2

Author	Country	Date	Material	Rearrange	Incr. Mit.	Bridges	C-mit	Freq. kc/s	Power W/cm²	Time
Wallace, Bushnell[2]	U.S.A.	1948	Root tips of Onion, Narcissus	+	−	−	+	400	8–10	–60 sec
Olivier[19]	Canada	1948	Root tips	−	+	−	−	960	0·16 A (0·35 A)	30 sec –10 min)
Conger[7], Newcomer	U.S.A.	1948	Tradescantia bud	−		+	+	9·9	250 V	?
Wallace[5]	U.S.A.	1949	Root tips, Narcissus					400	8–10	–60 sec
Dubow[26]	U.S.A.	1949	Drosophila		+			960	14	?
Loza[6]	France	1950	Root tips					400	1250 V	5 min–15 min
Carpio Orellana[27]	Spain	1951	Shoots of Vicia	+		+	+	400	1250 V	5 min–15 min
Carpio[28]	Spain	1951	Onion root tips	−	−	+	−	400	1250 V	30 sec –30 sec
Asche[23], Spencer[22], Goldman, Lepeschkin[29]	Germany, U.S.A., U.S.A.	1951, 1952, 1952	Root tips of Vicia, Root tips of Pea, Plants	−	+ −	+ −	+ −	1000 500 400 700 1000	1·5 10–20 ?	30 sec –30 sec ?
Selman[9], Newcomer[15]	U.K., U.S.A.	1952, 1954	Root tips of Onion, Root tips of Narcissus	−	+ −	+ +	? +	1000 400	–5 –20	–30 sec 1 min– 15 sec
Lehmann, Herrick, Krusen[20]	U.S.A.	1954	Root tips of Onion					800 1000	10 –30	2 min
Lehmann, Baldes, Krusen[21]	U.S.A.	1955	Root tips of Onion					1000	110	5 min
Baldes, Herrick, Stroebel[24]	U.S.A.	1957	Onion root tips			+	+	1000	20	?
Georgieva et al.[17]	Bulgaria	1962	Lucerne, Maize, Cucumber, Melon			+	+	?	9·9	5 min– 30 min

favourably with other known mutagens is also accepted. The wide variations in the observed and recorded effects of the various workers can presumably be explained by an examination of the materials and techniques applied. The extreme case, that of Hersch et al.,[1] has already been mentioned, but others exist, which could also account for such great differences. Thus Spencer reported a failure of ultrasound to produce mutations, or any cytological evidence that they might have occurred; he did however carry out his treatments on seed soaked for 6 hr and kept moist for a further 12 hr. His results thus refer only to those conditions. Again, doses are certainly not always measured in a similar fashion. Nor is all material used necessarily of a similar refractive index acoustically. In some cells chromosomes were relatively large and few in number, while others were very small but abundant. It is therefore unlikely that chromosomal abnormalities will be equally easily visible in both types of cell. It is not clear either if cells, with a large number of chromosomes, although obviously poor cytological material, are more affected by ultrasound than cells with few large chromosomes, but a polyploid will fairly obviously behave differently from a normal diploid cell in its action to ultrasound.

A difference in effect is also noted depending upon the position of the material relative to standing waves.[5] One investigation discovered that the effect varied with orientation of the material from horizontal to vertical[26] and another whether roots were positioned in nodes or anti-nodes.[29] In experiments with seeds, there will obviously be a marked difference in effect depending upon the orientation of the embryo to the ultrasonic waves.[6,8,22] There are thus a large number of variables which will have an effect upon the reaction of the cell to ultrasonic waves. It should again be stressed the importance of carrying out a fully controlled experiment into the effect of intensity and frequency upon the cell.

12.11 WHAT CAUSES THE ULTRASONIC EFFECT

Having discovered that ultrasound produced chromosomal breaks, and the resultant mutations, it remains to be seen why they occur. Ultrasound has three major physical characteristics which determine its biological action. These are:

1. High pressures and accelerations causing movements within cells
2. Generation of heat at points
3. Cavitation.

Much work has been carried out to discover which of these characteristics has been responsible for the mutagenic action. As early as 1949, Newcomer and Wallace[5] pointed out that it was uncertain if intracellular cavitation occurred. They concluded from their observations that the vibrations were responsible; the intensity of the vibrations was also such that secondary chemical changes took place, involving the colloidal materials of the cells as evidenced by changes in the staining ability of the cells. The degree of breakage which they observed indicated that a large amount

241

of energy had managed to penetrate through the cell walls of surrounding tissues, the alternate compression periods and rarefactions being responsible for the breakages. They recorded the increase in temperature of the treatment medium, water, and were of the opinion that the rise in temperature of 25°C, from 10°C–35°C was not sufficient to cause such damage, but they did not rule out the possibility that local spot heats had developed, due to differential absorption of the sonic energy by the highly variable colloids of the cells, and that they caused the effect. Newcomer thinks it unlikely that heat is a cause, as there is no coagulation of protoplasm observed.

Most evidence available is concerned with these points. Thus Carpio[28] and Carpio and Orellana,[27] although they do not rule out the thermal effect, consider that the regions of necrotic tissue which they saw, could be caused by local spot heats, but that the gross structural breakages were caused by mechanical vibrations and the large variations in pressure originating from cavitation, which were sufficiently intense to cause physiological changes within the cell. Spencer[22] considers however that the particle acceleration, which he estimates may produce as high speeds as 500 km/sec, are primarily responsible for the effects, leaving as they do, free valencies, as seats of chemical action. He does not rule out completely the occurrence of local point heats.

The majority of work on the thermal effects has been done by Lehmann and his co-workers.[20,21,25] They were not so much interested in the cytological aspect as the histological, and investigated the effect of different temperatures upon the general structure of the root tips and were able to obtain an effect, by soaking in water at 48°C, which was similar to that produced by ultrasound at increased pressures which ruled out the possibility of cavitation. This effect however, did not produce any chromosomal abnormalities. Baldes et al.[24] obtained yet another type of reaction using very intense ultrasound, 110 W/cm³, under a pressure of 30 atmospheres, which was not reproduced by heating the tissues to as high as 208°C. The rise in temperature due to the absorption of sound waves at this pressure was up to 150°C, equivalent to 60°C at atmospheric pressure. This reaction is therefore non-thermal and non-cavitational. Fry in 1953[30] came to a similar conclusion, viz, a non thermal reaction of unknown origin, which is not caused by cavitation.

For a long time it was considered that cavitation was the chief cause of the effect.[9,20] Thus Selman carried out his tests under increased pressure (10 atmospheres), eliminating cavitation and was unable to obtain similar results. He and others,[3,25] did not believe that intracellular cavitation could be the cause, as he agreed that because of the high viscosity of the cell sap the intensity necessary to produce cavitation would be too great. Cleavage of the chromosomes occurred in any case at an intensity well below the value at which intracellular cavitation could take place. His idea was of cavitation at some distant point, not necessarily closely in contact with the particular cell, which would transmit the energy by shock waves through the tissue. A similar idea was formed by Goldman and Lepeschkin.[29] Lehmann et al.,[20] however obtained chromosomal aberrations having treated the root tips in agar gel, and so they were forced to the conclusion since no cavitation occurs in this medium, that intercellular cavitation or intracellular cavitation must take place. Tolles[31] also produced similar cytological evidence using such low intensity ultrasound that no cavitation could be produced. It is unlikely that intracellular cavitation occurs for the reasons stated, hence we are forced to the conclusion that intercellular cavitation is responsible. This however would hardly seem to account for such large effects, and so by a process of elimination the mechanical characteristics would seem to be responsible, which was the view taken by Asche[23] originally. Experiments to investigate the mechanical effect of ultrasound are necessarily very complicated, as it is first necessary to rule out the effect of heat and cavitation. No reports of such an experiment have as yet appeared.

What chemical reactions are actually taking place is still uncertain, but there is evidence that depolymerization of macro-molecules plays a part. Starch was depolymerized in 1942 by Sutra[32] using ultrasound and by 1950 Laland et al.[33] had produced a depolymerization in nuceloproteins. Whether it is this depolymerization which is actually responsible for the rupture of the chromosomes, or whether the chromosomes are actually physically torn apart is not clear.[28] A similar type of reaction is thought to effect the lipo-proteins of the spindle, causing the C-mitosis effect. As Darlington[34] had earlier attributed the stickiness of chromosomes to a de-polymerization of thymonucleic acid, this seems a reasonable assumption, but Weissler says that cavitation is necessary for this effect. Agglutinations of chromatin have been attributed to trans-formations from the gel to the sol state which is another effect which has been discovered for ultrasound. Depolymerizations of protein molecules in enzymes have also been produced by ultrasound, which presumably accounts for the detremental effects of ultrasound on growth in some instances.

It will be obvious from the above that the problem of how ultrasound causes its effects is still largely a matter for dispute, there being various schools of thought of fairly contrasting opinion.

12.12 THE FUTURE OF ULTRASOUND AS A MUTAGEN

There is undeniable proof that ultrasound does produce mutations in animal and plant material. The rate at which it does this, is, however not equal to that at which X-rays and other mutations do, or so it would seem from the majority of evidence at hand. It is a justifiable criticism of all existing work on the subject that no comparison of other agents with ultrasound, using identical material and conditions has been carried out. Higher rates have been produced with other mutagens, but the techniques involved have been infinitely more complex and expensive than the ultrasonic equipment employed. The cheapest X-ray unit capable of producing mutations would presumably be several times the price of an ultrasonic machine capable of similar properties. Other physical mutagens, neutrons, alpha particles, and gamma rays have disadvantages, either from cost of production or precautions necessary for the user or both, but ultra-violet light is a mutagen which compares readily with ultrasound in its action. It is much lower in power than X-rays and is relatively cheap to use. Different wavelengths have quite different mutation-inducing properties however, although both gene and structural mutations are produced. Ultrasound in its turn produces both structural and gene mutations, but there is no evidence of differential effects with different wavelengths, although from the evidence quoted above there were such large variations in techniques and apparatus that it would be totally wrong to draw any hard and fast conclusions.

New chemical mutagens are being discovered every year, but it is only mustard gas and other closely related compounds which have been found to give an effect comparable to those from the highest practicable X-ray doses. Mustard gas, though relatively cheap to produce, presents various problems to the handler, which make it unacceptable as a quick mutagenic agent. For this reason ultrasound can compare very favourably with these chemical mutagens as well.

The exact mode of action of ultrasonic rays remains a problem for investigation, but it is fairly safe to say that the general rise in temperature which it produces can scarcely be responsible. Spot heats, due to differential absorption of the ultrasonic energy may occur, but, on account of experimental limitations, it is impossible to say to what temperature such areas rise, and whether the rise if sufficiently great would cause such an action. Even though there has been much evidence to the contrary, it is probable that cavitation is the cause of the mutagenic action of ultrasound. This is the view adopted by the majority of workers in the medical field as regards the biological affects. In this case it may either be a direct effect, because of the fantastic acceleration of the particles, or an indirect effect because of the shock waves produced through the tissue by the collapse of the cavitational bubbles. Experiments which have tried to eliminate cavitation by application of an external pressure have not always necessarily been successful in achieving this, as it is difficult to think of these pressures reaching the inter-cellular spaces. Nor has it presumably been justifiable to say that intra-cellular cavitation has been entirely absent, since the cell sap varies in its viscosity from near that of water to much higher values.

That there remain many unanswered questions regarding the mutagenic action of ultrasound, is obvious from the above discussion. That ultrasound is not as efficient at producing mutations as other agents is also accepted. But the great advantage of ultrasound, its ease of application to the material, is surely sufficient reason for a more thorough, comparative and controlled investigation to be made of its use as a mutagen. If once an optimum frequency and dose can be discovered for ultrasound, there is surely the chance that the average laboratory technician may find in his hands a machine capable of producing an infinite number of mutations, a facility which until now has been reserved for those in Breeding Stations and other special laboratories.

REFERENCES

1. HERSCH, A. H., KARRER, E. and LOOMIS, A. L., 'An attempt to induce mutations in Drosophila melanogaster,' *Am. Naturalist*, **64**, 552 (1930).
2. WALLACE, R. H. and BUSHNELL, R. J., 'Production of phenotypic and genotypic variations in seedlings by ultrasonic vibrations,' *Am. J. Botany*, **35**, 813 (1948).
3. BUSHNELL, R. J. and WALLACE, R. H., 'The induction of sex linked mutations in Drosophila melanogaster with ultrasonic treatment,' *Anat. Record*, **101**, 690 (1948).
4. WALLACE, R. H., BUSHNELL, R. J. and NEWCOMER, E. H., 'The induction of cytogenetic variations by ultrasonic waves,' *Science*, **107**, 577 (1948).
5. NEWCOMER, E. H. and WALLACE, R. H., 'Chromosomal and Nuclear Abberations induced by ultrasonic vibrations,' *Am. J. Botany*, **36**, 230 (1949).
6. LOZA, J., 'Recherches physiologiques et histologiques sur les effets provoques par les ultrasons chez les vegetaux,' *Rev. Gen. Botan.*, **57**, 594 (1950).
7. CONGER, A. D., 'The Cytogenic effect of sonic energy applied simultaneously with X-rays,' *Proc. Nat. Acad. Sci. U.S.* **34**, 470 (1948).
8. HASKELL, G. and SELMAN, G. G., 'Studies with sweetcorn. III Primary effects of treating seeds with ultrasound,' *Plant Soil*, **2**, 359 (1950).
9. SELMAN, G. G., 'The effects of ultrasound on mitosis,' *Exptl. Cell Res.*, **3**, 656 (1952).
10. SELMAN, G. G. and COUNCE, S. J., 'Abnormal embryonic development in Drosophila melanogaster induced by ultrasonic treatment,' *Nature*, **172**, 504 (1953).
11. BESSLER, W., 'Ultraschallwirkungen en embryonen von Triton alpestris,' *Strahlentherapie*, **89**, 292 (1952).
12. BRETTSCHNEIDER, H., 'Die Wirkung des Ultraschalls auf die Entwicklung des Hühnchens und des Froscheres,' *Strahlentherapie*, **87**, 517 (1952).
13. LOTMAR, R., 'Die Wirkung von Ultraschall auf verschiedene Entwicklung stadien von Drosophila melanogaster (Diptera),' *Strahlentherapie*, **87**, 517 (1952).
14. FRITZ-NIGGLI, H., 'Die Weinwirkung des ultraschalls auf die Entwicklung und mutationstrate der Tanfliege, (Drosophila melanogaster),' *Arch. Physik. Therapie*, **2**, 56 (1950).
15. NEWCOMER, E. H., 'Observations on dosage, the mechanism of action and the recovery of cells exposed to ultrasonic vibrations,' *Am. J. Botany*, **41**, 384 (1954).
16. OBOLENSKY, G., 'Les Ultrasons en biologie,' *Annee Biol.*, **61**, 465 (1957). 'Recherches sur quelques stimulations fonctionelles chez les plantes par les ultrasons,' *Rev. Gen. Botan.*, **65**, 297 (1958).
17. GEORGIEVA, R., NICOLOFF, H. and FILER, K., 'Cytological and genetic changes caused by ultrasound wave effects,' *Compt. Rend. Acad. Bulgare Sci.*, **15**, 3 (1962).
18. MISZYNSKY, K. A., 'Investigations on the mutations of Potato Virus X, induced by ultrasound, (in Polish), *Acta Soc. Botan. Polon.*, **23**, No. 2, 289 (1954).
19. OLIVIER, H., 'Etude cytotoxologique de divers agents physiques et chimiques,' *Rev. Can. Biol.*, **7**, No. 3, 62 (1948).
20. LEHMANN, J. F., BALDES, E. J. and KRUSEN, F. H., 'The effects of ultrasound on chromosomes, nuclei and other structures of the cells in plant tissues,' *Arch. Phys. Med. Rehabil.*, **35**, 141 (1954).
21. LEHMANN, J. F., BALDES, E. J. and KRUSEN, F. H., 'Destructive effects of high intensity ultrasound on plant tissues,' *Ultrasound in Biology and Medicine.* Symposium University of Illinois (1955).
22. SPENCER, J. L., 'Effects of intense ultrasonic vibrations on Pisum. I. On root meristems,' *Growth*, **16**, 243 (1952). 'II. Effects on growth and their inheritance,' *Growth* **16**, 255 (1952).
23. ASCHE, G., 'Kernabberationen durch Ultraschall,' *Strahlentherapie*, **85**, 215 (1951).
24. BALDES, E. J., HERRICK, J. F. and STROEBEL, C. F., 'Biological effects of Ultrasound,' *Intern. Conf. Ultrasound in Medicine, Los Angeles*, 111 (1957).
25. DUBOW, R. J., *Mutagenic effect of ultrasonic vibrations on Drosophila melanogaster*, Thesis, University of Connecticut (1949).
26. YAMAHA, G. and UEDA, R., 'Uber den Einfluss der Ultraschallwellen auf die Wurzelspitzenzellen von Vicia faba,' *Cytologica (Tokyo)*, **9**, 524 (1939).
27. CARPIO, M. D. A. and ORRELLANA, E., *Genet. Iberica*, **3**, 3 (1951).

28. CARPIO, M. D. A., 'Aportaciones para el estudio de las variaciones chromosomicas inducidas por ultrasonidos,' *Genet. Iberica*, **3**, 113 (1951).
29. GOLDMAN, D. E. and LEPESCHKIN, W. W., 'Cellular injury in standing sound waves,' *J. Cellular Comp. Physiol*, **40**, 255, 383 (1952).
30. FRY, W. J., 'Action of ultrasound on nerve tissue—a review,' *J. Acoust. Soc. Am.*, **25**, 1 (1953).
31. TOLLES, G., *Experimental techniques for the production of cytological and morphological changes in plants*, Thesis, University of Connecticut (1949).
32. SUTRA, R., 'Action des ultrasons sur l'amidon,' *Compt. Rend. Acad. Sci.*, **232**, 1490 (1942).
33. LALAND, S., OVEREND, W. G. and STACY, M., 'Some effects of ultrasonic irradiation of DNA,' *Research*, **3**, 386 (1950).
34. DARLINGTON, C. D., 'Chromosome chemistry and gene action,' *Nature*, **149**, 66 (1942).

13

CLEANING OF SURGICAL INSTRUMENTS

B. Brown, B.Sc., Ph.D., A.Inst.P.

13.1 INTRODUCTION

In this chapter the application of ultrasound to the cleaning of instruments used in surgery and medicine is considered. Cleaning of instruments such as scalpels, forceps, etc. is carried out prior to the sterilization process to which the instruments are ultimately subjected.

Sterlization refers to the freeing of an object from all living organisms, including bacteria, and in surgery and medicine the sterilization of instruments is extremely necessary in order to prevent infection. Sterilization can be accomplished in various ways and well known techniques include killing of the organisms by heat and by disinfectants. When objects are being sterilized by heat the heat can be applied either as dry heat or as moist heat. For treatment by moist heat articles are generally placed in a steamer or autoclave. Moist heat is more effective than dry heat, sterilizing at lower temperatures in a given time and in shorter times at the same temperatures. However dry heat is employed mainly for glassware, syringes, etc., which are not spoiled by the high temperature and are required dry. Whichever sterilizing process is used it is essential for the article concerned to be thoroughly cleaned beforehand. This cleaning process is necessary to remove any proteinaceous matter left on the surface or in a crevice of an instrument which may protect infectious bacteria during subsequent sterilizing process.

In the case of surgical instruments the usual method of cleaning is by hand scrubbing. This is a most unpleasant task and also takes up considerable time which could be spent in a more useful manner. Moreover, the method is unsatisfactory since it is quite impossible to clean the inaccessible surfaces of modern surgical instruments by hand scrubbing.

The introduction of ultrasonic cleaning techniques has overcome these disadvantages and released the staff formerly occupied in hand scrubbing so that they can undertake more interesting work within the hospital.

In the case of the cleaning of glassware, i.e. hypodermic syringes, etc., normal cleaning methods include the use of automatic pulse-jet glassware washers as well as hand washing. The cleaning problem here is not so severe as in the case of surgical instrument cleaning but even in this application ultrasonic cleaning has decided advantages over the other methods.

13.2 ULTRASONIC CLEANING EQUIPMENT

Ultrasonic cleaning basically consists of immersing the article to be cleaned in a suitable solvent through which ultrasonic waves are then passed. The process may be summarized as follows. High frequency electrical oscillations produced by an electronic generator are fed to a transducer which converts them to mechanical vibrations. By suitably coupling the transducer to the cleaning solvent the ultrasonic vibrations are thereby propagated in the solvent. If the energy and frequency of the ultrasonic waves are suitable their propagation through the liquid initiates cavitation. Cavitation refers to the rapid formation and subsequent collapse of innumerable minute bubbles or cavities due to successive rarefactions and compressions in the liquid. On the collapse of the cavities shock waves are produced and these impinge on any solid surfaces present in the liquid and very effectively scour the surface. Thus the effect is similar to mechanical scrubbing but acts much more efficiently, rapidly penetrating to every crevice of an instrument immersed in the solvent.

The range of ultrasonic frequencies employed is from 13 kc/s to about 1 Mc/s and the type of transducer used depends on the frequency. At high frequencies, of more than 100 kc/s, piezoelectric transducers made of quartz or barium titanate are used and in the low frequency range, from 13 kc/s to 40 kc/s both magnetostrictive and piezoelectric transducers are used. It has clearly been established that the intensity of cavitation increases as the ultrasonic frequency decreases and consequently most ultrasonic cleaning equipment works at fairly low frequencies of about 20 kc/s or less. In fact ultrasonic cleaning equipment working at frequencies in excess of 100 kc/s has largely been discontinued. The power outputs available in ultrasonic cleaning equipment range from a few watts to several kilowatts thus enabling a wide range of liquid volumes to be efficiently irradiated. Most hospital cleaning units provide a power output of 1 or 2 kW. The various types of transducers have already been discussed and hence only the factors which affect their suitability for use in cleaning equipment are considered here.

Magnetostrictive transducers have the advantage of being robust. They also have a high Curie point and this enables them to be used at high temperatures which is sometimes desirable. In one hospital cleaning unit currently under development, ultrasonic cleaning is combined with

Plate 13.1. Soniclean surgical instrument cleaner (Courtesy Dawe Inst. Ltd.)

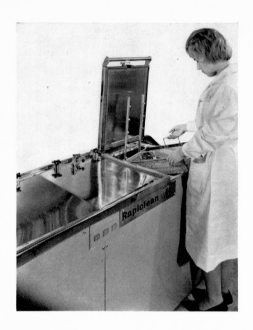

*Plate 13.2. Rapiclean 32
ultrasonic cleaning unit
(Courtesy Ultrasonics Ltd.)*

*Plate 13.3. Rapiclean 15/1000
(Courtesy Ultrasonics Ltd.)*

steam sterilization which takes place immediately after the cleaning process. Hence in this particular unit it is essential for the transducers to be able to withstand the high temperatures reached in the sterilization process. Barium titanate transducers are limited to use at a maximum temperature of about 70°C. The development of lead zirconate-titanate as a piezoelectric material has largely overcome this disadvantage of a low Curie point and also the use of sandwich type transducers seems to provide a solution to the non-robustness of pieozelectric materials.

It is often difficult for the user to decide which type of transducer is best for this purpose. Obviously when advertising equipment the manufacturers always stress the relative advantages of their particular type of transducer over other types. Provided that the consideration of robustness of transducers and a high Curie point are not applicable then for a particular cleaning application the factors which will influence a user to purchase a particular piece of equipment are reliable and efficient cleaning at the lowest cost. In this respect all ultrasonic cleaning equipment will obviously clean to some extent and for the cleaning of surgical instruments etc., several different types of equipment will accomplish the task successfully. Under these circumstances therefore the user, i.e. the hospital, must decide what importance must be attached to factors such as the time of cleaning, reliability of the equipment, quality of finish, servicing available, etc., before deciding on a particular type of equipment. It may be found that some equipment cannot remove hard encrusted deposits in a reasonable time and obviously, under these circumstances, it would be necessary to use a more powerful unit. It is common practice among manufacturers of ultrasonic cleaning equipment to refer to a 500 W generator and so on but it must be borne in mind that in certain types of equipment the power quoted is the maximum power, not the average power. To overcome this possibility of misleading their customers the manufacturers of ultrasonic equipment have adopted a nomenclature to give both the average power output and the peak power. Thus a 500/125 W generator refers to a generator providing an average output of 125 W with peak power of 500 W.

The design of ultrasonic cleaners varies from one manufacturer to another. Normally the transducers are connected to a cleaning tank containing a suitable solvent in which the articles to be cleaned are immersed. The coupling of the transducers to the tank depends on the type of transducer. Magnetostrictive transducers are usually attached to resonant coupling stubs which are bolted to the tank at their nodal points. Piezoelectric transducers are either cemented to the outside of the tank or constructed in such a form that they can be directly immersed in the solvent.

A certain amount of scattering of the ultrasonic waves takes place but mainly the cavitation is produced directly above the transducer face. If cleaning equipment has obvious gaps between transducers then it may result in certain parts of the liquid volume being less active than others.

Ultrasonic cleaning equipment for use in hospitals is made of stainless steel and is basically simple in design. The equipment usually consists

249

of an electronic generator to drive the transducers, together with two tanks, one for cleaning the articles and one for rinsing. The whole assembly is normally contained in one cabinet.

The electronic generator is normally simple in design supplying electrical oscillations at a fixed frequency and power output. In many cases no rectification is incorporated with a resulting pulsed or half wave output. There are few generator controls to make operation as simple as possible and usually these consist only of an on/off switch together with a crude tuning control to enable the generator output frequency to be tuned to the mechanical resonance frequency of the transducers being used.

Plate 13.1 shows the Type 1170C surgical instrument cleaner manufactured by Dawe Insts. Ltd. This consists of two flush mounting cabinets forming a single working top, one housing the ultrasonic generator while the other incorporates built in cleaning and rinsing tanks complete with close fitting lids. The transducers used are lead zirconate-titanate and work at a frequency of 25 kc/s. Twenty of these transducers are attached to the underside of the cleaning tank. The output of the generator is not continuous but pulsed at 100 c/s. Thus the power output is 1 kW peak, 500 W average. Either hot or cold water can be supplied to each tank by means of a swing arm tap. The rinse tank is provided with a spray mounted beneath the top edge and controlled by a separate valve. An outlet and overflow fitting are incorporated in each tank while a water level safety switch is fitted to the side of the wash tank. The whole unit is made of stainless steel with smooth surfaces and flush mounting panels to permit

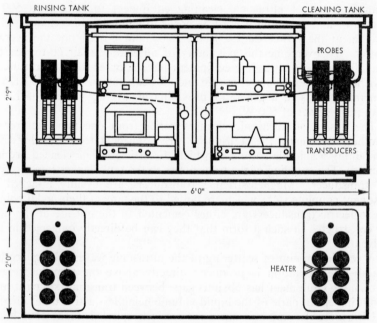

Fig. 13.1. A cross section through the Rapiclean 32 (Courtesy Ultrasonics Ltd.)

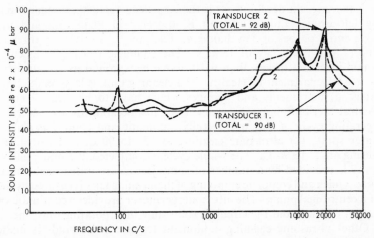

Fig. 13.2. Sound intensity output from 20 kc/s ultrasonic cleaning unit used in hospitals

hygenic cleaning of the exterior. Instruments to be cleaned are placed in a mesh basket with a metal bottom and are immersed in the solution contained in the wash tank. After ultrasonic cleaning the instruments are transferred in the same basket and rinsed in the rinse tank.

A hospital cleaning unit in which magnetostrictive transducers are used is made by Ultrasonics Ltd. and is shown in Plate 13.2. Fig. 13.1 shows a section through the cleaning unit. The transducers are attached to resonant probes which are fastened to the cleaning tank at their nodal points. It can be seen from the figure that in this equipment both the cleaning tank and the rinsing tank are fitted with ultrasonic transducers. Each tank is fitted with eight probes and four magnetostrictive transducers are attached to each probe. Both the treatment tanks and the transducer probes are made of 18/8/3 polished stainless steel. The equipment is tested up to 120°C and high temperature work presents no problems. The cleaning tank is fitted with a heater and this is thermostatically controlled. The output of the generator is continuous and supplies 1 kW to the transducers. The transducers actually work at a frequency of 13 kc/s which is in fact audible. However this noise problem is overcome by sound insulation of the whole unit. It is interesting to note that at one stage in the development of this equipment the frequency used was increased to 20 kc/s in order to be inaudible. However, this 'inaudible' sound was found to be annoying and the frequency spectrum, shown in Fig. 13.2, showed that audible sub-harmonics could be responsible. In addition due to the increase in frequency from 13 kc/s to 20 kc/s the intensity of cavitation fell off appreciably and eventually the original frequency of 13 kc/s was reverted to together with sound insulation. Tuning of this equipment is automatic and there are only three switches for tank selection, heating, and ultrasonic treatment. Instruments to be cleaned are placed in baskets and immersed first in the cleaning tank and then in the rinsing tank. Application of ultrasounds in both tanks ensures thorough cleaning.

251

A more recent development is the Rapiclean 15/1000 also manufactured by Ultrasonics Ltd. This unit is illutrated in Plate 13.3 and utilizes 'side entry' probes of 2 in diameter. Each probe is driven by three transducers at a frequency of 13 kc/s. The complete transducer assembly is sound-insulated to less than 6 dB above background as specified by the Scottish Department of Health. The cleaning tank is large enough for all types of instruments and syringes which have to be cleaned either in Central Sterile Supply Departments or in operating theatre suites. The operating cycle of this unit is fully automatic and comprises (1) a cold water spray, (2) ultrasonic cleaning at 75° to 90°C, and (3) ultrasonic rinsing at 75° to 90°C. The whole cycle is completed in 5 min. The water spray is provided by a number of spray jets incorporated in the cleaning tank. Quick and complete emptying of the cleaning tank is ensured by the use of a centrifugal pump. The ultrasonic generator provides a continuous wave output of 1 kW and the circuit is solid state incorporating only one valve.

Other ultrasonic cleaning equipment for use in hospitals is made by several firms including Kerry's Ltd., Lehfeldt and Co., Elliot-Acoustica, etc. At one time it was thought that ultrasonic cleaning might also sterilize the instruments but this is not so and at the present time a separate sterilizing process is necessary after the ultrasonic cleaning. In this connection, as mentioned earlier, an interesting development is currently being carried out in a Scottish hospital, where an attempt is being made to combine ultrasonic cleaning with subsequent steam sterilization in the same unit. This work is still in the experimental stage. Mention should be made here of a very recent report from America where a firm claims to have produced a new ultrasonic unit which works at 40 kc/s and not only cleans but sterilizes! However, the author has yet to see authenticated reports of results achieved with this new equipment.

In the United Kingdom the development of ultrasonic cleaning units for use in hospitals is complicated by the fact that nearly every hospital makes its own demands to an extent which means that the manufacture of a standard ultrasonic cleaning unit for hospital use becomes almost impossible. It is to be hoped that, in the near future, representatives of the hospitals and Ministry of Health will be able to reach a decision on the design of a standard ultrasonic cleaning unit.

13.3 CLEANING APPLICATIONS

Hospitals have been using ultrasound for several years now in order to clean various instruments and glassware before they are sterilized. In many hospitals the use of ultrasonic cleaning equipment is confined to the operating theatres. The actual location of the equipment is very important since no equipment of this nature is intrinsically safe for use in explosive atmospheres. Hence the ultrasonic cleaning equipment is normally located in a safe place near to the operating theatre.

In some of the larger modern hospitals all clinics and wards as well as the theatre suites are supplied with sterile instruments and dressings direct from the Central Sterile Supply Department (C.S.S.D.) and thus if ultrasonic cleaning equipment is used in C.S.S.D. all departments can have the added advantages of ultrasonic cleaning. Other hospitals have installed ultrasonic cleaning equipment in C.S.S.D. as well as in the theatre suites.

This latter scheme has been adopted at the hospital in Welwyn and the cleaning system is carried out as follows.[1] Immediately an instrument has been used it is dropped into a paper container which is closed. In each ward the containers are placed in a polythene bag inside a polypropylene bin. C.S.S.D. orderlies go round the hospital first thing in the morning collecting the polythene bags in closed aluminium trolleys so that by about 9.30 a.m. all of the instruments used during the previous day and night are in C.S.S.D. where they are sorted and loaded into stainless steel trays. Instruments with hinges are opened but otherwise the instruments are placed quite haphazardly in the tray to a depth of about 6 in. Some of the instruments may need presoaking in a bactericidal solution before the ultrasonic cleaning process but others can be immediately placed in the ultrasonic cleaning tank. After ultrasonic cleaning the instruments are then rinsed, following which they pass to a drying cupboard and thence to the sterilizers.

By this technique the instruments are efficiently and rapidly cleaned. Originally some difficulty was experienced on Monday mornings when instruments used over the weekend had to be cleaned, some of which contained dried blood 24 hr old. However by suitable choice of cleaning solvent in the presoak and in the ultrasonic cleaning tank cleaning is now accomplished with complete efficiency. As well as dealing efficiently with the routine cleaning of instruments the ultrasonic cleaning unit has also been successfully used to remove a thick $CaSO_4$ deposit from stainless steel beakers and dishes. This deposit had been gradually built up during the several months the dishes had spent in boilers. By ultrasonic cleaning what were apparently uncleanable vessels have been restored to new condition.

The actual cleaning solution used is very important. Alkaline, acidic and aqueous solutions have all been used successfully at various temperatures. Instruments cleaned include scalpel blades, forceps, hypodermic syringes, clips, needles, bowls and basins. Several papers have been published giving an account of the ultrasonic cleaning of specific instruments and one or two of these papers are mentioned below to provide an indication of the type of work carried out.

Myers and Goodman[2] have investigated the efficiency of ultrasonic equipment in cleaning old, well-used Spencer-Wells forceps, dissecting forceps, tissue forceps, etc., which had a coating of a deposit which constant routine scrubbing with soap and water would not remove. Rigid standards for testing the cleanliness of the cleaned instruments were not readily available and the only test applied was that after cleaning, the instruments should be bright shining steel, free from discolouration or foreign particles detectable by the naked eye. A preliminary screening of various detergent baths was carried out to find the best solvent. This was decided by cleaning a fresh pair of dirty forceps in each solution in turn for the same length of time. The aqueous solutions at 50°C used were as follows:

1 per cent centrimide
0·1 per cent benzalkonium chloride
0·1 per cent Nonidet P80
2 per cent Soft soap B.P.
0·5 per cent Teepol
0·5 per cent Penotrax
0·5 per cent Lissapol NX
0·5 per cent Penotrax in 2 per cent phosphoric acid
0·5 per cent Lissapol NX in 2 per cent phosphoric acid
0·5 per cent Teepol in 2 per cent phosphoric acid
0·5 per cent Lissapol NX in 2 per cent sodium hydroxide
0·5 per cent Teepol in 2 per cent sodium hydroxide
0·5 per cent Penetrax in 2 per cent sodium hydroxide.

These preliminary tests showed that instruments cleaned in the freshly prepared phosphoric acid bath plus detergent were much cleaner and brighter than those cleaned in any of the other baths. The 2 per cent sodium hydroxide bath plus detergents gave clean forceps but with a dull finish.

All further tests were therefore carried out in the acid baths. The ultrasonic cleaning equipment used magnetostrictive transducers working at 13 kc/s. In the majority of cases forceps were clean after 90 sec although a longer irradiation time, 120 sec, was often necessary to obtain a bright shining surface in the serrated forcep jaws. For the routine cleaning of new instruments it was not found necessary to use acidic solution and the simple detergent solutions at 50°C were sufficient. Experiments were repeated on old instruments with the solvent temperature at 90°C and this speeded up the cleaning process. All forceps were clean and shining within 100 sec.

The effect of the constant use of acid baths on stainless steel instruments was considered and manufacturers' opinions suggested that if the acid bath treatment was completed in 2 min little harm would occur. Other tests on needles were carried out and it was shown that all needles subjected to ultrasonic treatment could be cleaned satisfactorily within 2 min.

Beal and Skauen[3] have evaluated scientifically the cleaning of hypodermic syringes by hand washing, automatic washing and ultrasonic washing. Their procedure was as follows. Groups of 10 syringes were contaminated with Iodine 131 labelled blood, dried overnight and subsequently washed by hand, jet-pulse automatic machine or ultrasonic equipment. The syringes were then transferred to evaporating dishes and 1 l of distilled water was added to each group. After soaking for 24 hr the syringes were removed and the water evaporated to dryness. The resulting residue was taken up in water and an aliquot subjected to the usual radioactive count measurement.

The hand washing consisted of using a nylon test tube brush with the number of cleaning strokes standardized. The automatic jet-pulse washer provided a washing cycle consisting of 5 min washing, 3 min rinsing with tap water and a 30 sec rinse with distilled water. The ultrasonic cleaning equipment used utilized piezoelectric transducers. The syringes were loaded quite randomly in the ultrasonic cleaning bath and a treatment time of 10 min was used.

The results are reproduced in Tables 13.1 and 13.2. They show clearly that ultrasonic cleaning of syringes compares very favourably with both hand and automatic machine washing. The ultrasonic cleaning process always enabled areas to be cleaned which were difficult to reach by hand cleaning methods. Further, ultrasonic cleaning required less handling of the syringes than either hand or automatic washing. Beal and Skauen concluded that since ultrasonic cleaning equipment is relatively inexpensive and provides highly efficient cleaning its application to the cleaning of hypodermic syringes is well justified.

Table 13.1
(Typical results)

	Hand Washing	Ultrasonic Washing
Initial concentration of radioactivity in cpm of 10 syringes	500,000	500,000
Amount remaining after washing	3,446	906

Table 13.2
(Typical results)

	Automatic Washing	Ultrasonic Washing
Initial concentration of radioactivity in cpm of 10 syringes	80,000	80,000
Amount remaining after washing	180	76

The applications described above merely serve to illustrate the advantages of using ultrasonic equipment for the cleaning of surgical instruments and syringes. Several other workers have reported similar results and, in view of the advantages to be gained, there seems little doubt that more and more hospitals will use ultrasonic cleaning equipment.

REFERENCES

1. Anon., *Ultrasonics*, **2**, 1 (1964).
2. MYERS, J. A. and GOODMAN, J. E., *Pharm. J.*, **185**, 5069 (1960).
3. BEAL, H. M. and SKAUEN, D. M., *Ultrasonic News*, **3**, 3 (1959).

APPENDIX

ULTRASONIC DOSAGE FACTORS

It is recommended that in indicating the dose of ultrasonic radiation the following dosage factors should *always* be stated:

1. The nominal frequency of the ultrasonic radiation.

2. The total time over which the irradiation of tissue extends.

3. Whether the intensity of irradiation is maintained at a constant level throughout the period or is of varying intensity. If the intensity is not constant, the degree and periodicity of modulation or interruption.

4. Whether the transducer has a fixed relationship to the tissues during irradiation and if not, the extent of the relative movements.

5. The total power of ultrasonic radiation as a time average of the modulated but uninterrupted power.

6. Whether the radiation is in the form of approximately plane waves, focused, or divergent.

7. In the case of approximately plane waves the dimensions of the active area of the transducer.

8. In the case of focused transducers, the dimensions of the active area and the effective focal length, these depending on a knowledge of velocity of sound and acoustic path in the tissue.

9. In the case of transducers with lateral dimensions comparable with the wavelength, the active area and geometry.

10. In resonant systems the temperature of the transducer measured as close to the piezo-electric material or other active element as possible.

11. The temperature of the tissues being irradiated and of any coupling media between the transducer and the tissues.

If known, the following dosage factors should be stated and the method of measurement indicated:

12. The relationship between the peak radiated power and mean radiated power.

13. Where plane wave radiation is used, the relationship between the peak intensity and the average intensity over the surface of the transducer.

14. Where highly focused transducers are used the position of the plane maximum intensity and the distance in that plane from the point of maximum intensity to the nearest zone of minimum intensity.

15. Where weakly focused transducers or transducers using velocity transformers are used, the position of the plane of maximum intensity and the dimensions of the active area in that plane.

16. The proportion of the radiation that is of the fundamental frequency of the radiation and the proportion of the radiation that is of each harmonic or sub-harmonic frequency.

As tissues show variation in their acoustic characteristics and as the effects of duration, modulation and interruption of irradiation on its biological results are uncertain, it is recommended that derived factors such as "Watts per square centimetre" and "Joules" should not be used unless accompanied by the data from which they are derived.

INDEX